Social and Natural Biology

Social and Natural Biology

Selections from contemporary classics

CECIL E. JOHNSON / editor

D. VAN NOSTRAND COMPANY INC.
Princeton, New Jersey   Toronto   London   Melbourne

106649

Drawings by BERT MARSH

TO EDMUND C. JAEGER,

*Desert naturalist, who has carried on
the tradition of John Burroughs.*

Preface

The selections in this anthology represent a collaboration between students and teacher. They include essays recommended to students during informal talks on field trips as supplemental readings, and essays that they have brought to my attention. Inevitably, many of these essays are in the naturalist tradition and have served to enhance or illuminate experiences that we have shared on our field trips. Many of them are also concerned with some of the serious problems that man confronts in the mid-twentieth century—problems that have frequently become forcefully illustrated in my students' minds for the first time on a field trip when they have encountered the litter left by human visitors in a desert palms oasis or noted the layer of smog drifting below us from a mountain.

The major emphasis in the first section, titled *Evolution, Eugenics, and Population Prespectives*, is placed on human population dynamics. In the lead-off essay, however, one acquires some sense of the long span of evolutionary time as George Gaylord Simpson, the world-famed paleontologist, searches for artifacts of creatures that one lived in the distant past on the bleak, cold, and perennially windy fossil-paradise of Patagonia. A highly informative essay by the renowned East African anthropologist L. S. B. Leakey details his as yet unfinished lifetime hunt for evidences of man's own evolutionary forebears. Essays by Aldous Huxley, John Rock, Garrett Hardin, and the Population Reference Bureau cover such timely topics as overpopulation, birth control, and genetic improvement and their local, national, and global socio-political implications.

The second section of this anthology includes essays that over the years have heightened my students' interest in their natural environment. Through such selections, my classes have hiked the high mountain trails of the Sequoias with the nineteenth-century American naturalist John Muir, sailed on a leisurely trip into the Sea of Cortez to collect marine animals with John Steinbeck and Ed Ricketts, and become enthralled with Rachel Carson's vivid descriptions of natural beauty and her concern with conserving our natural heritage. It was my students who insisted that I dust off the volumes of John Burroughs that too often sit unread on the shelves of institutional libraries and include selections from his *Locusts and Wild Honey*. The final essay, Henry David Thoreau's "Winter Animals," is not only a classic of English prose, but it provides an unforgettable picture of what it must have been like at Walden in the snow-drifted winter when small animals visited Thoreau's cabin for their daily handouts.

The final section, *Animal Behavior*, is designed to bring readers into contact with the creative leaders in a suddenly mushrooming field of science. Konrad Lorenz, the father of animal behavior studies, captivates us with his description of the behavioral patterns of the world's tiniest mammals, the water shrews. Niko Tinbergen, a former student of Lorenz, reveals his astonishing powers of detailed observation in an essay on the sexual behavior of insects, fish, and herring gulls. George Schaller's graphic account of his forest life among wild African gorillas shatters many concepts of gorilla behavior which had been formulated by scholars observing them in zoos. The last essay in the volume is anthropologist-biologist Loren Eiseley's "The Bird and the Machine." Eiseley is not only a highly-trained scientist, but he is also one of the finest and most moving current writers of American prose. He writes in a style that is all his own, clean, sure, and unwavering. There are few passages more moving in the field of biology than Eiseley's description of his release of a small hawk that was destined for a zoo and its return to its mate.

We are often told that the era of the naturalist-biologist is dead: biology has become too complex for sophisticated scientists to concern themselves with lay essays in the tradition of Burroughs and Muir. Scientists such as Eiseley, who attempt to reach broad readership, make it possible for us to arouse enthusiasm in students for their natural environment. We may hope such students will become better informed citizens and perhaps impelled to channel their scientific talents into such vitally important fields as ecology and ethology—disciplines in which we need many disciples.

C.E.J.
Riverside City College
Riverside, California

Contents

Contents continued

Social and Natural Biology

SECTION 1

Evolution, Eugenics, and Population Perspectives

More than a million years ago an arboreal creature scurrying through the trees took to the grassy savannahs of Africa and thereby altered the destiny of its descendants. Man's span of time on earth since that event is only the flickering of an eyelash compared with the millions of years of evolution through genetic processes and natural selection that led up to that moment in which some protohuman animal broke with evolution as a blind, dominant force.

Fossil information gathered in the past few decades by such mid-African anthropologists as L. S. B. Leakey, Raymond Dart, and others has established that man's closest primate ancestors walked upright over the grasslands and challenged animals that possessed fangs, horns, hooves, claws, and much more speed with leg bones and jaw bones that could be used for crushing skulls and dismembering carcasses. Those primitive weapons employed by *Australopithecus africanus* at man's earliest appearance on the evolutionary stage were forerunners of new mechanisms of adaptation. Through the use and refinement of tools, man froze his own evolution. No longer imprisoned by chance genetic change, it became possible for him to direct the forces of his own adaptation and to modify and transform his environment.

Despite the fact that man has through successive agricultural, industrial, and scientific revolutions found increasing means to improve the lot of his species in the search for food and shelter, the problems of survival have become more acute than they were in the

1

dawn of man's history. The one quality that distinguishes man from all other earthly creatures—the ability to modify nature—has made possible a rapid increase in human numbers that could not have occurred if man were still chained by natural balances.

In the recent past, it took 1,600 years for the human species to double itself; now it has become apparent that the next doubling will take place in a mere thirty years. In the year 1750, there were only 0.7 billion people on the globe; and by 1900, only 1.6 billion. Today, over 4 billion people are scratching for food and space. Several decades ago, Aldous Huxley wrote: "By the year 2000 unless something appallingly bad or miraculously good should happen in the interval, six thousand millions of us will be sitting down to breakfast every morning. In a word, twelve times as many people are destined to double their numbers in one-fortieth of the time." Huxley's prediction failed to take account of radically new technological means of preserving man's health and lengthening life, and we can say now that his estimate will be exceeded by at least a billion additional persons.

Two regions of the world in particular, the Far East and Latin America, are faced with exploding populations, and per capita food production in those areas is now less than it was before World War II. The Chinese mainland in 1966 had a population of 900 million people and can be expected to have 1.5 billion people by the year 2000. Latin America is producing new human beings at a more rapid rate than any other area of the world. By the year 2000, its present population will have tripled and will have as many people as the U.S.S.R. and all of North Africa combined.

Africa, another potential trouble spot, is just beginning to feel its socio-political growing pains. By the year 2000, it will hold a population of 860 million, making it the second largest continent by numbers in the world.

The highly industrialized countries of the world, such as the United States, the Soviet Union, Great Britain, Canada, West Germany, Sweden, and a few others, are not only prosperous, but are beginning to learn that they must keep population within reasonable bounds. These affluent nations with their high level of technology have managed to develop an efficient, mechanized agriculture. In the United States, for example, only eight percent of the population are needed today on farms to produce food for the rest of the nation. The bulk of the population has time therefore for other pursuits than tilling the soil. This freedom has made it possible in the developed nations for man fully to employ his talents in altering his environment to educate more people, provide better housing, clothing, and medical attention, and make other astonishing improvements in his social well-being. The time may not be too far distant when, through eugenics, he can even alter and improve his descendants.

The jackrabbiting growth of the have-not nations, however, poses the frightening threat of undoing all of man's achievements, not to mention the immense toll in human misery already existing for those masses that make up the major portion of the human race. Starving people are ripe targets for the arrows of dictators, and in this era of nuclear power we already see totalitarian establishments weighing with equanimity their surplus populations as weapons— calculating them in equations of how many human beings they can afford to lose in an Armageddon struggle.

Man's break with undirected genetic change in the distant past tied his fate to an evolution through social and political means. He has always been a self-centered species, too often rearranging his environment to achieve short-sighted goals. Only in the twentieth century have we begun to see nations recognize that that which diminishes man's potentiality anywhere diminishes all men.

The prosperous nations have begun taking the necessary steps toward assisting have-not nations in raising living standards, but the myriad problems faced are formidable. In the have-not countries agricultural production is increasing at the rate of about one-half percent a year, as opposed to a population increase of 2.4 percent or higher. If world famine is to be prevented within our lifetimes, all the ingenuity possible must be exercised to integrate new technologies into the old agricultural traditions of backward countries.

There exists the awesome possibility that we may already be too late in facing the large responsibility that confronts us—that the population factor will outstrip the mandatory social action. United States foreign aid to underdeveloped countries would certainly be more realistic if we substantially increased funds to help establish family planning centers where they are most needed. Without such family planning—and it must happen soon—the major portion of foreign aid will continue to be drained off to support gargantuan increases in human numbers that can only further depress living standards.

At the height of his achievements in dominating his physical environment, man must face the most critical problems in his history. If he fails to use those adaptive mechanisms that freed him from an evolutionary mold, then it is possible that his time like that of many other extinct species will have come and evolution will pass him by.

GEORGE GAYLORD SIMPSON

Ancient Beasts

George Gaylord Simpson's book, Attending Marvels, *belongs in the company of Charles Darwin's* Voyage of the Beagle *and Rachel Carson's* The Sea Around Us. Attending Marvels *was written when Dr. Simpson was in his twenties, and in the beginning chapter we find him being shot at and temporarily caught up in a revolution. This was Buenos Aires, the fourth of September 1930, when as a young married man on the staff of the American Museum of Natural History he was selected to collect and study the fossils of cold, bleak, and perennially windy Patagonia.*

Patagonia, as Dr. Simpson so vividly describes, is dotted with corrugated iron houses and barren hills. It is also poorly endowed with resources except oil and wool, but Patagonia is a veritable treasure house of fossils, as earlier described by Charles Darwin in his Voyage of the Beagle.

George Gaylord Simpson is currently Agassiz Professor of Vertebrate Paleontology at the Museum of Comparative Zoology, Harvard University. Some of his better known books include The Meaning of Evolution, Horses, Life of the Past, The Major Features of Evolution, The World of an Evolutionist, *and his famous undergraduate biology text,* Life.

5

"The Señor doctor is crazy, isn't he?" asked Manuel, not realizing that I could not avoid overhearing him.

"I don't think so. Why?" put in loyal Justino.

"He came down to this desert for no reason! No one watches him and he still works hard! And what sort of work is that? Climbing around the barranca and getting all tired out, just to pick up scraps of rock. As if there were not rocks everywhere, even in that America of the North!"

"But those are not rocks. They are bones."

"Then why doesn't he stay in Buenos Aires and get bones from a slaughter-house, if anyone is fool enough to pay him for them?"

"They are not common bones. They are not sheep or guanaco. They are very old, so antique that they have turned to stone. They are bones of animals that now do not exist, and they are not found anywhere but here at Colhué-Huapí."

"The señor doctor is fooling you. Even if they were old bones they would not be any good. What would you do with them?"

"He says that some of them are the ancestors of our own animals and he wants to learn where they came from and what they were like millions of years ago. And others are strange beasts that are not like those of today. He will put them in a museum and people will come to see them because they are so queer."

"Oh, well, then maybe it does make sense. If many of those North American millionaires will pay to see them, then he can sell them at big prices. But then he should pay us more, because we are helping him and he is making his fortune."

"He says that no one pays to see the bones. And he does not sell them. He is just paid wages like us to come and find them."

"Why, then, with no one to watch him, he could stay in Buenos Aires and then go back to Nueva York and say he could not find any bones. No, friend Justino, it doesn't make sense. If the señor doctor is not crazy, he is too clever for you, and you are swallowing his lies."

And so the argument ended, as they always did, with each thoroughly convinced that he had been right all along. Manuel, like almost all the local inhabitants, was never able to see any logical reason or excuse for our activities. Rare Justino, on the contrary, took naturally to bone digging. He had tireless energy and a keen eye, as so many fossils now in New York testify. He also had that consuming curiosity which is the real reason for any scientific research, whatever higher motives we scientists sometimes like to claim for ourselves.

Yes, curiosity was the real reason why we were in Patagonia, and why others like us have been going there off and on for a century now. Indeed, there are only two valid reasons for ever visiting that bitter land, curiosity and desire for gain. Desire for gain may be more practical, but at present it is much less likely to be gratified and in the long run it is a good deal less important anyway. Those miserable flocks of sheep and that trickle of petroleum have no real significance. If they were to cease completely, the rest of the world would hardly know it, and human thought and progress would not falter in their stride. Patagonia's wealth of fossils is its real and essential contribution to the world. These fossils add chapters to human knowledge which are preserved nowhere else. And such knowledge has no ill application but can only enrich experience and give background and substance for intellectual advance. In the last analysis, most of what we are that beasts are not is due to this impractical but orderly curiosity which is called pure science.

The idea that we are the heirs of long ages of change and progress, and some real knowledge of the human rôle in the history of the earth, are relatively recent. Except for some fantastic guesses and a few neglected glimpses, this broader view of man's place in the universe has grown up altogether in the last hundred years.

By now everyone knows that life on the earth has not always been what it is today. In the mists of time loom antique monsters: scaly dinosaurs and hairy mammoths. Rhinoceroses once browsed in the lowlands of Florida. Diplodoci wallowed in Wyoming marshes. Mastodons blundered through primeval New England forests. Great marine reptiles once swam in seas where now the Himalayas stand five miles high, and strangely tusked beasts once dwelt in mountain basins now deeply buried below our present ocean level.

This prehistoric past is not a grab-bag of jumbled monstrosities. It is an orderly story as sequential as the history of human nations. Washington did not talk to Tutankhamen; and cavemen never saw living dinosaurs. The origin, spread, and disappearance of animal dynasties, their migrations, conquests, and failures, took place as definitely as any other part of history.

They now say that the earth, as a separate sphere with a hard surface, is a sprightly young planet aged at least 1,500,000,000 years. Starting with nothing much but a lot of shifting chemicals, it gave rise in the course of time to such things as *Brontosaurus* and marathon dancers, tree ferns and Pekingese dogs, mammoths and garter snakes, each in its own time and place.

The first hint that Patagonia can shed light on some of these ancient mysteries was due to Charles Darwin. In 1831, when he was a sporting and undistinguished student of theology, Darwin set out to circumnavigate the globe in a tiny ship, the *Beagle.* He was seasick most of the time; such disciplines prepare great minds. Those five years sobered him, and he returned a scientist who was to be a chief agent in revolutionizing human thought. Patagonia played a part in the development of Darwin's mentality, and he was a protagonist in the scientific development of Patagonia. Late in 1833 he landed on these shores and, ever alert for anything strange or new, he discovered here a few petrified bones. His shipmates grumbled at his bringing these on board the ship and ridiculed the ardent young naturalist. Fitzroy, the commander of the *Beagle,* did admit years later that the bones had been of some interest. This was handsome of Fitzroy, for that somewhat testy gentleman heartily disapproved of Darwin and even wrote a curious book, now forgotten by all but a few enthusiasts like me, in which he attempted to warn young minds against following the sinful teachings of the *Beagle's* naturalist.

The bones were taken back to England and there the great anatomist Richard Owen (he also later came to view Darwin with a somewhat jaundiced and distinctly suspicious eye) studied them. Owen recognized these fossils as the remains of extinct animals, weirdly unorthodox in structure, and quite unlike any found elsewhere on the earth. His work on them was the first publication suggesting the importance and interest of Patagonia's ancient life.

It seems cavalier to pass so briefly over three of the most

interesting men who ever lived: Darwin, Fitzroy, and Owen. All were great and brilliant men, as different in viewpoint and character as three men well could be, and yet strangely linked together by those few bones from such a far corner of the earth. However, I must avoid such a temptation to digress and will skip half a century of sporadic exploration in Patagonia. This is not a history, but an excuse, an excuse for my own presence in Patagonia.

It was in the eighties that the Ameghinos began their work, which was so extensive and so important that it is impossible to think of the prehistoric animals of South America without thinking of these two brothers: Florentino Ameghino, self-made savant; Carlos Ameghino, hardy and shrewd explorer.

Not long ago in Buenos Aires I attended services on the seventy-seventh anniversary of the birth of Florentino. The pupils of the Florentino Ameghino School laid a wreath before his marble effigy and sang a hymn chorusing "Gloria, Gloria a Ameghino!" They also recited in unison a poem entitled "The Wise Man of Monte Hermoso," picturing Ameghino as toiling up the sides of the mountain and on its peak, aloof from common mortals, envisaging glorious new conceptions of science, all undismayed by the fact that Monte Hermoso is not a mountain and that Ameghino's work there has been pretty thoroughly discredited. An orator then mounted the rostrum and declaimed an impassioned eulogy in which Florentino was compared with Aristotle, Newton, Darwin, San Martín (the George Washington of the Argentine), Einstein, and many others, to the distinct disadvantage of these worthies.

How encouraging that is to a poor bone-digger! One of us has schools, parks, streets, and towns named after him! The rest of us may be as obscure as last month's murderer or last year's Atlantic flyer, but our colleague Ameghino has already been dead these many years and yet is not only remembered but worshipped with a fervor almost religious. There must be a catch in it somewhere! There is, and this is it: Florentino is dead. Carlos, who did most of the hardest and most valuable work, is still alive and is even more obscure than most of the rest of us, so far as popular recognition goes. He was there at the celebration. No one seemed to mind, or even notice. There are no songs about him. "Glory to Ameghino" means glory to Florentino. Carlos spends his time waiting for the 300,000 pesos that the government once promised to pay him for the collection that he made.

Florentino did start it all. A son of poor Italian immigrants, he became a country school teacher. Walking on the pampa one day he found some bones, not very ancient, a few thousand years old, but still of a peculiar and extinct beast. He looked up the little that had been written on the subject, became enthusiastic, and decided to devote his life to this study. After working awhile in and around the Province of Buenos Aires, he became more ambitious and decided to collect in Patagonia, where it was already known that bones more ancient and even more strange occurred. He had no money, so he opened a stationery store in La Plata. The store came to be known as "El Gliptodonte"—glyptodonts, big armadillo-like armored brutes, animated tanks, were among Ameghino's favorite fossils. It was agreed that Florentino would stay home and try to earn a living, while his younger brother Carlos went off and collected bones in Patagonia.

Don Carlos spent twenty years in Patagonia, and if that land is unpleasant now, it was awful then. He wandered around, usually alone, on horseback or afoot, eating when and what he could or doing without, always collecting and studying. It wrecked his health, but he made one of the world's great collections of fossil mammals. Carlos published very little, leaving most of this to his more fluent and more sedentary older brother, but the real unraveling of the broad outlines of Patagonian geology was done by him. Of course he made some mistakes for the rest of us to correct, and left many gaps for us to fill in, but I should be very proud if I felt that I could have done as well.

Florentino named and described the new animals that Carlos found. I have not counted, but I imagine that Florentino named more different kinds of animals than any other man. He named so many that he ran out of simple names, which even scientists prefer, contrary to their popular reputation, and perpetrated such tongue-twisters as *Propalaeohoplophorus* and *Asmithwoodwardia* (after the famous English paleontologist, Sir Arthur Smith Woodward). As another wreath for his effigy and as revenge for his own tendencies in nomenclature one of the new animals found by us has been named *Florentinoameghinia*. He made known a whole new world. I am quite willing to join in the chorus of "Gloria, Gloria a Ameghino," but I do so with a mental reservation, because (and do not repeat this to my Argentine friends!) he had one very curious and sometimes very annoying failing. During his lifetime even his own countrymen viewed his work with apathy if not with hostility, and he was almost isolated from other students of the same subject. He became intensely individualistic and nationalistic. He thought that he had discovered the ancestors of all the animals of the world and of man. He thought that all the beasts and all of humankind had originated in the Argentine. Suggestions to the contrary only infuriated him, and when the facts opposed his idea of things (and they do show that he was very mistaken on this score) he ignored them or violently fitted them into his theories somehow.

Florentino finally became director of the National Museum. When he died, his body lay in state and the leading citizens of the republic paid tribute to him. Carlos still lives and I have spent many an hour drinking maté with him and talking over the old days. He still hopes to collect his 300,000 pesos.

There had been three American expeditions to Patagonia before ours. Back in the late nineties, while the Ameghinos were still at the height of their activity, John Bell Hatcher spent several seasons there, mostly in the Territory of Santa Cruz. His magnificent collection is at Princeton University and together with the collection in our own Museum made by Barnum Brown, who was with Hatcher for one season, it is the basis for a long series of ponderous and important reports, the last of which was published in 1932. Hatcher died not long after his return, another victim to Patagonia. In 1911–12 Professor F. B. Loomis of Amherst College spent a few weeks in the same region visited by our expedition, but devoting himself to a different subject of study. Finally, in 1926–27 E. S. Riggs of the Field Museum in Chicago made a large collection in Santa Cruz and southern Chubut.

So Darwin, Ameghino, Hatcher, Brown, Loomis, Riggs, and a good many others, too, have gone rooting around in the débris of the lost world of Patagonia, and what they have found is rather startling. If you dig bones in North America, you find ancient elephants, three-toed horses, rhinoceroses with paired horns, saber-toothed cats, and the like. They do not seem to belong in North

America, but that is only because they once lived almost everywhere and happened to become extinct here, and although they are not quite like anything living today, most of them belong to the same families and are not wholly unfamiliar. But down there in South America they found astrapotheres, and homalodontotheres, and sparassodonts, and toxodonts, and pyrotheres, and a lot of other -theres and -odonts with wholly unfamiliar names. It is baffling to try to describe these in terms of any animals living in the world today, for they have left no descendants nor even any distant relatives. They are not like the extinct animals of any other part of the world. To describe them you have to start from the ground up, or to compare them with half a dozen different animals at once, and then add a few original touches, like the fantastic combination beasts in children's stories. An astrapothere, for instance, was about the size of a rhinoceros but didn't look a bit like one. He was four-footed and had an ungainly body as if his inventor had not been able to draw well. He had a snout something like that of a tapir, and tusks something like those of a wild boar but bigger and not so curved. He had no front teeth in his upper jaw, and his lower front teeth were neatly scalloped; if they weren't so large they would make elegant lodge emblems. He probably ate bushes, twigs, leaves, and things like that.

The reason for this startling originality in the ancient life of South America is fairly clear. During most of the Age of Mammals, that is, during the last 60,000,000 years or so, when our animals of today were evolving into what they are, North America, Europe, Asia, and Africa were joined together off and on. When new kinds of animals developed on any one of them, these beasts would sooner or later get the urge to travel and in most cases succeeded in finding a land bridge and eventually in spreading over all of these continents. If the new type of animal was unusually intelligent, or fast, or otherwise well fitted to cope with things, it was successful and became more or less world-wide in its numerous varieties. If it were less well equipped, some enemy or competitor would come wandering along from some other continent and it would lose out and soon become extinct, without having time to become anything extremely unorthodox. So it happened that in spite of numerous local differences, these continents did develop more or less the same general type of animal life.

South America was different. At one time it, too, had a land connection with the rest of the world, but that was a very long time ago, before any of our modern animals had arisen, and the creatures that then wandered into South America were very ancient and primitive. They were stranded there. The crust of the earth, always restless, buckled and sagged a little, and near the beginning of the Age of Mammals South America became an island continent. There was no Isthmus of Panama, nor any other land connection with the other continents. So far as animals that can only travel on solid land are concerned, it was completely isolated. The ones that were there could not get out, and none of the modern types developing in the rest of the world could get in. This condition continued for a long time, for millions of years, and the mammals of South America, undisturbed by outside influences, evolved in their own way and into peculiar types never found on any other continent.

Finally the earth's crust heaved a little more—these changes are usually exceedingly slow, but with millions of years to work in they achieve great results nevertheless—and the Isthmus of Panama arose, a land bridge between North and South America. For a time it was probably even wider than it is now, and in any event it permitted land animals to wander back and forth between the two areas which had been separated for so long. Down from North America went cats, dogs, bears, mastodons, horses, peccaries, camels, and a whole host of creatures that had been developing in the rest of the world while South America was an island. Some of these, like the cats, dogs, and bears, survived in both continents, although generally in somewhat different forms. Others, although originating in North America, later became extinct in the north and survived only in the south. Thus it is that some species which we think of as typical of South America, such as its camels (llamas, guanacos, etc.) are really natives of North America. Others, like the mastodons, became extinct everywhere.

South America sent us some animals too, but not so many. A few, like porcupines or the Texas armadillo, are still with us, but others, like the ground sloths and glyptodonts, have since become extinct.

This irruption of animals from North America spelled the doom of most of South America's native fauna. In their continent-asylum they had never had to face such fierce and efficient competition, and relatively few of them were equal to it. The northern animals had already faced rivals and enemies from Europe, Asia, and Africa and had survived. They had learned to run a little faster, or to think a little better, or otherwise to take care of themselves a little more efficiently than the South-American stay-at-homes, and it was not long, geologically speaking, before the latter became extinct.

I am glad that South American politicians do not know about this. They would blame it on Yankee Imperialismo, too.

It was about or shortly after the middle of the Age of Mammals that the peculiarly South American animals reached their highest development. They had then been isolated long enough to have developed their own bizarre characteristics, and the fatal invasion from the north had not yet begun. The extinct animals of that epoch have also been the best known. Their remains happen to be very abundant, very well preserved, and scattered over a large area, especially in the territory of Santa Cruz. And because they are so abundant and well preserved, more attention has been paid to them. Most expeditions have concentrated on them because there they were sure of getting many and good specimens, and expedition leaders, like everyone else, wish to be successful and make a big showing.

Yet that leaves a great deal of curiosity unsatisfied. Those creatures are all very well and the vast labor that has now made them so well known, among scientists at least, was fine and necessary, but it does not complete the picture. What all students would like to know now, and what I particularly am keen to try to learn, is what the ancestors of those animals were like. Where did they come from? Scientists are agreed that they cannot have originated spontaneously in South America. Did they come from North America in the very remote past? or Australia? or Antarctica? or Africa? or all or several of these? And before they were shut up there in South America they must have borne some sort of relationship to the beasts of the rest of the world. Just what were these relationships?

And why and how did they develop their strange characteristics anyway?

The way to find out the answers to these questions, and others related to them, is to look for the remains of older animals. If we could find fossil animals that were living in Patagonia while South America was united to the rest of the world, along about the beginning of the Age of Mammals, or soon after it became isolated, they should go far toward solving these problems. They should not yet have lost definite traces of their origin, and they should show the very beginnings of the bizarre modifications undergone by their descendants.

The study of origins is always peculiarly difficult, and I suppose that is a large part of its fascination for me and for many others. The Ameghinos made a good start at this, as they did at most of the problems of the geologic history of their part of the world. Carlos did find the remains of very ancient animals in Patagonia, and Florentino named and described them. They were very scarce, and their remains were very poorly preserved. Most of them were represented only by isolated scraps or single teeth. From such poor material it was not possible in any case to figure out a great deal about the real characteristics and relationships of these oldest of South American mammals. Florentino was obsessed by that idea of his that all the world's animals originated in South America and these scraps were of crucial importance to his theories. In trying to interpret them he went perhaps even farther astray than usual. Students in other parts of the world saw or suspected that Florentino had not interpreted this part of the history correctly, but they were dismayed by the fragmentary nature of the evidence and the difficulty of studying it or of adding to it. Their very hesitancy was a tribute to the Ameghinos. For a long time other workers were content to collect in the richer deposits of later mammals and no really serious and extensive effort was made to add to or to improve on the collections of these earliest forms.

So it fell to our expedition to take the next step in this important and interesting work. The idea was not particularly original. Its necessity, from a scientific point of view, had struck many students, and in fact the first tentative suggestion which resulted in our work came from Professor von Huene, of Tübingen

University in Germany, who was unfortunately unable to carry through his plan for coöperation with us. That such an expedition as ours had not been undertaken before was due to the necessity for a combination of unusual circumstances, which happily fell to our lot. In the first place it was necessary to find a patron who was sport enough to back a long shot like this. We were almost in despair until we met Mr. H. S. Scarritt, who immediately supplied the essential backing for our expedition. Then it was necessary for the Museum authorities to permit such work, from the point of view of exhibition inevitably giving less showy, although from a scientific point of view more valuable, results than the same time and effort expended in some richer field. The authorities of the American Museum made no difficulties in this respect. Finally it was essential to obtain the full coöperation of the Argentine scientific and civil authorities. This, as has been seen, was also forthcoming, largely because of the friendly and disinterested spirit of the directors and staffs of the leading Argentine museums.

Of course we did not expect to solve all the problems that I have briefly sketched in this chapter. Perhaps they will never be completely solved. We did hope to make a substantial contribution to their solution, and so far the results have considerably exceeded our expectations. We were successful in making a large and good collection. It proves to contain a number of animals hitherto unknown, and, what is still more important, to contain good and relatively complete specimens of animals hitherto known from mere fragments. The study of this fine material is still in progress and it is too soon to say very much about the ultimate results. Anyway, that is a different story. Here I have only tried to show just why we were in Patagonia. For being in Patagonia without a reason, even such an involved reason as this, would imply a mental condition to which no one would confess.

Or perhaps Manuel was right.

This has been a long digression but it will be easier to see just what we are doing on this cliff at Lake Colhué-Huapí. It is more than a cliff; it is a long chapter in an only partly legible history.

The first day out of Comodoro, we saw that the land rises from the sea in a series of steep and very irregular terraces to the high, barren, windswept Pampa de Castillo. We went down the far side of this into the broad Valle Hermoso, a more sheltered tableland little over half as high. Across the Valle Hermoso the land rises again, much more gently, then drops abruptly to the basin of Lake Colhué-Huapí, part of the great depression known as the Sarmiento Basin, Cuenca de Sarmiento. This scarp south of Colhué-Huapí forms a belt of badlands, about six or seven miles long in its principal part and continued eastward and westward by somewhat similar scarps. This is the great "barranca south of Colhué-Huapí," nameless but famous.

The shore of the lake itself is formed in part by broad white dusty flats flooded at high water, in part by low, steep banks of clay and soil, and in part by higher vertical cliffs of rock brilliantly streaked red and white. Beyond these shores lies a strip of gently rolling land covered by sand and gravel dotted with barren knolls of somber shale. Above this rises the irregular line of the forecliff, vividly banded and spotted in crimson, orange, yellow, and white. It is clearly stratified, in some places horizontally, and in others at steep angles. Beyond this bright and rugged forecliff is the main barranca, rising to over four hundred feet from its immediate base and nearly eight hundred feet above the lake at its culminating point. It is formed by a great series of beds of volcanic ash, white or delicately tinted yellowish or pink except for a few outstanding strata that have weathered to an orange color.

In this ash series, particularly in the lower part, there are many beautiful minerals. Seams of snow-white or pink-streaked gypsum. Clear crystals of the same mineral, gleaming in the sun. Plates and fancifully contorted forms of white or bluish translucent chalcedony. Odd balls of tubes of chalcedony which often prove to be hollow and may be lined with myriads of small, clear, rock crystals or filled with yellowish, spongy, sugar-like quartz, looking very appetizing but harder than glass. "Desert roses," globules of complexly twinned crystals of calcite and barite, looking strangely like petrified flowers, usually white but sometimes pink or even black.

Closer inspection of the barranca makes one long very literally for the wings of a dove. Foot-by-foot investigation, the task of the bone hunter, often calls for a high order of mountaineering skill. There are steep rock slides, shale slopes where the weathered clay slides off the hard subsurface into an abyss below, vertical cliffs with narrow clefts as the only practicable passes. In the softer rocks the water or recurrent rains have worn numerous caves and dark holes which seem bottomless. The only trails are those of guanacos, crossing the slopes at every practicable point in an apparently aimless fashion. In only one place, where the barranca is lowest, have they worn a real highway, deeply rutted, where many tracks from the Valle Hermoso converge and then descend as a guanaco boulevard to the lake.

The barranca, burnt by the sun and swept by the wind, is not so barren as it seems. On closer acquaintance, it is found to be teeming with life. Up there, where there seems to be no smallest tuft of verdure, there are busy ant hills, numerous spiders and beetles, and stranger insects crawl, jump and fly. Birds are innumerable and ever present: eagles perching on the highest crags, and farther down, in nooks and caves, parrots and doves nesting and other birds seeking a restless living. Field mice and other rodents manage somehow to exist here. Guanacos, pasturing only on the gentler slopes above and below, yet spend much time on the cliff, as if for amusement.

This multitude of living creatures wandering over the surface of the barranca is as nothing, either in numbers or in variety, to the stranger and almost inconceivably ancient population that lies buried, awaiting resurrection, in the beds of ash and clay.

Here the sea once roared, and the deposits of its ancient shore now lie far down, near the shore of the present inland lake; in these rocks are the shells of small queerly distorted oysters and the teeth of sharks like none that now swim in any of the oceans. Then, slowly, the continent heaved and this region rose above the sea. For millions of years it was land and on it were spread out and piled up great thicknesses of volcanic ashes, carried by the wind and by streams from the volcanoes of the ancestral cordillera to the westward. Sometimes the earth yawned, and through fissures there welled up molten floods of black lava. Then the crust sank again, and the sea laid down beds of sand and gravel over the thick ash series. In this younger sea lived the enormous Hatcher's oysters, and in it also swam strange toothed whales and now extinct penguins, some of them taller than a man. Again the land rose and the sea withdrew to the east. After some chapters whose record has been destroyed here, but can be read in other parts of Patagonia, erosive forces, wind, rain, rivers, perhaps also glaciers, shaped the present surface, biting deeply into the beds of rock laid down in previous ages and exposing their secrets.

It might seem that animal life could not flourish in a region where so much radical remodeling of the face of the earth was going on, but these things were slow and seldom really violent. The last paragraph condenses over sixty million years of history, and in spite of their great aggregate changes most of those years were calm, and during most of them this region was peculiarly favorable to animal life. There was a tremendously long heyday here when the region was neither so dry nor so cold as it is now. Then vegetation flourished, even great trees—for there are their petrified trunks to prove it—and there also flourished a host of herbivorous animals, eating the vegetation, and another, but smaller, host of carnivorous animals, eating the herbivores.

This is all recorded in the barranca, and especially in its most prominent and most interesting part, that thick volcanic ash series that is intercalated between the two records of submersion below the sea. These ash beds represent so long a time, from forty-five or fifty to twenty-five or thirty million years ago, that evolution and migration brought about many changes in animal life during that span. The animals whose bones are preserved in the lowest, and hence oldest, strata of this series are all entirely different from those found in the highest and youngest levels. On the basis of these changes, the whole series can be divided into four successive geological formations, each with its typical fauna, and each with a definite designation. This designation is double, one name being derived from a locality where the formation is particularly well developed, and another from one of the most common or most typical animals found fossil in the beds. The oldest deposit of this ash series in the barranca is the Casamayor Formation containing the *Notostylops* Fauna. Next in order come the Musters Formation and its *Astraponotus* Fauna, then the Deseado Formation with the *Pyrotherium* Fauna, and finally, at the top of the barranca and just under the remnants of the second encroachment of the sea, the Colhué-Huapí Formation which contains the *Colpodon* Fauna.

There are three sorts of changes in their animal life that distinguish these successive deposits and permit their recognition.

Some of the animals in the older beds lived on, but the time is so great that they evolved into new species, and the descendants in the younger strata are unlike their ancestors in the older. Some of the ancient animals became extinct and left no descendants. And some of the younger animals have no ancestors buried in the older beds, but were immigrants whose ancestors had lived in some other part of South America. In these three ways, life was constantly changing, as it still is today.

The animals buried here would look absurdly strange to our modern eyes. Here in the oldest deposits, the Casamayor Formation, which particularly interested our party, is indeed a Lost World. There are just two sorts of animals that would not look wholly unfamiliar today: opossums and armadillos. These, too, have changed, but relatively little so that even at that remote time these creatures were already quite recognizable.

Among the other mammals the carnivores of that time were not wolves or cats or bears or any of the other sorts now so common, but were marsupials, pouched like opossums and with brains of very poor quality. They must have looked a little like our modern types of wild dogs, and some of them were as big as wolves and had great fangs. Even more common flesh-eaters were some of the reptiles, crocodiles and enormous snakes resembling pythons or boa-constrictors.

As is always and necessarily true in any animal society, plant-feeders were much more abundant than flesh-eaters. Most of these herbivores belonged to the distinctive group of South American hoofed mammals, almost confined to that continent, and now all extinct. Of these the most varied and most common subdivision was that which labors under the unhappily long but rather rhythmic name of homalodontotheres. These creatures had five toes, each ending in a hoof, stocky legs, long heavy tails, and disproportion-ately large heads. Although they must have fed entirely on leaves, twigs, bark, and the like, most of them had large, sharp fangs, used, doubtless, for fighting among themselves and against their enemies. They varied in size from little things no bigger than lap-dogs up to the largest creatures of their time, about the size of Shetland ponies. Later there were to be much larger animals in Patagonia, but at this most remote epoch of the Age of Mammals these had not yet evolved and their ancestors were still relatively small.

Then there were delicate and swift-running little beasts known as typotheres. Although they were hoofed, they must have looked, and probably also acted, very much like hares. *Notostylops,* a common mammal for which the fauna is named, also had the strange combination of gnawing teeth and hoofed feet. True rodents, akin to the porcupine and to the guinea-pig, were later to be very abundant in Patagonia, but they appear first in the Deseado Formation, above the middle of the barranca, and are quite lacking at the older levels. Where they came from is one of the things that we would particularly like to learn, but our work so far has cast no light on this mystery.

Throughout the whole thickness of the barranca there are astrapotheres, those ungainly, unbelievable brutes which I have already tried unsuccessfully to describe. They first appear, in the oldest strata, no bigger than sheep and with rather short tusks. As you climb up the cliff, up through time, their evolution takes place before your eyes, until at the top they are great beasts as big as elephants and with savage-looking, scimitar-like tusks four feet long.

The racial span of the pyrotheres was shorter, and their whole known history is recorded in the lower three-fourths of this barranca. When its highest strata were being formed the pyrotheres were already extinct. They also begin as rather small animals, unfortunately rare and still very imperfectly known, and end in the Deseado, the *Pyrotherium* Fauna, as animals nearly elephantine in size and also strongly elephantine in appearance. They had trunks, probably a little shorter than those of modern elephants, and they had tusks, two in the skull and two in the lower jaw. Their grinding teeth had two high, sharp, transverse crests. They had so many features in common with elephants that Ameghino claimed them to be the actual ancestors of these, and even the American student Loomis believed that there is some relationship. Now, however, it is widely agreed, and I strongly concur, that the resemblance is illusive. Pyrotheres and elephants had similar habits of life, and so came to resemble each other, much as the whales have come to resemble fish although they are very far removed in blood relationship, but the pyrotheres had a very different ancestry from the elephants. Among other things, this is shown as a result of our own study from which it appears that the oldest pyrotheres, which should be closest to any common ancestor, are much less like the ancient elephants than are the younger forms.

How all these animals came to be buried and preserved is graphically shown by the same sort of thing going on today in the Sarmiento Basin, here at the foot of our barranca and all around the lakes. The basin is slowly being filled by sand, silt, and eroded volcanic ash from the surrounding higher land. Rain washes down sediment, temporary streams are choked with it, and the wind gathers dust and sand from an enormous area and deposits much of it here in the lakes or along their margins. These deposits are forming not only in the waters of Colhué-Huapí and Musters but also and very extensively on the normally dry land along their shores, and the deposits are just as truly geological strata, in spite of their recent age, as are any similar beds that were laid down millions of years ago.

And the remains of animals are being buried in them, just as the remains of the vastly more ancient animals which we seek in the barranca were once buried. Here birds and mammals are constantly dying or being killed. Sometimes the bones are eaten, and usually they lie on the surface until they disintegrate, but a few happen to fall in mud or soft sand or to be covered by dunes or by flood deposits before they decompose. These are preserved and they will, in the course of time, become fossils.

The future history can be predicted, for it is exactly what has happened innumerable times before in just such basins during the great length of geologic time. Eventually the basins will be filled with sediment and the lakes will disappear. In time, thousands or perhaps millions of years hence, with the constant, gradual shifting of the earth's crust and the enduring play of the elements, streams will cut valleys back into the deposits that filled the basin, deposits now consolidated into layers of rocks of varying hardness by the pressure of their own weight and the chemical action of the water standing in or slowly seeping through them. These strata will again be exposed along the sides of the valleys and ravines, and some paleontologist of a higher race in that dim future can here collect relics of the twentieth century and study its quaint, extinct life, just as we are studying the life of the year 45,000,000 B.C. The bones now being buried will then have lost all their animal matter, and the chemical-laden groundwater will have deposited minerals in the pore spaces of their inorganic framework. They will be mineralized or fossilized bones, like those we are collecting.

This vivid present example shows, too, why we so seldom find more than one bone of the same animal, and almost never a really complete skeleton. Under such conditions animals are very rarely buried immediately or whole. Carnivores and carrion-eaters pull them to pieces. The bones lie around on the surface for a time and usually become widely scattered before any of them are buried. Most of them disintegrate: Perhaps a flood washed some of them away. Finally a few of the more resistant parts, particularly the teeth, may be covered over and preserved, but now so far apart that it would be impossible to find them all, or, having found them, to establish with certainty that they did come from the same animal.

A fair representation of the life of Patagonia is being preserved here. Guanaco, ostrich, and sheep bones will be common fossils in this geological formation of the future. In the deposits forming in the actual lakes, fish skeletons will probably not be uncommon. Other creatures will be much more rare, but probably almost every species that lives in central Patagonia, including man, will be represented by some fragments. Yet this will give the student of the distant future a pitifully inadequate idea of the life of South America at the present time, or even of Patagonia as a whole. This is another of the difficulties that beset paleontological research. In any one field, the collector will find only the remains of the animals that happened to live in one restricted area and under the particular conditions obtaining there. For instance, this deposit will contain no trace of deer, and yet deer are fairly common in Patagonia, back in the mountains. Still less will it contain any hint of the rich and very different life of other parts of South America.

So the past history of life on the earth has to be pieced together slowly and laboriously from many finds and from decades of work in different regions. The competent student needs constantly to visualize, and to allow for, the difficulties and the inevitable gaps.

Probably the procedure of hunting for fossils can already be inferred from what has been told of their occurrence. "How do you know where to dig?" is always the first question asked when a new acquaintance hears of my profession. The answer, of course, is that we dig where we see something to dig for. There is nothing esoteric about hunting for bones; we have no sixth sense and cannot see into the earth. The first step is to go where we know fossils do occur or where we think they might. Picking a likely place requires a fairly wide knowledge of geology and close study of any previous records of travelers and explorers in the area to be visited, but thereafter it is chiefly a matter of hard work. We hunt for fossils the way you might hunt for a lost collar button, with the difference that we do not know just what we are going to find and so must be on the lookout for everything, and that we have thousands of square miles to hunt in. Sometimes discouraging days, even weeks, may pass without finding anything, and then we may find a rich pocket where a large collection can be made in one quarry.

Having come to a place where fossils do occur, like this barranca south of Colhué-Huapí, we walk over it, eyes glued to the ground, examining, as nearly as practical, every square foot of the exposed rocks. When the fossils are small but sufficiently abundant or important to justify the effort, we may literally crawl for miles on hands and knees. Many specimens have already been washed out of the rock and lie loose on the surface. Then we must endeavor to find the exact layer in which they were buried, for more of the same specimen may still be embedded there, or there may be other things there, for fossils often tend to flock together and to be much more common in certain limited strata than in others. A large proportion of the things found are worthless, isolated scraps, not worth saving. Complete teeth are usually worth while, jaws always, and complete skulls are as precious as gems. Skeletons, with rare exceptions not including the deposits we studied in Patagonia, are so seldom found as to be quite priceless.

When a bone has been found partly embedded in the rock, it must be exposed carefully to determine its extent and value, and if it is found to be worth collecting, it must be removed without damage. This is more complicated than it sounds, and success requires patience and experience. If a large excavation is necessary, this is made in the ordinary way with pick and shovel, or even in some cases with a horse or tractor-drawn scoop or with dynamite—these latter were never required in our Patagonian work, however, as the largest necessary excavation was only a few feet deep, and the rock is generally easily broken with a pick. For usual prospecting, for small excavations, and for working close to the bone where delicacy is required to avoid injury to it, a special small pick, pointed at one end and adze-shaped at the other, and small enough to be swung easily with one hand, is used. This is the universal implement of the bone-digger and he feels completely lost without it.

Exposing the actual bone is still more delicate, for, like glass, fossil bone is usually hard but always extremely fragile. This fine work is done with small curved awls or, if the rock is very hard, with slender chisels. The resulting debris is brushed away with a whisk-broom or with a small dry paint-brush. If the specimen is uncracked, firm, and small it sometimes requires no further preparation than wrapping in cotton to avoid breakage in packing. Larger and more delicate or cracked specimens require special treatment. No more of the bone is exposed than is necessary to determine the size of the specimen and its general nature, and it is taken out still embedded in a block of the surrounding rock or matrix; freeing it entirely would weaken it and is such a long, slow operation that it should be done in a laboratory and not in the field.

Thin shellac is poured copiously onto the specimen, hardening the surface and helping to hold the whole mass together. The exposed bone is then covered with Japanese rice paper, also shellacked to make it adhere closely and dry to a thin, hard shell. This serves the double purpose of protecting and strengthening the surface and of keeping the bandages, if used, from sticking to the bone itself, from which they could then be removed only with difficulty and possible damage. The bandages are strips of burlap, three or four inches wide, soaked in flour paste or in plaster, and then pressed onto the specimen with the fingers. These bandages are overlapped and crisscrossed, and may be several layers deep depending on the requirements for strength. When dry, these form a hard protective casing which holds the specimen together and prevents injury to it during its travels back to the Museum. In some cases even this is not sufficiently strong, and then wooden splints are set into the bandages.

When a fairly large block must be removed, for instance a complete skull or several different bones of a skeleton which cannot safely be separated in the field, the upper side is first exposed, shellacked, papered, and bandaged. Then a deep trench is dug around the block, the sides are undercut as deeply as seems safe, and perhaps one or more tunnels are dug under it. Bandages are applied to the undercut sides and run through the tunnels as cinches. When all this is dry and firm, the one or more columns left supporting the block are broken, the block is carefully rolled over, the lower side trimmed of its excess matrix, then shellacked and bandaged in its turn.

With the use of this general method, with some little tricks of technique too detailed to specify here, and with some common sense, it is fair to say that there is no specimen so broken or so fragile that it cannot be preserved and taken back to the Museum without injury. One sometimes reads of marvelous discoveries of the bones of extinct monsters or of men which were so delicate and so old that they crumbled at a touch, preventing the writer from producing them as evidence of his tale. Such things do not exist. No bones are so crumbly that they cannot be collected by an experienced bone digger. Even if they are mere mounds of dust, that dust can be preserved and brought back in exactly the shape in which it was found.

Finding and collecting specimens is the main part of a fossil-digger's job, but if he does only that, his work is very inadequate. Each specimen must be numbered, and in a notebook under each number must be entered the exact spot where the specimen was found, a clear designation of the rock stratum from which it came, and other pertinent information such as the date and the name of the collector. When working in regions that are inadequately surveyed, it often also falls to the bone-digger to make at least rough sketch maps of his travels. He should be a fairly accomplished geologist and should study the composition and structure of the rocks in which his specimens occur, measure the thickness of the strata and determine any tilting or faulting that has taken place. Tasks of this sort are almost endless, and the senior member of such a party sometimes finds that most of his time must be devoted to other things than actual collecting. He always finds that his work does not end at sundown, as the notes for each day must be written or placed in permanent form while they are still fresh and exactly in mind, which often takes until far into the night. Everyone in the party is considered as on duty twenty-four hours a day, seven days a week, and holidays, if any, come only on particular great occasions or when work is impossible for some reason.

Even when collecting is completed, when the fossils are all securely packed in stout boxes, when local legal requirements have all been met, and when the shipment has actually reached the Museum—even then the work is only well begun. The rest takes place in the Museum, and invariably takes much longer than the time spent in the field. Preparators must clean each bone, removing the encasing matrix grain by grain. If soft, the bones must be carefully hardened, and if fragile, they must be reinforced with steel rods inside them or in some inconspicuous place along the outside. Fragments found scattered must be carefully matched, like a jig-saw puzzle, to see whether they will not fit together and make something more complete. Missing parts must be modeled in plaster, so far as this can be done with no possibility of error, by comparison with other similar specimens.

When this work is done, the specimens must be studied. They are carefully compared with all others known and the name of the animal to which they belong is determined. If they are of some creature not known before, a new name must be given to them and a description published. New or otherwise particularly important things must be photographed or drawn. The age of the strata from which the fossils came must be determined. Detailed reports on the results of the whole expedition must be written and published.

Finally, specimens must be selected and placed on exhibition. Iron supports have to be made to hold them, often a long and difficult task. The exhibition needs to be planned carefully, and comprehensible and enlightening labels composed and printed. Specimens not desired for exhibition must also be catalogued and then stored where they can be found readily when needed for study. In any collection there are numerous specimens, sometimes far the greater number, that are not exhibited. A specimen may have very great scientific value, and yet not have the properties of popular appeal, of completeness, of striking character, or of clarity in demonstrating some special point, that are requisite for appropriate exhibition in a large museum. The study collections of such an institution usually exceed the public exhibition both in bulk and in value.

Fossil hunting is far the most fascinating of all sports. I speak for myself, although I do not see how any true sportsman could fail to agree with me if he had tried bone digging. It has some danger, enough to give it zest and probably about as much as in the average modern engineered big-game hunt, and the danger is wholly to the hunter. It has uncertainty and excitement and all the thrills of gambling with none of its vicious features. The hunter never knows what his bag may be, perhaps nothing, perhaps a creature never before seen by human eyes. Over the next hill may lie a great discovery! It requires knowledge, skill, and some degree of hardihood. And its results are so much more important, more worth while, and more enduring than those of any other sport! The fossil hunter does not kill; he resurrects. And the result of his sport is to add to the sum of human pleasure and to the treasures of human knowledge.

L. S. B. LEAKEY

The Search for Man's Ancestors

L. S. B. Leakey's Adam's Ancestors *is scientifically accurate and is written in a most interesting manner so that both specialist and lay reader can glean the exciting information present. Not only is Dr. Leakey the most outstanding anthropologist living today, but he also travels the world, giving lectures to university students, faculty, and the general public. Some of the lectures he has given are the Herbert Spencer Lecture, Oxford University; Julian Huxley Memorial Lecture, Birmingham University; Regents Lecture, University of California; Siliman Lecturer at Yale, and others. Listed are a few of his publications*: Classification of the Bow and Arrow in Africa, Adam's Ancestors, The Stone Age Cultures of Kenya, Olduvai Gorge, Tentative Study of Pleiostocene Sequence, *and* Stone Age Cultures of North East Angola.

It is not so very long ago—a matter of about a hundred years only—that most people still accepted the opinion of Bishop Usher that man was created in 4004 B.C., and that Adam was the first representative of humanity on earth.

Today the position has changed to such an extent that the discovery of any new piece of evidence relating to human evolution is considered important news by the Press and is also often discussed at length in the wireless programmes of most countries.

Most educated people believe in evolution in the animal and

plant kingdoms, and consequently are more than usually interested in any light that can be thrown on the stages of evolution of man himself.

The first discovery to be made of an authenticated fossil human skull was that of the Gibraltar skull, found in 1848, but its significance was not realized until some twenty years later, by which time its pride of place had been taken by the discovery of the famous Neanderthal skull in 1856, which has given its name to a whole race of extinct humanity which, until relatively recently, was regarded as being in the direct line of ancestry leading to man as we know him today.

Since these early discoveries, finds of fossil human and sub-human remains have been made in ever-increasing numbers, and whereas most of the early discoveries were to a great extent accidental, and incidental to a search for other things, today the search for the ancestors and cousins of *Homo sapiens* is being conducted increasingly by trained scientists in a determined effort to clear up the story of man's early history.

The study of Prehistory is a complicated subject and is not only confined to the search for and interpretation of fossil human remains. This aspect of the subject is in fact only one very small part, although it is the central figure of the picture, so to speak, but the background is made up of studies of the climate, geography, cultures, and associated fauna and flora of the periods in the past history of the earth when man was gradually and slowly evolving into the creature we call *Homo sapiens* today. But before we pass on, in the succeeding chapters of this book, to discuss the many different component parts of the picture of Adam's ancestors, let us briefly consider some of the ways in which the evidence is found.

It has to be admitted that even today, when the search for Stone Age cultures and fossil humans is more scientifically organized than ever before, luck still plays a very major part in most discoveries of importance.

After all, the surface of the earth is immense, and a very large part of the earth's crust is covered up by vegetation and by surface

From *Adam's Ancestors* by L. S. B. Leakey. Reprinted by permission of Methuen & Co., Ltd., London, England. Copyright 1934. Harper & Row Publishers, Inc., New York.

deposits of humus and hillwash and other superficial deposits, so that, to a considerable extent, the search for evidence of man's past in geological deposits is governed by chance. Rivers and other forces of nature cut through geological deposits containing the evidence which we seek, and it is a matter of luck whether this erosion takes place at a time when some trained scientist is on the spot to recognize the hidden treasures so exposed.

Similarly, commercial undertakings carried out for the exploitation of river gravels and brick earths, or alluvial deposits containing gold or diamonds or tin are often the means by which deposits containing missing parts of the giant jigsaw puzzle are revealed. Here again it is a matter of pure luck whether a person qualified to recognize the stone tools and fossils is present before they are destroyed.

The old terraces of the Thames valley at Swanscombe have for a long time been exploited commercially for gravel and sand, and for years it has been known that they contained many Stone Age tools, washed into them when the geography of England was very different from today. The workmen soon learnt from visiting prehistorians how to recognize the commoner types of stone tool and most of these were preserved as the work progressed, and found their way to museums and private collections. It was, however, definitely a matter of luck that one of Dr. Marston's periodic visits to Swanscombe should have coincided with the uncovering of part of a fossil human skull—a piece of bone which many other visitors to the site might have failed to recognize—and thus lead to the preservation and study of the oldest human fossil so far discovered on English soil.

The Companhia Diamentes de Angola, in the course of their exploitation of old alluvial gravels containing a great wealth of diamonds, had to remove an immense overlying deposit of red wind-blown sand, and it was a matter of luck that the chief geologist to the company, in the person of Mr. J. Janmart, was interested in Prehistory and able to recognize stone tools when he saw them, thus leading to the discovery of a most important chapter in the story of the Stone Age cultures of the African continent, in a place where, but for this commercial exploitation of diamonds, little if any evidence would have been found.

It was a matter of considerable luck, too, that in 1926, the steamer in which I was crossing Lake Victoria from Kisumu to Entebbe had to change its sailing schedule and pass Rusinga Island in daylight instead of in darkness. This enabled me to examine the stratified deposits of rock on the island with field-glasses and make a note that the island looked a very promising place to search for fossils. This little incident led to my making my first visit to the island in 1931 and discovering, on my very first day there, some fragmentary fossil fragments of an ape jaw; a discovery which led up to the finding of the famous *Proconsul* skull by my wife on 2 October, 1948.

These three typical examples of the part which luck has played and must continue to play in the search for the evidence of the story of man's past, must suffice to make us remember always that the element of chance is very great and that we owe most of our knowledge of our past to this cause.

But it would be wrong to let you think that everything is a matter of luck, for it is not. No amount of luck, in the way in which nature or man exposes the deposits containing the evidence of man's past, would be of any use if there were not people with sufficient knowledge and training to recognize the finds. Moreover, it is not only in geological deposits that the evidence is to be found; many discoveries of fossil human skulls and stone implements are made in the accumulated debris in caves and rock-shelters and at such sites only excavation by persons who have been very carefully trained for the work can result in a proper interpretation of the story that is revealed by the digging of the deposits.

This fact is being more and more impressed upon us as we reconsider some of the work upon which the foundations of Prehistory were laid. A great deal of the early work on the Stone Age cultures to be found in caves was carried out in France, in the Dordogne, by people who inevitably—since they were pioneers in Prehistory—were not really trained to the work. The results of their work were magnificent, but the interpretation was oversimplified, so that for years it was believed that the sequence of evolution of Stone Age cultures was a simple series of successive stages, whereas, in fact, the story is far from simple, as we shall see in later chapters.

If we want to make a proper study of man's past in any particular area, one of the first things that has to be done is to study the evidence of what we may call Prehistoric Geography and Prehistoric Climate. This can only be done by the aid of geological studies.

Climate and geographical position have always played a most important part in determining where man made his home, where he hunted, and where he lived, just as they do today, and since neither the climate nor yet the geography of the world has remained the same over the long period of time since man first became man, and the still longer period when man's ape-like ancestors were slowly evolving to a human status, we must study the world changes of climate and geography before we can appreciate details of the story of man's past history.

As we shall see when we discuss early man's environment in more detail in the next chapter, there have been a number of major fluctuations in the climate of the world as a whole since the earth was formed, but it is the changes during the last million years or so that are the most important to us, for it was during this period that man was gradually making himself dominant over the rest of the animal kingdom.

Since these changes of world climate manifested themselves in the temperate zones by advances and retreats of the ice-sheets and in tropical and subtropical countries by alternating very much wetter and much drier periods than today, we clearly cannot study man's past without knowing something about the climate of the times. It would be useless to look for living-sites of prehistoric man at a place which—at the particular point of time in which you were interested—was covered by vast glaciers. Nor would it be any better to search in a place which, at the relevant time, was covered by the deep waters of a lake, or was so dry as to be completely waterless.

But equally, a locality which might have been quite uninhabitable at a certain point in the time-scale may have had a really suitable climate for human occupation at a later or an earlier date. Let me illustrate this point by reference to the prehistoric site known as Olorgesailie in Kenya Colony.

Today, the Olorgesailie area is practically a desert, and for the greater part of the year is uninhabited by man, for that reason. But when you begin studying the geological deposits of the area you can see that they are composed in large part of clays and sands and silts and gravels laid down in a lake.

Clearly, if there was ever a big lake in an area that is now desert this must have been at a time when the climate was much wetter than today, so it is first of all necessary to start to make a more detailed study of these old lake deposits, to see what story they have to tell.

Part of the deposits are very fine-grained silts, obviously laid down in calm and fairly deep water; it would be useless to look for Stone Age man's living-sites in these beds for they were formed under water. But at the top of the silts there is an irregular line separating them from the sands above. What does this mean? The lake must have dwindled so that the silts, laid down in the deep water, were exposed to the sun and wind, and a land surface formed; but probably the lake did not dry up completely, so that this would have been a land surface reasonably near to the waters of the lake while it receded. Such a land surface would have been an excellent place for Stone Age hunters to camp on, near to water for their own needs and with the likelihood that the wild animals of the time would be plentiful near the lake shore, as they are today in Africa by the shores of lakes, where man has not yet destroyed them. This old land surface, then, is worth exploring in more detail, and so you start your search, and if you are lucky—for clearly you cannot excavate the whole land surface—you find, as we did, the clear evidence of a camp site with hundreds of discarded stone implements and the fossilized bones of the animals which Stone Age man killed and ate.

Over this ancient land surface, with its Stone Age camp site, lies a thick layer of water-deposited sand, laid down in shallow water as the level of the lake responded to a fresh oscillation in the climate and started to rise again. The sandy nature of the deposit gradually changes to clay, betokening the presence of deep water again in the area. Above this clay is another irregular line separating it from another series of water-laid deposits. This is another land surface and, as before, it is worth investigating for possible human occupation sites. Actually, at Olorgesailie we found ten different old land surfaces, and on each, in due course, we located one or more camp sites of Stone Age man. Thus, the study of the geological deposits revealed the story of climatic changes in the area, as well as evidence of some of the stages of development of the Stone Age culture of that particular part of the world at the period corresponding to the formation of the series of deposits.

I mentioned that the sites of the old camps were marked by 'hundreds of discarded stone implements and the fossilized bones of the animals which Stone Age man killed and ate'. In finding these fossil bones we were particularly fortunate, for by no means all geological deposits are suitable for the preservation of bones and teeth as fossils, and they are one of the things we need most for the dating of any given geological deposit in order to be able to assign it to its correct position in the time-scale.

In working out the story of the earth's history geologists are dependent to a very considerable extent on the fossil remains of animal and plant life. Such fossil remains do not of course give an absolute date in terms of years, but they do provide an excellent clue to the relative date of one deposit compared with another. I shall discuss this a little more fully in the next chapter, but I will indicate here very briefly the methods that are used.

We know that evolution has not only taken place in the past but is still taking place, as you can see for yourself if you consider for a moment the history of the dog. The numerous races of present-day dogs, ranging from St. Bernards to Dachshunds, have all been evolved in the last few thousand years from one, or possibly a few, very generalized kinds of dog which were domesticated by man towards the end of the Stone Age. Of course, this very rapid evolution is unusual and has been greatly accelerated by man's careful selection of breeding stock. If thousands of years hence scientists find deposits containing fossil bones of Dachshunds and Pekingese and, shall we say, merino sheep, in the same deposit as the bones of the otter, rabbit, and fox, they will date the deposit by the creatures which are obviously *new* to the geological sequence and not by the fox or the otter whose bones will also be known as fossils in somewhat older deposits.

So, in studying the past, we can examine the fossil bones of animals which we find in deposits that we wish to date, and can say 'here is a fossil representing the straight-tusked elephant', or 'this is the tooth of some particular stage in the evolution of the horse', and by this means arrive at a backward limit of dating in the time-scale.

The estimation of the forward limit is not quite so easy, since it must be based upon negative evidence to a considerable extent; except when there is a good stratification and where the overlying deposits can also be dated.

It must also be remembered that in any area where the Stone Age culture sequence has been fairly fully worked out on a stratigraphical basis, it is sometimes possible to use the actual stone implements found at a site as evidence for dating a deposit.

Here I must digress for a moment to stress one very important point. Any conclusions which are based upon one or two specimens only, whether they are fossil bones or Stone Age tools, must be regarded with the gravest doubts, and it is essential to have a large assemblage of specimens—the larger the better—from any geological horizon or level in a cave deposit before drawing conclusions. And the conclusions must be based upon a study of the total assemblage and not by reference only to selected specimens.

This would seem to be such an obvious matter of common sense that it should be unnecessary to state it categorically in a book of this kind. But even today, when the study of Prehistory has had more than a hundred years in which to develop a code of procedure, it is unfortunately still easy to find examples of single selected specimens being used as a basis for dating purposes and causing erroneous conclusions to be drawn.

Just pause for a moment to consider the contents of the room or the house in which you are reading these words. In all probability there will be some objects such as candlesticks, for instance, which could as well belong to 300 years ago as to the present day. There will also be many objects whose first appearance in our culture can be dated to the present century—wireless, perhaps, or plastic cups, or stainless steel furnishings. There are also likely to be one or two objects in the house which, in their form and material, are genuine antiques that are not made at all today.

Now clearly, should all this material be buried and preserved, it would be most misleading to use either the antiques or the objects with a wide range of use in time, like the candlesticks, for dating purposes, and it would be upon a consideration of the whole assemblage, including the wireless set and other objects of the present century, that the scientist of the future would be justified in saying 'this level dates to about the twentieth century, although it contains several elements from an earlier period'.

Whereas the first discovery of an authenticated skull of fossil man was, as we have seen, made a little over a hundred years ago, the story of the discovery of the stone tools which represent part of his material culture dates back to a much earlier period.

So far as we know, the first person who found a Palaeolithic stone implement and actually recognized it as a relic of some culture long antedating the historical period, was John Frere, F.R.S., who in 1791 found a number of hand-axes of the culture which we now call the Acheulean, at Hoxne in Suffolk, and described them as 'belonging to a very remote period indeed, even beyond that of the present world'.

Prior to this, a pear-shaped stone implement had been found at what was then Gray's Inn Lane in London during 1690, in close association with the tooth of an extinct elephant, but the full significance of this discovery had not been appreciated.

The next important milestone was the demonstration, by Tournal in 1828, that man had been the contemporary of an extinct fauna of the Pleistocene Age in the deposits found in a cave at Bize. A few years later Schmerling confirmed this as a result of his excavations near Liége. But it was not until 1858 and 1859, after the discovery and study of the Neanderthal skull found in 1856 had caused such a sensation, that British scientists began to give serious consideration to the question of the great antiquity of the Stone Age.

It was in these years that a number of leading British scientists visited Abbeville and Amiens to examine for themselves the discoveries made by Boucher de Perthes, who, as early as 1847, had published his first account of the finding of unquestionable stone implements in ancient river gravels and other similar deposits in association with bones of extinct animals. As a result of this visit the British scientists became convinced of the claims that were being made for the antiquity of man, and a paper was read before the Royal Society in 1859, while in 1863 the first monograph on the subject appeared. This was the famous book by Charles Lyell, the geologist, entitled *Geological Evidence of the Antiquity of Man*.

The publication of this book marked a very important step forward in the study of Prehistory. From that date onwards new discoveries were made in quick succession, and the study of the Stone Age cultures, based upon an examination of the stratigraphical evidence, began to be seriously undertaken.

By the end of the century a vast amount of material had been accumulated and published, not only in Europe, but also to some extent in other countries such as South Africa and even Java.

During the fifty years of the present century (in spite of the interruption of two world wars) the study of the story of man's past before the dawn of history has advanced so rapidly that there is now practically no country in the world which has not yielded some evidence to help fill in parts of the picture. Naturally, one of the results of this mass of work is that we find that the story is a much more complex one than the earlier workers supposed. Many of the earlier conclusions, based mainly on work in South-west Europe, have got to be reconsidered and the evidence re-interpreted in the light of discoveries made in other countries and even other continents.

The picture, therefore, as it will be presented in the chapters that follow, differs in a great many respects from that which I gave in the edition of this book written in 1933. It is equally certain that some of the conclusions presented here will have to be revised within the next few years, as further work continues.

To conclude this chapter I want to try to answer a question which I am very frequently asked. How do remains of Stone Age cultures, and sometimes of the men who made them, come to be preserved in caves and in geological deposits? It is of the greatest importance to understand the answer to this question, for unless we do, we cannot hope to interpret correctly the results obtained by excavation.

Let us for a moment imagine that we can stand back and observe the sequence of events at a rock-shelter some twenty or thirty thousand years ago.

A Stone Age hunter is wandering down the valley in search of game when he espies a rock-shelter in the side of the rocky cliff above him. Carefully, and with the utmost caution, he climbs up to it, fearful lest he may find that it is occupied by the members of some other Stone Age family who will resent his intrusion, or possibly even that it is the lair of a lion or a cave bear. At last he is close enough, and he sees that it is quite unoccupied, and so he enters and makes a thorough examination. He decides that it is a much more suitable habitation than the little shelter where he and his family are living at present, and he goes off to fetch them.

Next we see the family arriving and settling into their new home. A fire is lit either from some embers carefully nursed and brought from the old home, or else by means of a simple, wooden fire drill. (We cannot say for certain what methods Stone Age man used for obtaining fire, but we do know that from a very early period he did make use of fire, for hearths are a common feature in almost any occupation level in caves and rock-shelters.)

Probably some of the family then go off to collect grass or bracken to make rough beds upon which they will sleep, while others break branches from bushes and trees in the near-by thicket and construct a rude wall across the front of the shelter. The skins of various wild animals are then unrolled and deposited in the new home, together with such household goods as they possess.

And now the family is fully settled in, and the day-to-day routine is resumed once more. The men hunt and trap animals for food, the women probably help in this and also collect edible fruits and nuts and roots. Gradually, rubbish starts to accumulate on the floor; decaying vegetation mingles with wood ash scraped from the hearth, and mixed with all this are the bones and teeth of the animals that have served as food. The stone and bone tools, which comprise the weapons and domestic implements of the family, break or become blunt through use, and they are discarded and new ones made. Blocks of suitable material collected during hunting expeditions have been brought to the new home, and from these flakes are knocked off to make new tools. This process involves the scattering of many waste flakes and chips over the floor, and these soon become incorporated in the debris in the same way as the tools that have become too blunt for further use. When the weather is fine a great deal of the work is done on the platform outside the shelter, so that deposits accumulate there too.

Years pass, the older members of the family die and—according to custom—are buried in the floor of the shelter; the younger members of the family grow up and marry, and all the time the home continues to be used, so that more and more debris accumulates on the floor. A large part of this debris is perishable material which by the process of decay turns into soil, throughout which imperishable objects of stone and bone are scattered.

Naturally enough, the deposits so formed do not accumulate evenly over the whole floor, and although the floor may have been level to start with (and even this is seldom the case) it very soon ceases to be so.

And so generations pass and a considerable depth of deposit is formed representing an occupation level, and then something happens which results in the shelter being vacated. When this occurs the shelter may perhaps be taken over almost immediately by some other Stone Age family—possibly of a different tribe and with a somewhat different culture—in which case we shall get a somewhat different occupation level superimposed upon the first one. On the other hand, the shelter may remain untenanted for a considerable period of time, in which case dust and leaves and other purely natural material will collect and gradually build up a sterile layer covering the occupation level, until the place is once more selected as a living site.

And so the story goes on; occupation levels alternate with sterile layers, blocks of rock fall from the roof, and slowly but surely the floor level rises.

If the shelter happens to be in a limestone cliff and the site is unoccupied during a period when the climate is very moist, a hard deposit of stalagmite may form over the floor and seal in the underlying deposits. On the other hand, if the shelter is not very high above the level of the river, a spell of heavy floods may result in the partial or complete scouring out of the unconsolidated deposits. Or, alternatively, a layer of water-laid sand may be formed.

Such occurrences and many other events will all leave their traces in the shelter, and if the eventual scientific excavation is carried out with patience and skill the evidence can be recognized and interpreted and the story worked out. If, however, the excavator is not well trained, or if he works too fast, part at least of the evidence will be lost. Above all, the excavator must be very critical, taking care not to confuse facts with his own theoretical interpretation of them, and seizing every opportunity to check and re-check each stage of his work.

Once the facts have been collected, it may be necessary to call in specialists in various branches of science before the data can be fully interpreted. The palaeontologist will have to help identify the various animal bones and teeth and state what conclusions as to geological age and climatic conditions may be drawn from them. The geologist and soil analyst may also be able to give aid in determining climatic conditions from soil samples of the deposits from different levels in the excavation, while the botanist may be able in some cases to identify certain trees and plants from well-preserved pieces of charcoal found in hearths. Even the physicist, by the latest methods of analysis of carbon 14, may be able to help to provide an approximate age from examination of the charcoal.

The stone and bone implements and even the waste flakes will also tell their own story, and so, when all the necessary collaboration has been achieved, the prehistorian will be able to present a reasonably accurate story of the sequence of events in the rock-shelter.

I have already indicated how Stone Age living sites may come to be sandwiched between geological deposits along the shores of a fluctuating lake, but many other types of geological deposit will also be found to contain stone implements. These, too, if properly studied and understood, will yield very valuable information about Stone Age man and his cultures.

Let us first consider the case of river deposits such as gravels, clays, and sands. These, if they were formed during the period when Stone Age man lived, will often be found to contain stone implements, sometimes in great quantity.

It is not difficult to understand how remains of Stone Age cultures came to be incorporated in river deposits if we think in terms of what is happening today. Who has not stood upon a bridge and, looking down into the water beneath, has seen lying on the gravel in the bed of the stream broken bottles, tin cans, bits of china, bones, and other relics of our present-day culture? All of these objects are now being slowly incorporated in the sands and gravels and clays of the river, and they have reached their present position either because they have been thrown in or else washed in by flood waters.

Stone Age man—especially at certain stages of his history—was particularly fond of living close to the banks of streams and rivers, probably because he had no vessels in which to store and carry water and therefore liked to live as close as possible to his water supply. Living thus—and by analogy with what happens today—it is quite natural that many of his cultural objects as well as the bones thrown away after his meals got washed into the rivers and incorporated in the deposits. Owing to changes of climate and topography, as we shall see in the next chapter, many of these old river deposits of Stone Age date lie, today, either on high-level terraces well above the present river levels, or in sunken channels; whole parts of these old deposits are sometimes washed into the present-day rivers, and in this way cultural material of a much earlier date, that was originally incorporated in the old gravels, gets re-deposited in younger gravels, bringing about a mixture of elements in the newly forming gravels.

Such a mixture of the remains of Stone Age cultures of several periods, in a single level of gravel or sand, is not an unusual phenomenon, and it is only by very careful examination of all the evidence that the story can be sorted out.

Another type of geological deposit which is often found to contain Stone Age man's tools, is that formed under glacial conditions. Considerable areas of the zones that at the present time have a temperate climate were, during the Stone Age, covered from time to time by ice-sheets. This was the result of world changes of climate which we shall discuss in the next chapter. Deposits formed under glacial conditions often consist of boulder clays and glacial outwash gravels. When an ice-sheet advances over the countryside it tends to plough up all the surface deposits that lie in its path and also to pick up most of this material and carry it forward. If the deposits so ploughed into and picked up already contained Stone Age tools of an earlier period, or if such implements were lying on the surface, they too were carried forward and churned up with the mass of other material. When further changes of climate resulted in the melting of the ice-sheets, all the mass of rubble and rock and earth that had been caught up in the ice was deposited in the form of boulder clays and outwash gravels. Thus it often happens that such glacial deposits contain Stone Age implements, but that does not mean that the men who made them were living in the area while the ice-sheets were there. It means rather that they had lived at some period before that particular advance of the ice.

From what I have said, it is clear that ordinary common sense is a very important factor in the interpretation of the past. To this must be added a great deal of scientific knowledge, if we are to obtain a proper picture of the climate, geography, and general environment which existed in the days when Stone Age man lived. In the next chapter we will consider some of the results of this study and try to see what the world was like when our prehistoric ancestors roamed over the land.

ALDOUS HUXLEY

The Politics of Ecology:
The Question of Survival

Aldous Harley Huxley, grandson of Thomas H. Huxley, the champion campaigner for Darwinism, and brother of biologist Julian Huxley, is one of the great men of letters in the English language. His Point Counterpoint, Brave New World, Ape and Essence, Chrome Yellow, Antic Hay *and others too numerous to mention comprise his literary contributions.* The Politics of Ecology *included in this anthology points out in a scientifically dramatic fashion the problems revolving around overpopulation.*

In politics, the central and fundamental problem is the problem of power. Who is to exercise power? And by what means, by what authority, with what purpose in view, and under what controls? Yes, under what controls? For, as history has made it abundantly clear, to possess power is *ipso facto* to be tempted to abuse it. In mere self-preservation we must create and maintain institutions that make it difficult for the powerful to be led into those temptations which, succumbed to, transform them into tyrants at home and imperialists abroad.

For this purpose what kind of institutions are effective? And, having created them, how can we guarantee them against obsolescence? Circumstances change, and, as they change, the old, the once so admirably effective devices for controlling power cease to be adequate. What then? Specifically, when advancing science and acceleratingly progressive technology alter man's long-established relationship with the planet on which he lives, revolutionize his societies, and at the same time equip his rulers with new and immensely more powerful instruments of domination, what ought we to do? What *can* we do?

Very briefly let us review the situation in which we now find ourselves and, in the light of present facts, hazard a few guesses about the future.

On the biological level, advancing science and technology have set going a revolutionary process that seems to be destined for the next century at least, perhaps for much longer, to exercise a decisive influence upon the destinies of all human societies and their individual members. In the course of the last fifty years extremely effective methods for lowering the prevailing rates of infant and adult mortality were developed by Western scientists. These methods were very simple and could be applied with the expenditure of very little money by very small numbers of not very highly trained technicians. For these reasons, and because everyone regards life as intrinsically good and death as intrinsically bad, they were in fact applied on a world-wide scale. The results were spectacular. In the past, high birth rates were balanced by high death rates. Thanks to science, death rates have been halved but, except in the most highly industrialized, contraceptive-using countries, birth rates remain as high as ever. An enormous and accelerating increase in human numbers has been the inevitable consequence.

At the beginning of the Christian era, so demographers assure us, our planet supported a human population of about two hundred and fifty millions. When the Pilgrim Fathers stepped ashore, the figure had risen to about five hundred millions. We see, then, that in the relatively recent past it took sixteen hundred years for the human species to double its numbers. Today world population stands at three thousand millions. By the year 2000, unless something appallingly bad or miraculously good should happen in the interval, six thousand millions of us will be sitting down to breakfast every morning. In a word, twelve times as many people are destined to double their numbers in one-fortieth of the time.

This is not the whole story. In many areas of the world human numbers are increasing at a rate much higher than the average for the whole species. In India, for example, the rate of increase is now 2.3 per cent per annum. By 1990 its four hundred and fifty million inhabitants will have become nine hundred million inhabitants. A comparable rate of increase will raise the population of China to the billion mark by 1980. In Ceylon, in Egypt, in many of the countries of South and Central America, human numbers are increasing at an annual rate of 3 per cent. The result will be a doubling of their present populations in approximately twenty-three years.

On the social, political, and economic levels, what is likely to happen in an underdeveloped country whose people double themselves in a single generation, or even less? An underdeveloped society is a society without adequate capital resources (for capital is what is left over after primary needs have been satisfied, and in underdeveloped countries most people never satisfy their primary needs); a society without a sufficient force of trained teachers, administrators, and technicians; a society with few or no industries and few or no developed sources of industrial power; a society, finally, with enormous arrears to be made good in food production, education, road building, housing, and sanitation. A quarter of a century from now, when there will be twice as many of them as there are today, what is the likelihood that the members of such a society will be better fed, housed, clothed, and schooled than at present? And what are the chances in such a society for the maintenance, if they already exist, or the creation, if they do not exist, of democratic institutions?

Not long ago Mr. Eugene Black, the former president of the World Bank, expressed the opinion that it would be extremely difficult, perhaps even impossible, for an underdeveloped country with a very rapid rate of population increase to achieve full industrialization. All its resources, he pointed out, would be absorbed year by year in the task of supplying, or not quite supplying, the primary needs of its new members. Merely to stand still, to maintain its current subhumanly inadequate standard of living, will require hard work and the expenditure of all the nation's available capital. Available capital may be increased by loans and gifts from abroad; but in a world where the industrialized nations are involved in power politics and an increasingly expensive armament race, there will never be enough foreign aid to make much difference. And even if the loans and gifts to underdeveloped countries were to be substantially increased, any resulting gains would be largely nullified by the uncontrolled population explosion.

The situation of these nations with such rapidly increasing populations reminds one of Lewis Carroll's parable in *Through the Looking Glass,* where Alice and the Red Queen start running at full speed and run for a long time until Alice is completely out of breath. When they stop, Alice is amazed to see that they are still at their starting point. In the looking glass world, if you wish to retain your present position, you must run as fast as you can. If you wish to get ahead, you must run at least twice as fast as you can.

If Mr. Black is correct (and there are plenty of economists and demographers who share his opinion), the outlook for most of the world's newly independent and economically non-viable nations is gloomy indeed. To those that have shall be given. Within the next ten or twenty years, if war can be avoided, poverty will almost have disappeared from the highly industrialized and contraceptive-using societies of the West. Meanwhile, in the underdeveloped and uncontrolledly breeding societies of Asia, Africa, and Latin America the condition of the masses (twice as numerous, a generation from now, as they are today) will have become no better and may even be decidedly worse than it is at present. Such a decline is foreshadowed by current statistics of the Food and Agriculture Organization of the United Nations. In some underdeveloped regions of the world, we are told, people are somewhat less adequately fed, clothed, and housed than were their parents and grandparents thirty and forty years ago. And what of elementary education? UNESCO recently provided an answer. Since the end of World War II heroic efforts have been made to teach the whole world how to read. The population explosion has largely stultified these efforts. The absolute number of illiterates is greater now than at any time.

The contraceptive revolution which, thanks to advancing science and technology, has made it possible for the highly developed societies of the West to offset the consequences of death control by a planned control of births, has had as yet no effect upon the family life of people in underdeveloped countries. This is not surprising. Death control, as I have already remarked, is easy, cheap, and can be carried out by a small force of technicians. Birth control, on the other hand, is rather expensive, involves the whole adult population, and demands of those who practice it a good deal of forethought and directed willpower. To persuade hundreds of millions of men and women to abandon their tradition-hallowed views of sexual morality, then to distribute and teach them to make use of contraceptive devices or fertility-controlling drugs—this is a huge and difficult task, so huge and so difficult that it seems very unlikely that it can be successfully carried out, within a sufficiently short space of time, in any of the countries where control of the birth rate is most urgently needed.

Extreme poverty, when combined with ignorance, breeds that lack of desire for better things which has been called "wantlessness"—the resigned acceptance of a subhuman lot. But extreme poverty, when it is combined with the knowledge that some societies are affluent, breeds envious desires and the expectation that these desires must of necessity, and very soon, be satisfied. By means of the mass media (those easily exportable products of advancing science and technology) some knowledge of what life is like in affluent societies has been widely disseminated throughout the world's underdeveloped regions. But, alas, the science and technology which have given the industrial West its cars, refrigerators, and contraceptives have given the people of Asia, Africa, and Latin America only movies and radio broadcasts, which they are too simple-minded to be able to criticize, together with a population explosion, which they are still too poor and too tradition-bound to be able to control by deliberate family planning.

In the context of a 3, or even of a mere 2 per cent annual increase in numbers, high expectations are foredoomed to disappointment. From disappointment, through resentful frustration, to widespread social unrest the road is short. Shorter still is the road from social unrest, through chaos, to dictatorship, possibly of the Communist party, more probably of generals and colonels. It would seem, then, that for two-thirds of the human race now suffering from the consequences of uncontrolled breeding in a context of industrial backwardness, poverty, and illiteracy, the prospects for democracy, during the next ten or twenty years, are very poor.

From underdeveloped societies and the probable political consequences of their explosive increase in numbers we now pass to the prospect for democracy in the fully industrialized, contraceptive-using societies of Europe and North America.

It used to be assumed that political freedom was a necessary pre-condition of scientific research. Ideological dogmatism and dictatorial institutions were supposed to be incompatible with the open-mindedness and the freedom of experimental action, in the absence of which discovery and invention are impossible. Recent history has proved these comforting assumptions to be completely unfounded. It was under Stalin that Russian scientists developed the A-bomb and, a few years later, the H-bomb. And it is under a more-than-Stalinist dictatorship that Chinese scientists are now in process of performing the same feat.

Another disquieting lesson of recent history is that, in a developing society, science and technology can be used exclusively for the enhancement of military power, not at all for the benefit of the masses. Russia has demonstrated, and China is now doing its best to demonstrate, that poverty and primitive conditions of life for the overwhelmingly majority of the population are perfectly compatible with the wholesale production of the most advanced and sophisticated military hardware. Indeed, it is by deliberately imposing poverty on the masses that the rulers of developing industrial nations are able to create the capital necessary for building an armament industry and maintaining a well equipped army, with which to play their parts in the suicidal game of international power politics.

We see, then, that democratic institutions and libertarian traditions are not at all necessary to the progress of science and technology, and that such progress does not of itself make for human betterment at home and peace abroad. Only where democratic institutions already exist, only where the masses can vote their rulers out of office and so compel them to pay attention to the popular will, are science and technology used for the benefit of the majority as well as for increasing the power of the State. Most human beings prefer peace to war, and practically all of them would rather be alive than dead. But in every part of the world men and women have been brought up to regard nationalism as axiomatic and war between nations as something cosmically ordained by the Nature of Things. Prisoners of their culture, the masses, even when they are free to vote, are inhibited by the fundamental postulates of the frame of reference within which they do their thinking and their feeling from decreeing an end to the collective paranoia that governs international relations. As for the world's ruling minorities, by the very fact of their power they are chained even more closely to the current system of ideas and the prevailing political customs; for this reason they are even less capable than their subjects of expressing the simple human preference for life and peace.

Some day, let us hope, rulers and ruled will break out of the cultural prison in which they are now confined. Some day . . . And may that day come soon! For, thanks to our rapidly advancing science and technology, we have very little time at our disposal. The river of change flows ever faster, and somewhere downstream, perhaps only a few years ahead, we shall come to the rapids, shall hear, louder and ever louder, the roaring of a cataract.

Modern war is a product of advancing science and technology. Conversely, advancing science and technology are products of modern war. It was in order to wage war more effectively that first the United States, then Britain and the USSR, financed the crash programs that resulted so quickly in the harnessing of atomic forces. Again, it was primarily for military purposes that the techniques of automation, which are now in process of revolutionizing industrial production and the whole system of administrative and bureaucratic control, were first developed. "During World War II," writes Mr. John Diebold, "the theory and use of feedback was studied in great detail by a number of scientists both in this country and in Britain. The introduction of rapidly moving aircraft very quickly made traditional gun-laying techniques of anti-aircraft warfare obsolete. As a result, a large part of scientific manpower in this country was directed towards the development of self-regulating devices and systems to control our military equipment. It is out of this work that the technology of automation as we understand it today has developed."

The headlong rapidity with which scientific and technological changes, with all their disturbing consequences in the fields of politics and social relations, are taking place is due in large measure to the fact that, both in the USA and the USSR, research in pure and applied science is lavishly financed by military planners whose first concern is in the development of bigger and better weapons in the shortest possible time. In the frantic effort, on one side of the Iron Curtain, to keep up with the Joneses—on the other, to keep up with the Ivanovs—these military planners spend gigantic sums on research and development. The military revolution advances under forced draft, and as it goes forward it initiates an uninterrupted succession of industrial, social, and political revolutions. It is against this background of chronic upheaval that the members of a species, biologically and historically adapted to a slowly changing environment, must now live out their bewildered lives.

Old-fashioned war was incompatible, while it was being waged, with democracy. Nuclear war, if it is ever waged, will prove in all likelihood to be incompatible with civilization, perhaps with human survival. Meanwhile, what of the preparations for nuclear war? If certain physicists and military planners had their way, democracy, where it exists, would be replaced by a system of regimentation centered upon the bomb shelter. The entire population would have to be systematically drilled in the ticklish operation of going underground at a moment's notice, systematically exercised in the art of living troglodytically under conditions resembling those in the hold of an eighteenth-century slave ship. The notion fills most of us with horror. But if we fail to break out of the ideological prison of our nationalistic and militaristic culture, we may find ourselves compelled by the military consequences of our science and technology to descend into the steel and concrete dungeons of total and totalitarian civil defense.

In the past, one of the most effective guarantees of liberty was governmental inefficiency. The spirit of tyranny was always willing; but its technical and organizational flesh was weak. Today the flesh is as strong as the spirit. Governmental organization is a fine art, based upon scientific principles and disposing of marvelously efficient equipment. Fifty years ago an armed revolution still had some chance of success. In the context of modern weaponry a popular uprising is foredoomed. Crowds armed with rifles and home-made grenades are no match for tanks. And it is not only to its armament that a modern government owes its overwhelming power. It also possesses the strength of superior knowledge derived from its communication systems, its stores of accumulated data, its batteries of computers, its network of inspection and administration.

Where democratic institutions exist and the masses can vote their rulers out of office, the enormous powers with which science, technology, and the arts of organization have endowed the ruling minority are used with discretion and a decent regard for civil and political liberty. Where the masses can exercise no control over their rulers, these powers are used without compunction to enforce ideological orthodoxy and to strengthen the dictatorial state. The nature of science and technology is such that it is peculiarly easy for a dictatorial government to use them for its own anti-democratic purposes. Well financed, equipped and organized, an astonishingly small number of scientists and technologists can achieve prodigious results. The crash program that produced the A-bomb and ushered in a new historical era was planned and directed by some four thousand theoreticians, experimenters, and engineers. To parody the words of Winston Churchill, never have so many been so completely at the mercy of so few.

Throughout the nineteenth century the State was relatively feeble, and its interest in, and influence upon, scientific research were negligible. In our day the State is everywhere exceedingly powerful and a lavish patron of basic and *ad hoc* research. In Western Europe and North America the relations between the State and its scientists on the one hand and individual citizens, professional organizations, and industrial, commercial, and educational institutions on the other are fairly satisfactory. Advancing science, the population explosion, the armament race, and the steady increase and centralization of political and economic power are still compatible, in countries that have a libertarian tradition, with democratic forms of government. To maintain this compatibility in a rapidly changing world, bearing less and less resemblance to the world in which these democratic institutions were developed—this, quite obviously, is going to be increasingly difficult.

A rapid and accelerating population increase that will nullify the best efforts of underdeveloped societies to better their lot and will keep two-thirds of the human race in a condition of misery in anarchy or of misery under dictatorship, and the intensive preparations for a new kind of war that, if it breaks out, may bring irretrievable ruin to the one-third of the human race now living prosperously in highly industrialized societies—these are the two main threats to democracy now confronting us. Can these threats be eliminated? Or, if not eliminated, at least reduced?

My own view is that only by shifting our collective attention from the merely political to the basic biological aspects of the human situation can we hope to mitigate and shorten the time of troubles into which, it would seem, we are now moving. We cannot do without politics; but we can no longer afford to indulge in bad, unrealistic politics. To work for the survival of the species as a whole and for the actualization in the greatest possible number of individual men and women of their potentialities for good will, intelligence, and creativity—this, in the world of today, is good, realistic politics. To cultivate the religion of idolatrous natonalism, to subordinate the interests of the species and its individual members to the interests of a single national state and its ruling minority—in the context of the population explosion, missiles, and atomic warheads, this is bad and thoroughly unrealistic politics.
Unfortunately, it is to bad and unrealistic politics that our rulers are now committed.

Ecology is the science of the mutual relations of organisms with their environment and with one another. Only when we get it into our collective head that the basic problem confronting twentieth-century man is an ecological problem will our politics improve and become realistic. How does the human race propose to survive and, if possible, improve the lot and the intrinsic quality of its individual members? Do we propose to live on this planet in symbiotic harmony with our environment? Or, preferring to be wantonly stupid, shall we choose to live like murderous and suicidal parasites that kill their host and so destroy themselves?

Committing that sin of overweening bumptiousness, which the Greeks called *hubris,* we behave as though we were not members of earth's ecological community, as though we were privileged and, in some sort, supernatural beings and could throw our weight around like gods. But in fact we are, among other things, animals—emergent parts of the natural order. If our politicians were realists, they would think rather less about missiles and the problem of landing a couple of astronauts on the moon, rather more about hunger and moral squalor and the problem of enabling three billion men, women, and children, who will soon be six billions, to lead a tolerably human existence without, in the process, ruining and befouling their planetary environment.

Animals have no souls; therefore, according to the most authoritative Christian theologians, they may be treated as though they were things. The truth, as we are now beginning to realize, is that even things ought not to be treated as *mere* things. They should be treated as though they were parts of a vast living organism. "Do as you would be done by." The Golden Rule applies to our dealings with nature no less than to our dealings with our fellow-men. If we hope to be well treated by nature, we must stop talking about "mere things" and start treating our planet with intelligence and consideration.

Power politics in the context of nationalism raises problems that, except by war, are practically insoluble. The problems of ecology, on the other hand, admit of a rational solution and can be tackled without the arousal of those violent passions always associated with dogmatic ideology and nationalistic idolatry. There may be arguments about the best way of raising wheat in a cold climate or of re-afforesting a denuded mountain. But such arguments never lead to organized slaughter. Organized slaughter is the result of arguments about such questions as the following: Which is the best nation? The best religion? The best political theory? The best form of government? Why are other people so stupid and wicked? Why can't they see how good and intelligent *we* are? Why do they resist our beneficent efforts to bring them under our control and make them like ourselves?

To questions of this kind the final answer has always been war. "War," said Clausewitz, "is not merely a political act, but also a political instrument, a continuation of political relationships, a carrying out of the same by other means." This was true enough in the eighteen thirties, when Clausewitz published his famous treatise; and it continued to be true until 1945. Now, pretty obviously, nuclear weapons, long-range rockets, nerve gases, bacterial aerosols, and the "Laser" (that highly promising, latest addition to the world's military arsenals) have given the lie to Clausewitz. All-out war with modern weapons is no longer a continuation of previous policy; it is a complete and irreversible break with previous policy.

Power politics, nationalism, and dogmatic ideology are luxuries that the human race can no longer afford. Nor, as a species, can we afford the luxury of ignoring man's ecological situation. By shifting our attention from the now completely irrelevant and anachronistic politics of nationalism and military power to the problems of the human species and the still inchoate politics of human ecology we shall be killing two birds with one stone—reducing the threat of sudden destruction by scientific war and at the same time reducing the threat of more gradual biological disaster.

The beginnings of ecological politics are to be found in the special services of the United Nations Organization. UNESCO, the Food and Agriculture Organization, the World Health Organization, the various Technical Aid Services—all these are, partially or completely, concerned with the ecological problems of the human species. In a world where political problems are thought of and worked upon within a frame of reference whose coordinates are nationalism and military power, these ecology-oriented organizations are regarded as peripheral. If the problems of humanity could be thought about and acted upon within a frame of reference that has survival for the species, the well-being of individuals, and the actualization of man's desirable potentialities as its coordinates, these peripheral organizations would become central. The subordinate politics of survival, happiness, and personal fulfillment would take the place now occupied by the politics of power, ideology, nationalistic idolatry, and unrelieved misery.

In the process of reaching this kind of politics we shall find, no doubt, that we have done something, in President Wilson's prematurely optimistic words, "to make the world safe for democracy."

A Proper Public Policy on Birth Control

John Rock, Harvard Professor Emeritus of Medicine, helped develop the first oral contraceptive. He is also a prominent Roman Catholic layman. In his book The Time Has Come *he talks to the reader in a very kindly and personal way about the problem of overpopulation and population control. Dr. Rock's book does not antagonize the Catholic segment, but it does place the problem before them. Protestants, Jews, and others will not be offended. He says the time has come when we must cease our bickering about birth control and do something about it. Dr. Rock vividly recalls the words of his village priest, and these words have been a guideline in his life. He said, "John, always stick to your own conscience. Never let anyone else keep it for you." And after a momentary pause, he added, "And I mean anyone else."*

If the controversy over local birth-control regulations is not to be repeated in community after community or to be transformed, with even greater damage, into a nationwide battle concerning federal policy on birth control, it will require great effort from all of us to work out peaceful solutions. The discussion thus far, I hope, has indicated clearly that the real doctrinal differences between Catholics and non-Catholics need not prevent initiation of a proper public policy—a live-and-let-live policy which will protect the rights and privileges of all groups. A formula for this can be arrived at by generalizing the principles used in the settlement of complaints within the New York hospitals.

First, however, it is important to consider to what extent Catholic teaching may encompass toleration. There is considerable confusion among Catholics on this point, and many have found themselves torn between their sincere respect for democratic principles, which imply a spirit of individual liberty, and their devout adherence to religious authority. Two Church principles seem to compound this confusion: The principles that natural law, which has been interpreted to forbid birth control, is binding on all, and that "objectively error has no rights." Both doctrines are often taken to infer an obligation on Catholics to use all means at their command—legislative, judicial, administrative—to prevent any use of artificial birth control, which they regard as evil.

If this were a valid position, there would be little hope for harmony. If, however, Catholic principles will support tolerance, then great strides can be made toward resolution of the conflict over public policy. Most Catholics, I believe, would be quite relieved to find their religious and their civic beliefs at peace with each other. And, of course, there are no requirements in Protestant or Jewish tenets that compel their imposition on Catholics.

Is such charity permissible to Catholics? Unequivocally, yes. I have been taught to believe that the Church's mission is to teach and to utilize persuasion and reason in doing so. Attempts to impose the Church's teachings by political fiat stem from an unwarranted extension of the Church's duty, as well as from a sad misunderstanding of what constitutes a democratic, pluralistic society. The Church, it seems, has paid an extravagantly high price for these misconceptions.

A more valid attitude, it appears to me, is that of those Catholic writers I have cited earlier who have discussed the implications of the Connecticut law and the New York controversy. These commentators dealt with specific situations. To my knowledge, a comprehensive consideration of the general question—would Catholic doctrine permit a public policy of toleration on birth control?—is to be found only in Father de Lestapis's recent book. His discussion[1] is quite illuminating and of particular interest, since it reflects a European, and not an American, Catholic background.

In nations of divided beliefs which are contemplating the legalization of birth control or have already done so, the French Jesuit says, Catholics must bear witness to their beliefs and the State should not restrain them from doing so. "It is for [Catholics] to *convince* the world of this, provided of course that they are given sufficient chance to do so, and that *they themselves respect the liberty of others,*" he writes.

Should Catholics grant freedom to others "even when they are quite certain that the doctrine opposed to their own leads to an inevitable social evil?" he asks.

His reply is that even a *Catholic government* may find it preferable "to close its eyes to a limited diffusion of contraceptive methods. In spite of the fact that objectively error has no rights and even the erring conscience has no right to profess error publicly, the psychological and moral state of society may in certain circumstances demand some toleration in the interests of public order."

In support of this position, Father de Lestapis cites a number of acknowledged authorities. He quotes Aquinas to the effect that "human law is not obliged to forbid all the immoral acts from which virtuous people abstain, but only the most heinous, those from which the majority of men are able to abstain, and especially those which harm other people and the repression of which is seen to be indispensable if a human society is to be preserved. Consequently human governments can legitimately refrain from preventing certain blameworthy deeds, for fear they should otherwise hinder the good or incite men to worse crimes."[2]

A similar point is cited from an address by Pope Pius XII to Italian jurists in December 1953. "The obligation of repressing moral and religious offenses cannot be an ultimate norm of action," the Pontiff declared. "It must be subordinated to higher and more generous norms which, in certain circumstances, allow and even perhaps make it obvious that it is better not to prevent error in order to bring about a greater good."[3]

---

[1] *Family Planning and Modern Problems,* pp. 256ff. (Emphasis added.)
[2,3] Quoted in *ibid.,* p. 258.

Finally, Father de Lestapis refers to a lecture given in 1959 by Cardinal Lercaro, Archbishop of Bologna, on religious tolerance and intolerance. "Which is the greater good?" the Cardinal asked. "It is respect for truth and the way the human mind reaches it. None should be forced against his will to accept the Catholic faith. Respect for truth demands freedom of consent. A truth which is imposed is not accepted as truth. . . . When truth is imposed, it is because religion is confused with politics."[4]

On the specific question of public policy on birth control, Father de Lestapis concludes that the extent of toleration cannot be defined *a priori,* but must be negotiated among the major components of the society like "a treaty to define a frontier." "We can envisage a whole sliding-scale of prohibitions and, to counterbalance it, activities which are tolerated," he states.[5]

Unfortunately this attitude of toleration is not always in evidence. One of the last acts of Representative Louis Rabaut, of Michigan, before his death in 1961, for example, was to use his post as chairman of the House Appropriations Subcommittee, which controls the District of Columbia's purse strings, to block funds for birth control in the District's health clinics. The funds—$5,000—had been appropriated by Congress after they had been requested by the District's commissioners and health officials, who felt that such a program would be in the best interests of the community's health. But the Michigan congressman managed singlehandedly to veto the use of the appropriation, declaring that "it would be a bad example to a lot of little towns."[6] As could have been anticipated, *Christian Century* editorialized: "As a Roman Catholic layman, Congressman Rabaut is an ardent foe of birth control. He has a right to his personal opinion. But he has no right to use his control over the District of Columbia budget to inflict his religious and sociological views on district residents."[7]

The late congressman, interestingly, was one of 166 prominent Catholic laymen who joined in what was a most important statement during the 1960 election campaign—the Statement

[4] Quoted in *ibid.,* p. 259.
[5] *Ibid.,* p. 259.
[6] Detroit *Free Press,* Oct. 14, 1961.
[7] Nov. 1, 1961.

on Religious Liberty which assured non-Catholics that the election of a Catholic President would not imperil their religious freedom. "We believe in the freedom of the religious conscience," the Statement declared, "and in the Catholic's obligation to guarantee full freedom of belief and worship as a civil right. . . . We believe that among the fundamentals of religious liberty are the freedom of a church to teach its members and the freedom of its members to accept the teachings of their church."[8]

Whatever may have been Congressman Rabaut's interpretation of this doctrine in regard to birth-control policy, apparently most of the others who signed this Statement were much more tolerant. The Planned Parenthood Federation conducted a poll of these distinguished Catholic educators, lawyers, editors, and public officials, asking if they agreed that non-Catholic doctors and laymen should have "freedom of conscience and action concerning birth control" and that public officials should respect such freedom of religious belief in policies affecting medical institutions. Surprisingly nearly half the signers—the late congressman was not one of them—responded. Their replies provide a good clue to the attitudes of informed Catholic laymen. According to Mr. Cass Canfield, president of the polling group, the responses revealed "a substantial body of opinion among Catholic lay leaders considerably more permissive in terms of the rights of non-Catholics to contraception than has been traditionally associated with the Roman Catholic Church."[9] While adhering strictly to the Catholic position on artificial contraception, 60 per cent of the respondents *nevertheless* agreed that non-Catholics should have freedom of conscience and action on birth control, and more than half agreed that public officials should respect these beliefs. There were no replies which could be classified as completely negative.

Mr. Canfield commented: "Almost three out of four either agreed directly with our formulation of the birth control issue or took the opportunity to state forthrightly their opposition to anti-birth control laws. Most of the remaining respondents reflected varying degrees of permissiveness. The position of almost all who

[8] *The New York Times,* Oct. 6, 1960.
[9] *Results of a Poll of 166 Catholic Laymen,* released October 31, 1960, by the Planned Parenthood Federation of America, New York.

answered, if implemented, would require at least some—in most cases, major—changes in public policy on birth control. . . . It is apparent that the settlement of on-going controversies in this field could be advanced immeasurably if this important section of Catholic opinion is recognized and heard."

Here then is a wide-open bridge on which Catholics and non-Catholics can meet. A workable arrangement lies in a public policy of toleration which accepts the fact that differences exist between the religious groups on birth control. In the face of such disagreements, the only democratic solution is the enactment of laws and the adoption of policies for each public body which respect the deeply held convictions of all groups. Only in this way can each separate group feel satisfied that public power is not being used to impose on them practices and beliefs to which they do not subscribe.

The New York City hospital settlement, in fact, was a rare example of a formally adopted compromise which applied this tolerant approach. By extracting the general principles embodied in this resolution, we can discover ground rules for settling disputes over public policy in this field.

The rules, I believe, are such as these:

1. Family planning, whether by contraception or continence, is both a religious matter, involving the individual consciences of husbands and wives, and a medical problem, involving considerations of the health and well-being of families and, thus, of society.

2. The State has no competence—and no right—to legislate on the religious aspects of the problem.

3. In the medical programs operated by the State, however, proper medical care normally requires the provision of family planning services. In these programs, all restrictions on birth control, written or unwritten, should be removed.

4. In public facilities, no one should be compelled to accept birth control, or to participate in a birth-control program, against his will.

5. All methods of family planning, including the rhythm method, should be offered so that the adherent of any faith will be able to choose a method that accords with his own conscience.

These principles are broad enough to permit the government to adopt properly neutral policies on birth control in all of the areas which have been disputed. They would apply not merely in public hospitals and health departments but also in the medical care programs provided to recipients of welfare, in the technical assistance programs on medical matters offered by the United States to other nations, and in the formulation of guidelines for publicly financed medical research programs.

Some Catholic writers, while agreeing generally with this approach, have sought to limit its application to one or another public institution and deny its validity to the whole gamut of public programs. Mr. St. John-Stevas, for example, deems the New York compromise "reasonably satisfactory" as far as public hospital policy is concerned. But he cites, as an example of a government "exceeding the bounds of neutrality," the resolution discussed in Chapter 8, by Pennsylvania's Board of Public Assistance permitting case workers to refer clients for birth-control services.[10] He also asserts that the hospital situation is "distinguishable" from the foreign-aid program, finding that a policy based on the New York settlement "would not commit the municipality to a policy of generally furthering birth control. The foreign aid programme, on the other hand, is an act of policy involving the whole nation as such."[11]

I must confess that I cannot understand these subtle distinctions, and Mr. St. John-Stevas does not elaborate them. I fail to see the difference in over-all policy between a doctor in a public hospital providing birth-control service to a patient, and a case worker in a public welfare agency that lacks this medical service referring the client for needed family planning guidance to another agency which can supply a doctor. I do not understand why the giving of assistance in answer to a request by another country would be any more "an act of policy involving the whole nation" than the giving of service in a publicly financed hospital in answer to a request by a patient. In my view, these situations are not distinguishable in principle one from the other. Each of them is a medical program operated by the body politic with public funds, and the principle of respect for the rights, and needs, of others ought to apply across the board.

[10] *Birth Control and Public Policy,* p. 58n.
[11] *Ibid.,* p. 61n.

The basis for an equitable public policy on birth control lies in an honest and forthright examination of where family planning fits appropriately into publicly financed programs. Instead of attempting to draw distinctions which are untenable, Catholics would be better advised to sit down with their Protestant and Jewish colleagues and work out the details of a sound public policy for all publicly financed programs—hospitals, health departments, welfare services, foreign-aid programs, and medical research.

This viewpoint is shared by informed leaders on all sides—including Catholics. Father O'Brien, of Notre Dame, has stated his belief that in such conferences a proper policy for all public institutions could "be amicably established."[12]

The public policy approach I am suggesting has also been recognized by a leading moral theologian. In the context of a critical article expressing disapproval of my views on the oral contraceptive pills, John J. Lynch, S.J., of Weston College, states that "little fault can be found with the doctor's sentiments" on the question of public policy.[13]

The need for interfaith and interdisciplinary conferences to develop a sound public policy on birth control likewise was vigorously presented to the House Foreign Affairs Committee in April 1962 by James L. Vizzard, S.J., director of the Washington office of the National Catholic Rural Life Conference. Testifying in support of the foreign-aid bill in behalf of both the Conference and the Catholic Association for International Peace, Father Vizzard cited religious differences over birth control and declared:

> It seems to me that in a relatively short time effective public policy will have to be adopted in the critically important area of population growth and economic development. . . . An important public service needs to be performed in bringing together for intensive discussions the best minds from all sciences and disciplines. . . . Efforts would be made to enlarge as far and as clearly as possible the areas of agreement and to define as sharply and narrowly as possible the area of irreconcilable disagreement. . . . I suggest that if bitter conflict

[12] "Let's Take Birth Control Out of Politics," *Look,* Oct. 10, 1961.
[13] "Notes on Moral Theology," *Theological Studies,* Vol. 23, No. 2 (June 1962), p. 239.

is to be avoided in the near future, a conflict which can be destructive to our foreign aid program, a proper foundation must soon be laid for the development of public policy on this most delicate and vital issue.[14]

Thus the basis for a consensus on public policy exists. We can choose either to formulate policy peacefully and with deliberation or to engage first in a series of damaging battles before the same essential policy is adopted. Which course we choose will depend on our maturity as Catholics, Protestants, Jews, and, if I may say so, human beings.

[14] National Catholic Rural Life Conference release, April 18, 1962.

POPULATION REFERENCE BUREAU

World Population Projections, 1965–2000

The Population Reference Bureau (PRB) is a public service organization devoted to a broad program of education on population trends and problems. The PRB does not attempt to influence legislation regarding birth control. It operates on the premise that people will make their own decisions provided they have the facts and understand what those facts mean.

The United Nations demographers have gazed into their modern statistical crystal balls and come up with some startling projections. If the present trend of population growth continues, world population will reach 7.4 billion by the year 2000. If certain other trends develop, the world total could fall short of this by 2 billion. As matters now stand, the higher figure appears to be the more likely, barring famine, nuclear war, disintegration, or some new and "miraculous" form of fertility control.

The gain of 4.1 billion in only 35 years would exceed the present total world population of 3.3 billion by nearly a billion! The current trend, long continued, is viewed as "calamitous."

The United Nations estimates revealed that over 85 percent of the increase will be in the high-birthrate, "developing" countries of Asia, Africa, and Latin America. This continues a trend which

From *Population Bulletin,* Vol. XXI, Oct. 1963. Reprinted by permission of the Population Reference Bureau. This Bulletin is based on material prepared by Kaval Gulhati.

has been building up since 1900. Then, with world population totalling only 1.6 billion people, just over two thirds lived in Asia, Africa, and Latin America; less than one third lived in Europe and Northern America. By 1965, these proportions had shifted to three fourths and one fourth, respectively.

Projections to the year 2000, based on current trends, indicate that four fifths of the world's people will then be living in Asia, Africa, and Latin America. Northern America and Europe (including the U.S.S.R.) will have shrunk to less than one fifth of the total. World projections are somewhat moot because of the big question regarding Mainland China, discussed below.

The ranking of the ten largest nations will also show some interesting changes by the year 2000. In 1965, the list included five "developed" countries. By 2000, this number may be reduced to three, with West Germany and the United Kingdom being replaced by Nigeria and Mexico. The total population for the "top ten" nations will grow to 4.7 billion, if present trends continue.

The United Nations Report,* from which these projections are taken, represents the fourth time the U.N. has scanned the demographic radar. The previous reviews were published in 1951, 1954, and 1957. The current Report notes that growth has tended to be more rapid than anticipated:

In 1957, as in the previous studies, three variants, "high," "medium," and "low," were calculated to which a fourth variant is now added, referred to as "continued recent trends." Actually—disregarding details of secondary importance—the assumptions of the new "continued recent trends" variant, particularly the assumption of constant fertility, resemble the previous "high" variant, whereas the new "high" variant assumes appreciable fertility declines in many parts of the world before the end of the century. As new data show world population currently growing at a faster rate than was projected in 1957, the new "continued recent trends" variant carries the world total by the year 2000 to 7,410 million, as compared with 6,900 million for the "high" variant in the 1957 projections. The new "high" variant, although it is higher than the

* *Provisional Report on World Population Prospects as Assessed in 1963.* United Nations, New York, 1964.

previous one for 1980, implies enough reduction in rates of growth afterward so that an end-century total of 6,828 million results, which is somewhat less than the previous "high" variant.

Demographically, the nations of the earth fall into two clearly defined sectors, "developed" and "developing." The "developed" countries—the industrialized, urban nations of Europe, Northern America, U.S.S.R., Oceania, and Japan, with a total of 900 million people—have control of fertility.

The slow rate of population growth in the Western developed nations is due to a "demographic transition" which began early in the 19th century with a slow decline in death rates. This was followed in a generation or so by a decline in birth rates due to spontaneous action by individuals. Today birth rates and death rates are in approximate balance, with a consequent slow rate of population growth. (The United States has been an exception, with a "controlled birth rate" and a continuing "baby boom" which only recently appears to be ending.)

In the developed countries, the close balance between low birth and death rates has resulted in a relatively unchanging rate of population growth.

The remainder of the world, the so-called "developing" countries, has traditionally high fertility and low or declining mortality. It is the 2.4 billion people in these countries who are most acutely caught in the looming population crisis. No major region in the developing countries is now measurably passing through the transitional phase from high to low fertility. A few small countries like Taiwan and South Korea may be entering such a phase.

Although there is no general measure of the terms "developed" and "developing," the U.N. Report points out that, with few exceptions, the level of human reproductivity is the characteristic which best separates the "developing" countries from the "developed" countries. With very minor exceptions, there is no overlap in the birth rates of the two sectors. Thus, the level of fertility defines these two groups more clearly than any other socio-economic measure, such as per capita income, industrialization, urbanization, or literacy.

Most of the developing countries have birth rates* in the range of 39 to 50. In the developed countries, birth rates range from 17 to 25. In the world at large, death rates do not cover so wide a spectrum because recent dramatic declines in many developing countries have largely eliminated the high mortality of the past. They mostly range from 10 to 30 in the developing countries and from 8 to 12 in the developed countries.

The rate of population growth is determined by the difference between the birth rate and the death rate (the "rate of natural increase"). Gains or losses through migration have been an important factor in the past and even in some limited areas today. In the crisis in the developing countries today, migration is of minor importance.

The current high rates of population growth are due to the growing imbalance between births and deaths. The annual rate of population increase in the developing countries ranges from 1.0 percent to 3.5 percent—and even more. In most of the developed countries, it ranges from 0.5 percent to 1.7 percent. At a 3.5 percent rate of growth, a population doubles in 20 years. This means more than a 30-fold increase in a century. A 0.5 percent annual increase requires 139 years to double the population.

The few developing countries which show low rates of growth still have high fertility, but this is balanced by high mortality. If the death rate declines, population growth would accelerate.

Whether the world has reached the point of most rapid population growth depends on the future and unpredictable interplay between shifting birth and death rates. There is a widespread assumption that the death rate will continue to decline. If this happens and if the birth rate in the developing countries remains at present levels, other countries might reach—or even exceed—the alarming 4.3 percent annual rate of growth now reported by Costa Rica. It is conceivable, therefore, that even the highest U.N. projection for a world population of 7.4 billion by 2000 could be exceeded.

There is an ardent hope that a general decline in fertility is

---

* Birth and death rates are in terms of 1,000 of the population per year.

imminent in the developing countries. New fertility-control techniques enhance this possibility. (Such developments in Taiwan and South Korea are described in a later section.)

How Projections Are Made

The construction of population projections, using the most advanced demographic techniques, is not an exercise in crystal gazing. It is a sophisticated and ingenious procedure which can be outlined here only very sketchily.

The starting point is population data—the more detailed and accurate, the better—for a nation, for a region, or for the world. The essential information includes the total population and such components as breakdowns of the population by age and sex; death rates for the total population and for its age-components; birth rates and other special measures of fertility.

Most of the developed countries have the essential census and vital statistics data in considerable detail. While many countries of the world have taken censuses since 1960, there are still important gaps. Vital statistics are still far from adequate in many countries. Where such data are lacking, much skill and ingenuity are employed in developing from other data estimates adequate to fill these gaps.

The basic demographic data for a nation or a region being at hand, the projection process computes the movement of this population into the future, usually in five-year intervals: so many babies are born; so many people die in each age-cohort. The surviving 0-4-year-olds in 1965 become the 5-9-year-olds in 1970, etc.

If birth rates and death rates never changed, it would be a simple matter to forecast future populations with great accuracy. That vital rates may—and do—change greatly complicates matters. Future population depends on how these variables shift and the rate and magnitude of the shifts.

To meet this difficulty, a series of projections is prepared which, hopefully, will bracket the range of possibilities. These are based on different sets of assumptions regarding changes in birth and death rates both for the world and for regions, especially for the two main demographic groupings. The thinking on which some of these assumptions are based is set forth in the U.N. Report:

Plausible prospects of future population growth differ substantially for populations of the two types. Barring events that cannot now be foreseen, the scope of plausible future variations, both in fertility and in mortality, is much wider in the "developing" than in the "developed" regions. In the former, failure of mortality to decline where it is still high would certainly be regarded as a calamity and is not contemplated in this report. An even greater calamity would eventually ensue, at least in the remote future, if fertility decline were to be postponed indefinitely while mortality decline continued. Declines of both fertility and mortality must therefore be assumed in the "developing" countries, though the assumption has to be varied from area to area as regards plausible timing and speed of declines. In the "developed" regions, currently prevailing trends may continue well into the future though reasonable allowance has to be made for possible changes in trends, particularly as there remains some scope for moderate variations of fertility in response to changes in economic and social circumstances.

The big question—what will happen to fertility *and* mortality —cannot be disposed of by verbal fiat. The assumption that mortality will continue to decline is made in the face of ominous developments in certain stress areas, discussed below. In the U.N. projections, a continuing mortality decline is assumed for developing countries.

The "high," "medium," and "low" projections are based on different assumptions regarding the timing of fertility declines in Asia, Africa, and Latin America. Birth rates there have mantained their previous high level in the 40–50 range, with a few relatively minor exceptions—Chile, Taiwan, Ceylon, Singapore, and Hong Kong. During the past 50 years, death rates have declined by 50 percent or more and now stand at 25 to 30 in Asia and Africa and even lower in Latin America. The "continued recent trends" projection assumes that this pattern will persist. If it does, world population could considerably exceed 7 billion by the year 2000.

Depending mainly on how rapidly fertility declines in developing areas, the "low" and "medium" projections show a world population ranging from 5.3 to 5.9 billion in the year 2000;

the "high" projection totals 6.8. Even were the "low" projection to be realized, the sobering fact remains that this shows a two-thirds increase over present world population.

In evaluating these "radarscopings" of future population growth, it cannot be too strongly emphasized that the realization of the projections depends on many additional factors too complex and unpredictable to measure. The major assumption which is not explicitly stated is that there will be nothing more than brushfire wars, no economic crises, no major pandemics, etc., etc. The statement quoted above that "calamity . . . is not contemplated in this report" and that "declines of both fertility and mortality must therefore be assumed" borders on verbal magic. These and other calamities may not be contemplated, but they could happen. A grim confrontation which would have changed the Asian demographic situation hovered over the subcontinent for two tense weeks in September.

Also necessarily ignored in these assumptions is the alarming fact that food production around the world is not keeping up with population growth. If the projections of population growth in the developing countries are to be realized, a massive revolution in agriculture on a scale apparently not now contemplated must be achieved. The looming threat of famine cannot be exorcised merely by ignoring it.

The value of projections of future population growth is that they do give a picture of what might happen if everything went according to "plan"—if the assumptions were realized; if none of the calamities happened.

In the past, U.N. projections have tended to be low. The addition of a new "continued trends" projection may indicate that the projectors are not too sure that calamity-averting declines in fertility will take place.

With death rates still declining and persisting birth rates, a population of 7.4 billion people 35 years hence is definitely a possibility. If this prospect is indeed "calamitous," then humane and effective steps to avert it are indicated. This review of the areas and a few of the major nations is geared to the "continued trends" projection. The tables in the appendix give the "medium" and "low" projections. The "high" and the "continued trends" do not differ greatly.

The "Continued Trends" Projection

World population is estimated to be growing at a rate of 2.1 percent a year. Each year about 125 million babies are born, 55 million people die, leaving some 70 million human beings added to the worlds total population. If this trend continues, *world population will gain over 100 million each year by 1980 and over 200 million by 2000:* a number that would exceed today's total U.S. population.

In the first half of the 19th century, the rate of world population growth was less than 1 percent per year. It took 50 years, from 1900 (1.6 billion) to 1950 (2.5 billion), to add one billion more people. If current trends proceed unchecked, the next billion will be added in only 13 years—by 1978.

World population is projected to increase by 125 percent between 1965 and 2000. During the previous 35 years (1930-1965), the comparable increase was 60 percent. Latin America had the highest increase (130 percent) and Europe, the lowest (25 percent). In the next 35 years, Latin America's population is expected to triple, while Europe's would increase by slightly more than one fourth.

"Continued trends" show every continent having a larger increase between 1965 and 2000 than between 1930 and 1965. Africa is expected to increase by 177 percent, compared to 90 percent in the previous three decades. Asia would jump from a 64-percent to a 139-percent increase. Among the developed areas, the U.S.S.R. is expected to have the highest gain from a previous 31 percent to an anticipated 72 percent. Northern America's growth would increase from 60 to 80 percent; Europe's gain would be least, from 25 to 29 percent.

Latin America's high rate of population growth gives it the dubious distinction of being the fastest growing major area in the world. Its average annual rate of growth between 1930 and 1965 was close to 2.5 percent. At this rate of growth, a population doubles in less than 29 years. A continuation of present trends would give Latin America a rate in excess of 3.5 percent. This would mean a doubling of the population in 20 years, or a tripling in only 31 years.

In comparison, Europe's rate of growth over the past 35 years has been about 0.7 percent. The same rate is projected to the year 2000. At this low rate of growth, Europe's population will take some 100 years to double.

In terms of massive numerical gains, Asia, with her huge population base, far exceeds Latin America. One half of the world's 2 billion people lived in Asia in 1930; a growth rate of 1.4 percent annually produced 1.8 billion by 1965. The over-all projected growth rate of 2.5 percent to the year 2000 would result in about 4.4 billion people in Asia alone. This would be a billion more people than the entire world population today.

Latin America, whose present population is 248 million, and Africa, with 311 million, would each accumulate over a half billion more people by 2000. The U.S.S.R. (234 million) and Northern America (215 million) would both add about 170 million; Europe (443 million), about 128 million; and Oceania (17 million), only 16 million.

Population Density

The world's population continues to expand, but the earth's land area remains the same, some 52 million square miles (excluding Antarctica). Density per total area tells only part of the story, for hardly more than a third of the land surface of the earth is habitable under present conditions. In 1930, there were 40 people per square mile of the world's land surface. Today, there are 63; by 2000, there will be 142.

Europe, the continent with the smallest land area, now has the highest density of population in the world: 233 people per square mile. Asia, with the next largest area, has a density of 177 people per square mile. Next to Eurasia, Africa is the earth's largest land mass, and has a density of 27. Latin America, Northern America, and the U.S.S.R. are about the same size and have densities of 31, 26, and 27, respectively. Oceania, with the smallest population, has the world's lowest density of only 5 people per square mile.

By 2000, Asia's projected density of 423 would be nearly a four-fold increase over the 1930 figure. Europe, with a density of

301, will rank a low second. Latin America's density will increase over 200 percent between 1965 and 2000, ranking third with a count of 96 persons per square mile. Northern America and the U.S.S.R. will remain neck-and-neck, with densities of 47 each.

How are so many people, particularly on the Asian continent, going to be supported on a shrinking per capita land base? In urban, industrial Europe, the world's most crowded continent today, there are about three acres of land per person; by 2000, there will be only two. But rural, undernourished Asia is moving headlong toward having only one and a half total acres per person: only a fraction of an acre of arable land per capita. Europe is able to accommodate its overcrowding by packing most of the people into the cities.

The trek to the cities today is world-wide. Urban living under decent conditions requires heavy investments in housing, water supplies, highways, and other services. Even in the developed countries, the provision of essential amenities for decent living is not keeping up with the population trend. This is embarrassingly obvious even in the affluent United States. In the developing countries, the situation borders on the desperate.

Cities like Calcutta are notorious for water shortages, water contamination, and wretched slum conditions. Since urban housing in developing nations is so inadequate, many great and teeming "slum-cities," dotted with isolated pockets of affluence, undoubtedly are in the making. A recent United Nations report* equates urban population increase to the increase in slums:

The outstanding phenomenon of the age is urbanization. It is the most visible expression that one can find of the will of people to advance. The reasons for the movement may be complex but it is essentially an expression of man's search for work and income. Like the migrations of lemmings, nothing seems to stop it—not the scarcity of good jobs, not the absence of decent shelter, nor the presence of real hardship. Give a man a job, any kind of a job, or even the hope and expectation of a job, however illusory, and he will make a shelter for himself (witness the squatter towns) or he will be content with any

* U.N. Economic and Social Council. *Social Aspects of Housing and Urban Development.*

kind of existing shelter (witness the slums of Harlem or the bazaars of Calcutta).

The increase in urban population which is the result of this movement is, in developing countries at least, almost exactly equivalent to the increase in the extent of slums. Almost nowhere has there been enough or, indeed, any good housing to receive the migrants.

Outlook By Regions

The United Nations report divides the world into eight major areas and 24 regions within these areas. Briefly reviewed here are the areas, the regions, and some countries of especial significance. The categorizing of these divisions borders on the intriguing. The "area" designated "Mainland East Asia" breaks down into three "regions": Mainland Region (99 percent China); Japan; and Other East Asia.

Today, Asia contains 56 percent of the world's people. On the basis of the continued trends, Asia will have 4.4 billion people in 2000, or nearly 60 per cent of the total.

The continent's current total population of 1,842 million is about equally divided between the two major regions of East Asia and South Asia. The latter has a faster rate of growth, close to 3 percent, compared to East Asia's 2 percent, based on the assumption that Mainland China's birth rate is 38. On this basis, South Asia's expected population of 2.6 billion by 2000 will exceed East Asia's expected total of 1.8 billion by over 40 percent.

Children under 15 and people over 65 constitute the "dependent age group." Not being in the labor force, they are regarded as economically unproductive. Children are a high-consumption group, requiring extensive investments in education, housing, food, clothing, hospitals, and other facilities. In the developing nations, over 40 percent of the population consists of children under 15, as compared with 30 percent in the United States and 25 percent in Europe. The very nations which can least afford such a heavy load bear the heaviest burden in this respect.

East Asia

Mainland Region. This is the world's most populous region, with an estimated 715 million people in 1965. All but 1 percent live in Mainland China; the remainder live in tiny Hong Kong and sparsely populated Mongolia. The population of this region is expected to more than double by 2000. The people of Mainland China alone would increase to 1.5 billion.

The population of China, being the largest in the world, requires a special focus. One out of every five persons in the world today is a Chinese. According to the continued trends estimate, this ratio would be the same 35 years hence. Demographic statistics on Mainland China are scarce and of questionable quality. Estimates for the 1965 population range from a low of 673 million to a high of 764 million. The U.N. estimates for the year 2000 range from 1,498 million to 882 million, a difference of 616 million. "Present uncertainty as to the size and current trends of the Chinese population is so great that such a variety of possibilities must be allowed for," according to the United Nations Report.

The "continued trends" projection assumes a rapidly declining death rate and questionably low birth rate of 38. Life expectancy at birth is projected to rise from 42.5 years in 1955-60, to 52.5 years in 1975-80, and to 63.2 years in 1995-2000. The latter figure is comparable to the level now prevailing in countries such as Ceylon and Singapore, where recent public health achievements have been outstanding.

Japan. The seventh largest nation in the world and the fifth largest in Asia, Japan has a population of 98 million. Its annual rate of population growth, 1.1 percent, is lower than that of the United States and several European countries. Japan's projected population is expected to reach 130 million by the year 2000.

Japan is the only Asian country which has completed its demographic transition, having today a close balance between a low death rate (6.9) and a low birth rate (17.7) in notable contrast with nearly all of Asia where births range from 40 to 50.

The contrast between Japan and her neighbors is further highlighted by a comparison with Pakistan whose estimated population today is 106 million—just 8 million more than Japan's. By 2000, Pakistan's projected population will total over 300 million.

The Japanese islands have a land area of only 143,000 square miles—approximately the size of Montana. With a density of 685 persons per square mile, Japan is one of the world's most crowded countries. By 2000, Japan will have packed in another 200 persons in each square mile.

Other East Asia. This area has a relatively small population of 54 million. However, with an accelerating growth rate already well over 3 percent, its numbers may triple by 2000.

Taiwan and South Korea are two countries in this region that appear to be approaching a breakthrough in fertility control. Taiwan's birth rate today is 34.5, the death rate, 5.7. This gives a rate of population growth close to 3 percent.

Thirty-five years ago, the island had a population of only 4.6 million. By 1965, this had grown to 12 million, including the migration from the Mainland in 1950. Were this trend to continue, Taiwan's population would total 39 million in 2000.

In Taiwan, an intensive campaign to control fertility is under way. The birth rate has declined to its present level from 39.5 in 1960.

South Korea's population of 29 million would more than triple by 2000 if the present birth rate of 47 remains unchanged. The South Korean government is actively concerned with checking the rapid rate of growth.

The intensive campaign now under way to reduce birth rates in these two countries may signal the first breakthrough in achieving a more favorable balance between the birth rate and the death rate in the developing countries.

As in all the developing countries, more than two fifths of the population of Korea and Taiwan are children under 15. These large cohorts of children moving into their high-fertility years represent a huge potential for continued growth. Even with rapid acceptance of contraception, the population in the developing countries can be expected to grow rapidly for a number of years.

If current efforts succeed in bringing birth rates into line with the modern low death rates, then by 2000 there will be a favorable shift in the age structure of both Taiwan and Korea, with an increasing proportion in the productive age group, 15 to 64.

South Asia

Middle South Asia. With a population of 656 million this region is second only to Mainland China. If present growth trends continue, there would be an increase to 1.7 billion by 2000.

India and Pakistan, with a combined population of 590 million, are the largest countries in this area. (India's 484 million exceeds the population of Europe.) If the present high rates of growth continue, the populations of both nations would almost triple by 2000. India would have 1.2 billion people; Pakistan, over 300 million.

India's population entered a new phase in the 1930's. The population stood at 270 million in 1931. In the next 34 years, 214 million more people were added. In the 35 years prior to 1930, only 34 million were added to India's population. The continued trends projection for the next 35 years shows a gain of 716 million.

The Indian birth rate is estimated to be over 40. Life expectancy at birth has risen from 27 years in the 1920's to nearly 45 years today, and it is projected to reach 63 years by 2000. India's death rate has dropped from over 32 in 1951 to below 20 in 1965, and this decline is expected to continue.

Pakistan, a neighbor of both India and China, has a growth rate of 2.7 percent a year, according to the current U.N. estimate. This rate doubles the population in only 26 years. Pakistan's estimated birth rate of about 50 is higher than India's, but the mortality level is about the same in both countries.

Although the 1961 Census of Pakistan counted 93.8 million people, Pakistan's Planning Commission recently revised this upward by 7.7 million to push it over 101 million.

The U.N. medium projection for Pakistan assumes a 50-percent cut in the birth rate by 1995. Should this happen, Pakistan will have 227 million people in 2000—nearly 100 million less than the 314 million expected if the current trend continues.

The U.S. Bureau of the Census in a recent report on Pakistan's population estimated the rate of growth to be 3.2 percent, higher even than the Planning Commission estimate. This rate would double the population in 22 years and give a population in 2000 totaling nearly 400 million.

Active programs to reduce the birth rate are under way in both India and Pakistan. In neither country has any decline in the birth rate been observed, although considerable optimism has been expressed in both countries that a breakthrough is imminent. Time is running out in the subcontinent if population growth is to be checked before a multiplication of people overruns the resources to support them.

The U.S. Census report on Pakistan* made an observation on possible changes in mortality which might further accelerate the growth rate in this and other developing areas of the world:

> In the short run, the process of modernization could actually have the effect of increasing the level of effective fertility and possibly the level of actual fertility. Improvements in prenatal care will probably reduce pregnancy wastage and thus increase the proportion of conceptions which result in viable births. Lower infant and child mortality will increase the proportion of live births surviving to adulthood. Moreover, improvements in health care and a more adequate diet for the adult population may tend to reduce fertility impairment and thus increase the likelihood of conception. Finally, there is also evidence that some couples in marginal but improving economic circumstances conclude that since their condition is improving, they can afford more children.

South East Asia. This region's population of 251 million exceeds Latin America's entire population of 248 million but constitutes only 14 percent of Asia's total. By 2000, there could be nearly 700 million in this region.

Indonesia, which ties for fifth place with Pakistan among the world's largest nations, is Southeast Asia's most populous country. It has an estimated population of 106 million; the other eight nations in this region have populations of less than 35 million each.

South West Asia. Only 68 million people live in this region which contains less than 4 percent of all Asians. The region's rate of population growth is high (over 3 percent annually), and a continuation of present trends could result in a population of about

* U.S. Department of Commerce, Bureau of the Census. *Projections of the Population and Sex:* 1965-1986.

200 million by 2000. This would still give this region less than a 5 percent share of Asia's projected population of 4.4 billion by the year 2000.

Turkey's 32 million people make it the most populous country in this region.

Latin America

Latin America is far and away the most rapidly growing major area on earth. Its present population of 248 million is comparable to the U.S.S.R.'s 234 million and Northern America's 215 million. By the year 2000, Latin America's projected population of 750 million could be nearly as large as the U.S.S.R. and Northern America combined.

Tropical South America. With 133 million people, this is Latin America's most populous region. In mid-1965, well over half the population of Latin America lived in this region.

The continued trends projection to 2000 assumes a constant high birth rate of 45 and steadily declining mortality. On this assumption, expectation of life at birth would rise from about 58 years today to 73 years by 2000. The annual rate of population increase would rise from the 1960-70 average of 3.7 percent to over 4 percent in 1990-2000. Total population in 2000 could reach 431 million. This number is nearly 75 percent larger than the entire population of Latin America today.

The outlook for rapid declines in fertility in this region remains bleak, though a recent surge of interest may herald a change. The medium projection assumes a reduction in the birth rate from 45 to 30.4 by 2000. Even were this to happen, the population would total 350 million.

Brazil is by far the most populous country in this region, with 81 million people. It has the eighth largest population total in the world.

Middle America. With a population of 56 million, this is the world's fastest growing region. The current annual rate of

population increase is 3.8 percent. By 2000, the population of this region could increase three and a half times—from 56 million to 195 million. Nearly three fourths of all the population of Middle America is in Mexico.

Temperate South America. This region has a population of only 36 million, increasing at 2 percent annually. Projections to 2000 show no acceleration in the rate of growth and indicate an expected population total of 68 million.

Argentina's 21 million people comprise nearly two thirds of the present population of this region.

Caribbean Region. This is a region which consists of numerous islands. Its total population, 23 million, is growing rapidly and could triple by 2000. The islands are small, and current densities run high. Barbados, for instance, already has over 1,500 persons per square mile.

Like Asian and African populations, all of Latin America (except Temperate South America) has a high birth rate. Between 40 and 50 percent of the population consists of children under 15. The death rate in virtually every Latin American country is well below the Asian and African levels.

Africa

Africa ranks after Asia and Europe as the third most populous continent. The five regions into which it is subdivided contain 311 million people. By 2000, Africa's expected population total of 860 million will make it second largest in the world.

Western Africa. With 100 million people, this is Africa's most populous region. By 2000, the population is expected to more than triple to 318 million, a number exceeding Africa's total population today. Nigeria's 58 million people constitute the largest national population in all of Africa and account for one fifth of the continent's total inhabitants.

Eastern Africa. With an estimated population of 83 million this is Africa's second largest region. The projected population in 2000 is 193 million. Ethiopia, with 20 million people, is the largest country in this region.

Middle Africa. This region contains exactly 10 percent of Africa's entire population today. Its 31 million people are projected to increase to about 64 million in 2000. Congo (Leopoldville) with about 15 million people stands first.

Northern Africa. This region's 76 million population is expected to triple to 228 million by 2000. A scant half of the people in Northern Africa (29 million) are found in Egypt.

Southern Africa. Only 20 million people live in this region—90 percent of them in South Africa. The continued trends show a tripling by 2000.

Europe

Europe stands at the opposite pole demographically from Latin America: population there passed its apogee of growth over a half-century ago. It now has a population of 433 million, and the continued trends projection gives it only 571 million 35 years hence. It will increase not by three times, but by a *third*.

Today the population of Latin America is little more than half that of Europe. If the trend holds, Latin America's population will exceed that of Europe by nearly a third 35 years hence.

In Europe, modern death rates are balanced by modern birth rates. The continent as a whole has an annual rate of increase of less than 1.0 percent a year.

Today Europe is the second most populous continent. The continued trends projection shows it fourth in 2000, exceeded by Asia, Africa, and Latin America.

Western and Northern Europe. These two regions have a rate of population growth of 0.7 percent per year, the lowest in the world. At this slow rate of growth, a population doubles in about 100 years. On the continued trends assumption, the populations of each of these regions will increase by less than one fourth. Western Europe will increase from 139 to 172 million, and Northern Europe will increase from 80 to 98 million.

West Germany with a population of 56 million is Europe's most populous country and ninth largest in the world.

The United Kingdom (54 million) ranks tenth. Its rate of population growth, 0.5 percent per year is among the lowest in the world.

Southern and Eastern Europe. These regions have populations of 123 million and 102 million, respectively. Both regions are growing at a rate of 1.0 percent per year. If current trends continue, by 2000 Southern Europe would have 165 million people and Eastern Europe, 136 million people.

Italy is the largest country in Southern Europe, with a population of 51 million and a rate of population growth of 0.6 percent per year. Projections to 2000 indicate a 25-percent increase, giving a total population of 64 million.

Poland, with a present population of 32 million, is Eastern Europe's most populous nation.

As a result of Europe's low birth rate (generally below 20), only about 25 percent of the total population is under 15. The European birth rates effectively match modern low death rates. The resulting growth rates of less than 1.0 percent a year are in sharp contrast with annual growth in the developing countries which is twice to three times as rapid.

Northern America, U.S.S.R., and Oceania

Northern America (the United States and Canada) has a population of 215 million and a growth rate of 1.6 percent per year. The continued trends projection to 2000 gives a total of 388 million people, or an 80-percent increase in 35 years.

Ninety percent of northern America's population lives in the United States; 10 percent, in Canada. Birth rates in both nations are below 24 (21.2 in the United States; 23.8 in Canada), and death rates are under 10 (9.4 in the United States; 7.6 in Canada).

U.S.S.R., a "region" in the U.N. classification, has a current population of 234 million. This is expected to increase by nearly 75 percent, to 402 million in 2000.

Australia and New Zealand. These two countries, with 14 million, contain over 80 percent of Oceania's entire population. The annual rate of growth is 1.6 percent with a projected growth to 24 million by 2000. In contrast to the more populous parts of the world, this vast area—mostly water—has only a miniscule population, numbering less than the combined populations of New York and New Jersey in 1965.

Oceania's other two regions, *Melanesia* and *Polynesia,* have populations totalling only 2 million and 1 million, respectively. By 2000, the combined population of these two regions will be about 8 million.

From Projections to a Program

In discussing the assumptions in this Report, it was noted that a rise in the death rate or an indefinite continuation of high birth rates would be "calamitous." Beyond that lie the questions as to the magnitude of these calamities and the steps which might be taken to avert them. It is not a part of such an exercise to explore the grave questions of truth and consequences, world-wide, which these projections raise.

If these projections are taken as a point of departure for a realistic survey of the outlook around the world—and in the developing countries especially—they will serve a very useful purpose.

There is no lack of evidence to indicate that looming preludes to disaster may profoundly change the trends indicated by these projections.

One appraisal urgently needed was underlined at the U.N. World Population Conference in Belgrade in September. The Director-General of one of the U.N. Special Agencies—the Food and Agriculture Organization—for the third time in recent months warned that food production is not keeping up with population growth.

Dr. Sen said in part:

It is now less than seven years since there was any appreciable increase in food production per head of the world's population, seven very lean years for the developing countries. In two regions in particular, the Far East and Latin America, per caput production is still less than it was before the war, more than a quarter of a century ago. Many countries in these regions have been able to maintain their wholly inadequate dietary levels only by reducing exports, or by increasing imports of food, including in some cases a very heavy dependence on food aid.

The general outlook is indeed alarming. In some of the most heavily populated areas the outbreak of serious famines within the next five to ten years cannot be excluded. And it is simple arithmetical conclusion that if food output everywhere just kept pace with population growth at the present level of consumption, by the end of this century the number of people who would be subject to hunger and malnutrition would be double what it is today.

Mr. President, the next two or three decades will be a critical period in man's history, and will either see the beginning of mankind as a whole taking responsibility for its destiny or a drift towards disaster. But inaction will be a counsel of despair. Man with his inexhaustible resources of intelligence and inventiveness is capable of meeting the challenge. What is necessary is to put moral ardour and unbending will into the heart of this intelligence. Only thus will human fellowship and human rights acquire their true meaning.*

If the warning contained in the United Nations Report is given the attention it deserves it could mark a turning point in developing an adequate and integrated program to check the still accelerating rate of population growth.

Recent developments suggest that time may be ripe for mounting such a program. The United Nations has moved into a position to take action. The resolution by the Economic and Social Council has set the stage for the creation of a comprehensive program. Two major U.N. agencies—Food and Agriculture Organization (FAO) and the World Health Organization (WHO) are concerned with essential aspects of the problem.

Governments in over a dozen of the developing countries have adopted policies directed toward bringing fertility into balance with modern mortality. The Swedish Government is actively cooperating with some of these governments.

The United States is committed to cooperation around the world in such manner as may be proper and feasible. Many private

* Food, Population and Human Rights," address delivered by Dr. B. R. Sen, Director-General of Food and Agriculture Organization, at the World Population Conference, Belgrade, 30 August 1965.

organizations and foundations also are variously engaged in this area. Among the most active are the Population Council, the Ford Foundation, The American Friends Service Committee, and the International Planned Parenthood Federation.

These are some of the encouraging straws which show a strong wind of change blowing around the world.

Lest these hopeful developments lead to complacency, however, two facts must be emphasized:

1) Present trends give no assurance that an early decline in the world birth rate can be anticipated. Even if a crash program of fertility control were to be instituted tomorrow, the population of the world would increase very rapidly for the next decade or longer.

Current programs to control fertility in the developing countries are not on a scale to be effective in the period of grace that is still remaining.

2) An adequate program to increase food production to meet this burgeoning of people is not now operative.

It has been said and said again by a chorus of the more optimistic experts that "we know enough to feed all people." On paper, this is true! In terms of the magnitude and urgency of the problem, the present efforts to increase food production are pathetically inadequate to put this knowledge to work.

So there the matter stands today. Some of the elements of the present situation present disturbing paradoxes, of which the situation in the United Nations and in the Government of the United States is symbolic. Both these far-ranging agencies are committed to the proposition that there is a job urgently needing to be done. Both appear to be treading water as far as moving from high-sounding resolutions to action. By its very nature, the United Nations World Population Conference at Belgrade added nothing to the development of a plan. Several departments in the United States Government have begun to stir. It is reported that a "White House Task Force has issued a private call to key agencies to come up with 'imaginative and far reaching' plans for 1965." Perhaps the report of this Task Force will propose a comprehensive and effective formula.

It is a big assignment which would involve intimate cooperation between the United Nations, the governments of the developing countries, and both governments and private organizations in the developed countries. For such a program to succeed, a broad spectrum of technical skills and services must be drafted to get this complex undertaking on the road. This would have to be on a far greater scale than anything now contemplated. There has been talk of a "Manhattan Project" for population control. This would be far more complex than releasing the energy of the atomic nucleus.

Without question, if the human mind were urgently focused on these two crucial problems of food and fertility, the essential steps to avert catastrophe could be taken.

The great question is: *Will they be taken?*

ROBERT C. COOK
Editor

POPULATION REFERENCE BUREAU

World Population Data Sheet

The Population Reference Bureau's Population and Vital Rates for 135 Countries will provide up-to-date population estimates by continent and country, a population doubling table, the annual rate of increase, and birth rates per 1,000 population. In these troubled times it is imperative that the informed citizen know something of the statistical data revolving around population dynamics so that he can draw his own conclusions concerning the possible courses of action which must be taken if mankind is to survive.

The population doubling chart will be extremely helpful because it makes possible projections of population growth to the year 2,000 and beyond and the pinpointing of potential trouble spots.

POPULATION AND VITAL RATES FOR 135 COUNTRIES.
Reprinted by permission of the Population Reference Bureau.

Region & Country	Population estimates mid-1966 (millions)	Annual rate of increase from 1958-1964 (percent)	Number of years to double population†	Birth rate per 1,000 population‡	Death rate per 1,000 population‡	Population projections to 1980 (millions)§	Population under 15 years (percent)‡
WORLD		(1.7)	(41)	(34)	(16)		(37)
AFRICA		(2.3)	(31)	(47)	(23)		(43)
NORTHERN AND EASTERN AFRICA		(2.3)	(31)			(231.9)	(42)
Algeria	11.4	0.9	78	46-50			44
Burundi	2.9	2.5	28			4.2	
Ethiopia	23.0	1.8	39			29.0	
Kenya	9.6	2.9	24	48-55		13.6	46
Libya	1.7	3.7	19	35-43			44
Madagascar	6.6	3.1	23	42-50	17-21		38
Malawi	4.1	2.8	25			6.1	45
Mauritius*	0.8	2.9	24	35.5	8.6	1.1	45
Morocco	13.7	2.8	25	44-50		22.4	46
Mozambique*	7.0	1.3	54			9.1	
Rwanda	3.2	3.1	23				
Somalia	2.6	3.5	20				
S. Rhodesia*	4.4	3.3	21	46-53		7.1	46
Sudan	13.9	2.8	25	48-55		19.3	
Tanzania	10.7	1.9	37	42-51		14.6	43
Tunisia	4.8	2.0	35	45.1		6.5	41
Uganda	7.7	2.5	28	42-48		10.0	41
U.A.R. (Egypt)	30.4	2.7	26	41-44	16-18	46.8	43
Zambia	3.8	2.9	24	49-54		5.7	45
WESTERN, MIDDLE, AND SOUTHERN AFRICA		(2.3)	(31)			(217.7)	(44)
Angola*	5.2	1.4	50			6.0	42
Botswana1	0.6	3.1	23				44
Cameroon	5.3	2.1	33	44-52	24-30		
Cent. African Rep.	1.4	2.2	32	42-50	26-32	1.6	40
Chad	3.4	1.5	47	45-50	25-31		
Congo (Brazzaville)	0.9	1.6	44	43-51		1.1	
Congo (Democratic Rep.)	16.0	2.1	33	40-48		21.5	39
Dahomey	2.4	2.9	24	47-55	20-26	3.0	46
Gabon	0.5	1.6	44	32-40		0.5	29
Gambia	0.3	2.4	29				38
Ghana	7.9	2.7	26	47-54		12.3	45
Guinea	3.6	2.8	25	53-57	33-35	5.0	42
Ivory Coast	4.0	3.3	21	49-56			43
Lesotho2	0.8	1.7	41			1.0	43
Liberia	1.1	1.4	50			1.2	37
Mali	4.7	2.3	31	55-63	26-32	6.4	48
Mauritania	0.9	2.2	32				
Niger	3.4	3.3	21	49-57	24-30	4.5	46

Region & Country	Population estimates mid-1966 (millions)	Annual rate of increase from 1958-1964 (percent)	Number of years to double population†	Birth rate per 1,000 population‡	Death rate per 1,000 population‡	Population projections to 1980 (millions)§	Population under 15 years (percent)‡
Nigeria	58.7	2.0	35	47-55		91.2	
Senegal	3.6	2.3	31	40-47	23-29	4.4	43
Sierra Leone	2.3	2.1	33				37
South Africa	18.3	2.4	29			26.8	40
Southwest Africa*	0.6	2.0	35			0.9	40
Togo	1.7	2.8	25	50-59	26-32	2.3	48
Upper Volta	5.0	2.5	28	46-52	27-32	6.3	42
ASIA		(1.8)	(39)	(38)	(20)		(39)
SOUTH WEST ASIA		(2.4)	(29)	(42)	(18)	(103.0)	(43)
Cyprus	0.6	0.8	88	23-26	6-8	0.7	37
Iraq	7.3	1.7	41	47-53			45
Israel	2.7	3.6	20	25.4	6.2	3.1	35
Jordan	2.0	3.1	23	44-49		3.4	45
Kuwait	0.5	11.4	6	40-46	6-9	1.0	38
Lebanon	2.4	2.4	29			3.1	
Saudi Arabia	6.9	1.7	41			9.4	
Syria	5.5	3.2	22			9.3	46
Turkey	32.0	2.8	25	40-46		48.5	41
Yemen	5.0	2.2	32			6.9	
MIDDLE SOUTH ASIA		(2.0)	(35)	(41)	(21)	(954.2)	(42)
Afghanistan	15.9	2.7	26	45-53		22.1	
Bhutan	0.8	2.4	29			1.0	
Ceylon	11.5	2.6	27	34-37	8-10	18.3	41
India	494.1	2.3	31	40-43	21-23	682.3	41
Iran	24.0	2.5	28	42-48	23-27	33.1	45
Nepal	10.3	1.7	41	41-48		14.1	39
Pakistan	121.1	3.2	22	49-53	17-21	183.0	46
SOUTH EAST ASIA		(2.4)	(29)	(43)	(18)	(369.2)	(42)
Burma	25.2	2.0	35	43-50		35.0	
Cambodia	6.5	3.0	24	47-53		9.8	44
Indonesia	106.8	2.2	32	43-48	19-23	152.8	42
Laos	2.0	2.3	31	45-49	22-24	2.9	
Malaysia³	9.7	3.3	23	39.1	8.1	14.9	44
Philippines	33.5	3.3	21	44-50		55.8	47
Singapore	1.9	3.1	23	29.9	5.5	3.2	43
Thailand	31.5	3.0	24	41-49		47.5	43
Viet-Nam, North	19.6	3.4	21				
Viet-Nam, South	16.7	3.3	21	41-48			
EAST ASIA							
China (Mainland)	735-765 (No exact data)						
China (Taiwan)	12.9	3.4	21	32.7	5.5	17.2	46
Hong Kong*	4.0	4.4	16	26.9	4.6	5.5	40
Japan	98.9	1.0	70	18.6	7.1	111.1	26
Korea, North	12.5	3.0	24	36-42	10-14	17.5	
Korea, South	29.2	2.9	24	40-45	13-17	43.4	44
Mongolia	1.1	2.9	24	38-44	10-14	1.7	30

Region & Country	Population estimates mid-1966 (millions)	Annual rate of increase from 1958-1964 (percent)	Number of years to double population†	Birth rate per 1,000 population‡	Death rate per 1,000 population‡	Population projections to 1980 (millions)§	Population under 15 years (percent)‡
AMERICA		(2.2)	(32)	(32)	(11)		(37)
NORTHERN AMERICA		(1.6)	(44)	(23)	(9)	(267.3)	(31)
Canada	20.0	2.0	35	21.4	7.5	26.3	33
United States	196.8	1.6	44	19.4	9.4	240.9	31
MIDDLE AMERICA		(2.7)	(26)			(125.3)	(44)
Barbados⁴	0.2	1.0	70	25.9	7.8	0.3	41
Costa Rica	1.5	4.3	17	40.8	8.8	2.4	48
Cuba	7.8	2.1	33	32-37	7-10	10.0	36
Dominican Republic	3.8	3.6	20	47-51	14-17	6.2	47
El Salvador	3.0	3.3	21	46.5	10.5	4.6	45
Guatemala	4.6	3.3	21	43.5	16.8	6.9	
Haiti	4.8	2.3	31	45-50	20-25	6.9	43
Honduras	2.4	3.3	21	46-50	14-17	3.7	51
Jamaica	1.8	1.8	39	39.4	7.9	2.1	41
Mexico	42.2	3.2	22	45.3	9.5	70.6	44
Nicaragua	1.7	3.1	23	45-50	13-16	2.8	48
Panama	1.3	2.8	25	39.1	9-12	2.0	43
Puerto Rico*	2.7	2.0	35	30.2	6.6	3.1	39
Trinidad & Tobago	1.0	3.1	23	27.6	6.1	1.5	43
SOUTH AMERICA		(2.7)	(26)			(247.0)	(41)
Argentina	22.7	1.6	44	21.8	8.3	29.0	30
Bolivia	3.7	1.4	50	42-46	20-23		
Brazil	83.9	3.1	23	40-44	10-13	123.7	43
Chile	8.8	2.3	31	32.8	11.2	12.4	40
Colombia	18.4	3.2	22	42-46	13-17	27.7	
Ecuador	5.2	3.1	23	46-51	15-18	8.0	45
Guyana⁵	0.7	2.8	25	39.9	7.6	1.0	46
Paraguay	2.1	2.6	27	42-46	12-17	3.0	43
Peru	12.0	3.0	24	42-46	13-15	17.6	45
Uruguay	2.7	1.4	50	24-27	7-9	3.1	28
Venezuela	9.0	3.4	21	47-51	8-12	14.9	45
EUROPE		(0.9)	(78)	(19)	(10)		(25)
NORTHERN AND WESTERN EUROPE		(1.0)	(70)	(18)	(11)	(235.4)	(23)
Austria	7.3	0.5	140	17.9	13.0	7.3	23
Belgium	9.5	0.6	117	16.4	12.1	10.1	24
Denmark	4.8	0.7	100	18.0	10.1	5.2	24
Finland	4.6	0.8	88	17.0	9.7	5.3	28
France	49.6	1.3	54	17.7	11.1	53.3	25
Germany, West⁶	57.6	1.3	54	17.9	11.2	58.5	23
Iceland	0.2	1.9	37	25.1	6.9	0.2	35
Ireland	2.9	0.0	—	22.2	11.5	2.9	31
Luxembourg	0.3	0.9	78	15.6	11.8	0.4	22

Region & Country	Population estimates mid-1966 (millions)	Annual rate of increase from 1958-1964 (percent)	Number of years to double population†	Birth rate per 1,000 population‡	Death rate per 1,000 population‡	Population projections to 1980 (millions)§	Population under 15 years (percent)‡
Netherlands	12.5	1.4	50	19.9	8.0	14.1	29
Norway	3.8	0.8	88	17.5	9.1	4.3	25
Sweden	7.8	0.6	117	15.9	10.1	8.4	21
Switzerland	6.1	2.1	33	18.7	9.3	6.3	23
United Kingdom	54.9	0.7	100	18.4	11.5	57.3	23
EASTERN EUROPE		(0.7)	(100)	(18)	(9)	(113.6)	(27)
Bulgaria	8.3	0.9	78	15.4	8.0	9.3	25
Czechoslovakia	14.3	0.7	100	16.4	10.0	15.8	26
Germany, East	17.0	−0.2	—	16.5	13.4	17.6	24
Hungary	10.2	0.4	175	13.1	10.7	10.7	24
Poland	31.9	1.3	54	17.3	7.4	38.0	32
Romania	19.2	0.8	88	14.6	8.6	22.3	27
SOUTHERN EUROPE		(0.8)	(88)	(21)	(19)	(137.8)	(26)
Albania	1.9	3.1	23	35.2	9.0	3.0	
Greece	8.6	0.7	100	17-19	7-9	9.5	26
Italy	51.9	0.7	100	19.2	10.0	56.4	25
Malta	0.3	0.1	700	17.8	9.4	0.4	
Portugal	9.2	0.7	100	22.9	10.1	9.8	29
Spain	31.9	0.8	88	21.3	8.7	36.0	27
Yugoslavia	19.7	1.1	63	20.9	8.7	22.8	31
OCEANIA		(2.2)	(32)	(27)	(10)		(31)
Australia	11.6	2.1	33	19.6	8.8	14.6	30
New Zealand	2.7	2.2	32	22.8	8.7	3.7	33
USSR	234.3	1.6	44	18.5	7.3	277.8	31

WORLD AND REGIONAL POPULATION (millions)

	WORLD	Africa	Asia⁷	Northern America	Latin America	Europe⁷	Oceania	USSR
Mid-1966	3,346	314	1,864	217	252	448	18	234
1980 projections‖	4,330	449	2,461	262	378	479	23	278

NOTES: Data are compiled from United Nations and other reliable sources.
Blank space indicates lack of reliable information.
()Figures for a region or the world. The PRB's former estimate of 3,308 for world population for mid-1965 has been revised downward to 3,281. This gives an increase of 65 million between mid-1965 and mid-1966. The 1958-1964 annual rate of change of world population is low compared with estimates of the present rate of change. The U.N. estimates that the 1960-70 annual rate of increase will be 2.0 percent.
*Non-sovereign country.
†Assuming continued growth at the 1958-1964 annual rate.
‡Latest available year.
§U.N. projections as assessed in 1963.
‖U.N. projections, medium variant (1966).
[1]Declared independent September 30, 1966. Formerly Bechuanaland.
[2]Declared independent October 4, 1966. Formerly Basutoland.
[3]Figures other than the population estimates exclude the Constituent States of Sabah and Sarawak.
[4]Declared independent November 30, 1966.
[5]Declared independent May 26, 1966. Formerly British Guiana.
[6]Excludes West Berlin, population 2.2 million.
[7]Excludes USSR. The figure for Asia may be higher if accurate statistics of the population of mainland China were available.

GARRETT HARDIN

Genes and Personal Decisions

Garrett Hardin, distinguished professor of biology from the Santa Barbara campus of the University of California, in his book Nature and Man's Fate, *wrestles with some of the most urgent political and ethical problems of the mid-twentieth century. His book entitled* Biology: Its Human Application *is widely used in liberal arts courses.*

When Mendel's work was rediscovered in 1900, its importance was immediately recognized. In part, this was because Mendel now had a champion, William Bateson, who played for genetics the role T. H. Huxley had earlier played for evolution. Bateson "sold" Mendelism to his fellow scientists, and tirelessly explained it to the public at large. He was still explaining it during the First World War, when he contributed his bit to the defense of England by giving lectures on the subject to the troops in France. One wonders what the young men thought of it all, whether they caught even a little of the intellectual excitement behind the fractions ¼, ¾, ⅞, and ¹⁄₁₆; and whether they appreciated the splendid opportunity they were being given to develop their minds during their hours out of the trenches instead of degrading their bodies. History does not record. We do know, however, that Bateson, during one of his gay canters through a field of fractions, was caught up short when a soldier commented that *this Mendelism is just scientific Calvinism.* And so it is, the lecturer had to admit, with a shock of recognition. For seventeen years he had been busily occupied with the numbers game of genetics without once seeing what it all added up to: a rebirth, in modified form, of Calvin's doctrine of predestination, the belief that man's fate is determined for him at the time of conception, a determination that was (in Calvin's mind) irrevocable.

Genetics *is* a form of Calvinism—but it is Calvinism with a difference. That there is a sort of predestination at the time of conception is true: what genes an individual has is determined by what sperm unites with what egg. The genes of the gametes become the genes of the zygote, and (by repeated equational division) of all the cells of the adult body. In the formation of the next generation of gametes, chance enters in during the reduction division, in the assorting of the various alternative alleles, but the distribution must always be made from the genes available in the individual as a result of the earlier fertilization. Chance, operating within predestined boundaries, determines the possibilities of the succeeding generation.

Biological truth is richer than simple Calvinism. An example will help make the point. Among laboratory mice there are some animals that are very sensitive to noise. Put such a mouse in a metal tub and rattle keys against the side of the tub and you will cause the animal to go into convulsions and probably die. Susceptibility to such "audiogenic seizures," as they are called, is inherited. But one cannot say that a mouse of a susceptible strain is predestined to die of an audiogenic seizure, for it may never be exposed to the risk. Its death is not really predestined (not by genetics, at any rate); what is predetermined is its reaction to an environmental event that may, or may not, transpire.

The mice are worth following further. One can develop a strain that is practically pure for this type of reaction. Suppose we maintain such a strain in accoustically quiet surroundings, generation after generation: what will happen? The animals will, of course, live to a ripe old age without seizures. As generation succeeds generation, will the susceptibility to seizures disappear? *Not at all.* If, say, after twenty generations the colony should once again be subjected to

From *Nature and Man's Fate* by Garrett Hardin. Copyright 1959. Reprinted by permission of Holt, Rhinehart and Winston, Inc.

raucous noise, convulsions and death will result just as surely as they would have at the beginning of the experiment. It is this sort of inevitable reaction that makes one regard genes as a kind of Calvinistic fate. It is probably because of this similarity that so many intelligent people reject genetics, consciously or otherwise; aware as they are of the many good effects that have come from revolutionary destruction of old ideas of caste and "divine right," they regard genetics as a dangerous counter-revolutionary movement. The impulse to reject is understandable. But if truth is our god, we must accept it even when unpleasant. We must also try to discern the lineaments of truth as closely as possible if we are not to be led astray by first impressions. We must study the gene more closely.

The Gene Becomes Subtle

The great physicist A. A. Michelson was once asked why he spent so much time determining the exact value of the velocity of light. In reply, he began by halfheartedly uttering some fashionable statements about the Value to Science, about Contributions to Knowledge, and so forth; but abruptly he interrupted himself, as his honesty got the better of his intentions, and laughingly said, "But the real reason is because it is such fun!" Few motives are more effective than this in getting the work of science done, and those fields of science that are the most fun generally advance the fastest. Certainly this has been true of genetics during the first half century of its existence. Seldom has a science been more fun to develop. Probability theory holds a strange fascination for many minds, and in genetics men found a new science in which there was endless delight working with permutations and combinations, and in seeing the predictions beautifully verified in flies or corn plants: $\frac{1}{4}$, $\frac{1}{2}$, $\frac{3}{4}$, $\frac{7}{8}$, $\frac{9}{16}$, $\frac{13}{16}$, $\frac{15}{16}$—there was no end to the fractions predicted and verified. It was a wonderful game.

But to play this game, it was almost necessary to be able to mate organisms at will, and one had to study only genes that were 100 percent determinative in their effects. It was because of the first need that most geneticists worked only with non-human organisms: and the second consideration caused them to work with only highly selected genes. Not all genes behave in a completely predictable way, even in a homozygous stock. Genes that produce only statistically predictable effects are often referred to, by the laboratory geneticist, as "bad" genes, meaning *bad for my work*—bad for the game of genetics. If you look through the published literature of the early period of genetics, you find few references to these "bad" genes; for the most part such genes were just thrown out of the game. Who wants to play with messy counters?

When we come to consider human genetics, however, such a cavalier attitude toward what is, is inappropriate, for the simple reason that we *are* human. The genes that contribute to epileptic seizures are "bad" genes in the laboratory geneticist's sense; but they are *bad* also in a humane sense, so we cannot ignore them, however esthetically unsatisfying the research may be.

Because of the difficulty of the work, much of human genetics has so far had to develop in partial independence of Mendelian theory. No one thinks for a moment that the genetics of human beings is fundamentally different from that of other organisms—in fact, year by year, we succeed in "mendelizing" more of the human data. But the facts of our heredity are so important to us that we must work as well as we can with the crude data even before we have succeeded in tying them firmly to theory.

The figures in Table 1 will give some idea of what we are up against. Here are listed various *congenital* defects, that is defects that are present at birth. Congenital abnormalities may or may not be hereditary. Congenital albinism *is* hereditary. Congenital syphilis is *not* (the child has merely been infected by its mother). Congenital blindness sometimes is, sometimes is not. What about the defects listed in the table? Are they hereditary? If they are, we might expect the figures shown in the right hand column to correspond with one or another of the well-understood Mendelian probabilities, *e.g.,* 1 in 2, 1 in 4, 1 in 16, etc. Inspection shows few familiar figures. One of these is listed opposite "hyperdactyly." If we were told that one child of a family had too many fingers or toes, we could predict that his subsequent siblings would have a fifty-fifty chance of also having extra digits, for we know that hyperdactyly is caused by a rare dominant gene, and it is unlikely that both parents have the gene. Observation shows that the prediction is correct: the risk figure for later siblings is approximately ½. But what about the other risk figures listed: $\frac{1}{7}$, $\frac{1}{25}$, $\frac{1}{60}$, etc.? What formal sense can we make of these? Not much. Plainly, more than "school genetics" is involved. Fortunately we can say something about the additional factors or

TABLE 1

Approximate incidence of selected congenital malformations, showing increase in risk for later children in a given family once it is known that one child of the family has the defect. (From Anderson and Reed, 1954.)

Congenital Malformation	Incidence in Population	Risk Figure for Later Siblings
All malformations	1 in 65	1 in 20
Central nervous system malformations (35%)		
Anencephalus	1 in 450	1 in 50
Spina bifida	1 in 375	1 in 25
Hydrocephalus	1 in 550	1 in 60
Mongolism	1 in 600	1 in 20
Muscular-skeletal malformations (25%)		
Harelip with or without cleft palate	1 in 1000	1 in 7
Cleft palate alone	1 in 2500	1 in 7
Hyperdactyly	1 in 1200	1 in 2
Syndactyly	1 in 2000	1 in 2
Clubfoot	1 in 1000	1 in 30
Congenital hip dislocation	1 in 1500	1 in 20
Cardiovascular malformations (20%)		
Patent ductus arteriosus	1 in 2500	1 in 50
Genitourinary malformations (6%)		
Hypospadias	1 in 1000	1 in 50 (?)
Gastrointestinal malformations (3%)		
Tracheo-esophageal fistula	1 in 6000	less than 1 in 100
Atresia ani	1 in 5000	less than 1 in 100
Multiple malformations (11%)		

principles that are probably involved in such ratios, principles for which there is adequate scientific evidence among non-human animals and plants whose reproduction can be experimented with.

First subtlety: *many different genes may have similar effects.* For example, there is a dominant gene for whiteness in chickens:

there is also another gene for whiteness that is recessive. The experimenter who assumed that whiteness was always brought about by a single gene would be quite unable to explain some of the odd ratios obtained from different matings. Among humans, there is evidence that at least two different genes may produce diabetes, one being dominant, the other recessive.

Second subtlety: *two or more genes may have to act together* to produce a given condition. The ability to hear (among humans) is known to require both of two different dominant alleles, which may be called *D* and *E*. A person who has one or more of each of these, *D-E*, can hear; all other genetic types are deaf (*e.g., dd E-, D-ee* and *ddee*). It is thus possible not only for two normal parents to have a deaf child (parents being, say, DdEE x DdEE) but also for two deaf parents to have a child who hears (*e.g.,* parents thus: *ddEE x DDee*). To those who do not understand genetics, such apparently contradictory results seem wholly mysterious.

Instances in which different genes have to act together to produce a normal structure or function are not the exception, but the rule. We know of biochemical functions that demonstrably depend on the coaction of as many as a dozen genes; the trend of genetic knowledge is such that we expect someday to find that almost all of the principal functions of the body require at least dozens, and maybe hundreds, of coacting genes. Whenever we have not yet identified the principal genes involved in a variable characteristic, it will be difficult for us to make simple sense of the "risk figures" that are produced by unidentified genes.

Third subtlety: *genes can kill.* When this happens, primary genetic ratios may be altered by the differential survival of the various genotypes. An interesting example has turned up in the silver-fox business. A generation ago a fox rancher in Wisconsin found among his standard silver foxes one animal with an interesting type of fur to which the name "platinum" was given. When this type was bred with the silvers, about half the offspring were silver, half platinum. Since silvers bred true, it looked as though platinum was caused by an ordinary dominant gene, say *P*. On this hypothesis, two platinum fox parents, if derived from mixed parentage, should produce among their offspring, ¾ platinum and ¼ silver. But the prediction is not verified. If one breeds two platinum foxes and then counts and classifies the pups after they are weaned, one finds only ⅔ platinum and ⅓ silver. How come?

The answer becomes apparent when one observes the litters soon after birth. In the litters of platinum x platinum there are some foxes that are white. These die soon (always before weaning time), and the vixen, good housekeeper that she is, eats them. The primary genetic ratio is one of ¼ silver: ¾ platinum: ¼ white, which is modified by death of the homozygous platinum (white) to a ratio in the living adult foxes of ⅓ silver: ⅔ platinum. It is not possible to have a pure-breeding platinum strain.

Several points should be made in this connection. The platinum gene is of the sort usually called *lethal* or *sublethal* genes. The distinction between the two is not fundamental. If a gene kills before birth, it is called a lethal. Such a gene is "yellow" in mice, and "minor brachyplalangy" in man; both, when homozygous, kill their possessors in embryo. If the gene kills after birth, it may be called sublethal, particularly if it kills late. But where does one draw the line? Genes are known that have lethal effects at all periods of life, from the zygote stage to old age. Indeed, from a general point of view, one might say that everyone has lethal genes, but in some of us their effect is so slight that they take threescore years and ten to kill. The facts form a continuum, to which we must apply discrete terms as best we can.

It may seem strange that the white fox should die. Whiteness is not, by itself, a lethal characteristic: albinos, which owe their whiteness to a different gene, live. The important point is that a gene has many effects, and the superficial—*i.e.,* "surface"—effects from which we give the gene its name may be superficial in the metaphorical sense also, that is, of little basic importance. The platinum gene evidently modifies the biochemistry in such a way that various effects are caused, one of which is a change in fur color. The biochemical modification of the homozygote is so severe that it soon kills the pup. *How* the gene kills is a matter for further biochemical research.

The platinum gene raises a terminological question: Is it a dominant gene or a recessive one? With respect to coat color it is dominant; with respect to lethality, it is recessive (fortunately for the fox rancher's business). Clearly, it is purely a matter of convenience how one calls the gene; some genetical fence-straddlers like the term "semi-dominant."

Fourth subtlety: *the "penetrance" of a gene may be incomplete.* For example, the gene for Huntington's chorea, a disease characterized by involuntary jerking movements of the body, is unquestionably a dominant gene, and yet there are two features of its inheritance that require explanation: (1) in families born to a heterozygous parent and a homozygous normal parent, the affected offspring are not quite as common as simple Mendelian theory would predict; and (2) there are records of choreic individuals being born to parents neither of whom showed the characteristic. We

TABLE 2

Progressive increase in proportion of individuals showing clinical symptoms of Huntington's chorea in a sample of 460 patients who eventually showed the symptoms. (Julia Bell, 1934.)

Age Attained	Percentage Showing Symptoms by This Age
4	1
9	2
14	5
19	11
24	19
29	31
34	49
39	66
44	79
49	88
54	94
59	97
64	98
69	99
74	100

"explain" both these observations by saying that the gene for Huntington's chorea has less than 100 percent "penetrance"; that is, that although it is a dominant gene—*i.e.*, a single dose of it is enough to produce the condition—nevertheless, heterozygous individuals do not always show the effect of the abnormal gene. It is as though the gene could not penetrate through to the soma. Hence the term "penetrance."

It is apparent that penetrance is not entirely satisfactory, as a concept. It has the smell of a term invented "to save the appearances," to save Mendelian theory from the threat of its exceptions. It clearly explains nothing. Can we, however, find an explanation for the facts that impelled us to invent the term? In many instances, we can. The incomplete penetrance of Huntington's chorea is explained almost entirely by the variable period taken for the development of clinical symptoms. From Table 2 we learn that at age thirty-four less than half the people who will eventually be choreic are so. Suppose a genetically choreic individual who has not yet developed the symptoms has children (by a normal mate) and then dies before he himself is old enough to be choreic. Some of his offspring may eventually exhibit the disease, thus confronting us with what appears to be an anomaly: offspring affected by a dominant trait being born to unaffected parents. Anomalous—yet now completely explicable. The word "penetrance" can be given operational meaning, in the case of Huntington's chorea.

TABLE 3

Relation of age of mother to various abnormalities that are congenital (but may or may not be hereditary). The frequency of the youngest age group is arbitrarily expressed as 1, and the others are stated relative to this figure. (From Stern, 1949, after Penrose, 1939).

Mother's Age	Frequencies of Nervous System Abnormalities	Frequencies of Mongolism
16–20	1	1
21–25	2.7	0.7
26–30	2.3	1.3
31–35	4.3	3.0
36–40	6.0	9.3
41–45	10.0	34.3
46–50	7.0	146.2
Number of cases	144	224

For other genes, other meanings may develop. Sometimes an abnormal condition may develop only if two different abnormal genes are present; if we are aware of only one gene, the *apparently* irregular expression of this gene we will attribute to "incomplete dominance." In other instances, the clinical expression of abnormal genes depends on certain environmental conditions that may not always be present. For example, Mongolian idiocy has genetic causes; but an important role in producing it is played also by environment—*i.e.*, by the uterus, the environment of the developing embryo. Most Mongolian idiots are born to mothers near the end of their child-bearing period; the "penetrance" of the genes is very incomplete, particularly among young mothers (*see* Table 3). What are the effective differences between the uterine environments of young and older mothers? We don't know.

Fifth subtlety: *"variable expressivity."* How delicately the organism's potentialities are poised on the environment is shown by a wide variety of phenomena lumped under this term. The two different abnormalities, harelip and cleft palate, may be caused by identical genes interfering with normal embryogeny to different extents, simple harelip resulting from a minimum of interference. Males are more often affected, and more severely, than are females; in some sense that we don't understand, the male body is a different environment for the genes than is the female body. Identical twins may even be affected differently, indicating a hair-trigger sort of situation in development. (Both environmental and genetic factors are as nearly alike as can be in identical twins.) So delicate a hair trigger almost makes one wonder—in a moment of weakness— whether there was any wisdom in the old Norwegian law that forbade the hanging of hares in public view for fear that the pregnant women passing by might thereby be caused to produce children with harelips! The abnormality of hyperdactyly must also be delicately controlled, for not only does the number of extra fingers or toes vary among different affected individuals, but in a single individual the number of digits on the left appendages is often different from the number on the right.

Sixth subtlety: *environmentally caused defects may be indistinguishable from genetically caused ones.* The development of a human being is a complicated process. Each structure of the adult has its embryonic beginnings as one cell or a small group of cells called a *primordium.* Primordia are particularly susceptible to damage, and of course anything that injures the few cells of a primordium may destroy or greatly alter the normal adult structure that should grow out of it. Slight interference with the sensitive primordia of the hands may result in lack of hands, or in presence of webbed fingers, or in shortened fingers, or any of a number of other defects. The timing of the interference is all important in determining the result: each primordium has only a short period during which it may be easily affected. The same interfering agent, acting before or after this period, may be quite without effect. (Here we see another general explanation of the phenomena of imperfect penetrance and variable expressivity.) The interfering agent may be either genetic or environmental. In experimental animals a great variety of defects has been produced by treating pregnant mothers with different toxic chemicals, in various concentrations, and at various periods during the pregnancy. Many of these environmentally produced defects are—to the eye—indistinguishable from gene-produced defects; they are, therefore, called *phenocopies.* It is suspected that with continued trials we may be able to produce a phenocopy of almost every known genetic trait. The phenocopy, of course, does not breed like the genotype it mimics. A phenocopy web-toed animal breeds like a normal animal: its genes have not been affected—merely their mode of expression in the particular individual.

The consequences of accidental toxemias in human beings indicate that phenocopies occur here, too. We know that not all congenital defects are hereditary (*i.e.,* gene-caused); some of them—apparently the lesser fraction—are phenocopies. One of the best-proved agents for producing congenital defects is rubella, or "German measles." About 1940, Australia was so unfortunate as to suffer an acute epidemic of this disease, but the world was fortunate in that an unusually acute observer, a Dr. Gregg, was on the scene. He noted a fact which surely had long been true (though never before noticed) that a woman who has rubella during the first two months of her pregnancy is very likely to produce a defective child. The first month of embryonic life is the most sensitive period. The commonest defects in the offspring born of mothers who contract German measles are congenital cataract of the eyes (blindness), defective development of the internal ear (deafness) and imperfect division of the right and left chambers of the heart (resulting in "blue babies"). In other cases, the disease causes grossly abnormal brains, mongolism, or spontaneous abortion. Since this discovery, it has become common practice for humane obstetricians to induce abortion in patients who contract rubella in the first two months of pregnancy. (The human embryo, incidentally, at two months true age is only two inches long.) Where patient or doctor is a conscientious Roman Catholic, this mode of escape from the burden of fate is closed.

The "Heredity Versus Environment" Fallacy

In writing of phenocopies and genotypes I have carelessly written as if a defect were caused by genes *or* by the environment—*either/or*. This is not true, of course. Every structure and function, normal or abnormal, is caused by the interaction of hereditary and environmental factors. We can often "get away with" such careless expressions only because some characteristics are completely indifferent to *existing* environmental variations (for example, albinism) or similarly indifferent to existing hereditary variations (an example of this is harder to find, but perhaps susceptibility to the common cold will answer). Many abnormal characteristics demonstrably depend on interaction of both heredity and environment. *Diabetes mellitus* exemplifies this principle well. The evidence that genes are involved is quit convincing, but only a small fraction of those who are genetically diabetic become so clinically. Diet and psychological factors are known to play a role in producing the diabetic condition among those who are genetic candidates for it. Similarly complex interactions of heredity and environment are found in what are called "epileptic seizures." The study of "brain waves" shows that epileptics can be differentiated from "normals," but that many unaffected persons have the epileptic type of brain wave. Apparently all persons with this type of wave are susceptible to epilepsy, but they will not, in fact, have seizures unless they are subjected to a suitable rigorous environmental stress. One recalls the history of the Russian novelist, Dostoevski, who became seriously affected with seizures after his prison wardens had pretended, with complete realism up to the last possible moment, that they were going to execute him. The "joke" was too much for

Dostoevski, who undoubtedly had the genes for susceptibility to seizures. Others, of different genotypes, have survived equally grueling treatments without conspicuous damage. Viewing Dostoevski's life with a genetic bias, one might say, "He suffered from seizures because of his genes." Viewing it with an environmental bias, one could say, "His seizures were caused by his experiences." Both statements are partial truths. Dostoevski's genes were a sort of predestination for him—but only in determining his reactions to certain sorts of environments, which he might or might not encounter during his life. The predestination of genes is, in general, only a partial one, subject to some environmental modification.

Can I Accept Myself?

Genetic knowledge raises questions that are centuries old, but which many men in recent times had thought no longer valid. In old-fashioned language, the principal questions are two: (a) How can I find out my predestination? and (b) How can I accept it? We will take up the second first.

The acceptance of personal limitations is a problem that faces everyone; in a sense, it is independent of genetic knowledge, for a limitation must be accepted whatever its source. One's personal "talents," strengths, defects—call them what you will—play a role in the structuring of one's life analogous to the part played by the strength of materials used in constructing a building. They determine which of an infinity of designs for living are possible, which not. There is this important difference, however: whereas the strength of a building material is not influenced by what one thinks it is, the strength of a personal characteristic is. To an amazing extent, courageous refusal to accept an apparent limitation often brings about the displacement of the limit. By refusing to accept his stammering as an ultimate limitation, Demosthenes became a great orator; many a circus strong man has begun life as a sickly boy. On the other hand, the futile butting of ambitious heads against the stone walls of genuinely immovable limitations has produced personal tragedies without number. Such are the Scylla and Charybdis of the personal maturation process.

Genetics makes us aware of another facet of the problem, the acceptance of one's genetic limitations. It is a curious thing how we do not want to admit defects that are genetically determined—curious, because what can we be less "responsible" for than our genes? We didn't pick our parents. Yet the feeling of responsibility is there, perhaps because of an early psychological "identification" of the child with the parent. Whatever the cause, the issue of responsibility for ancestry is a minor one; the important responsibility is that for children. No one wants to produce a child that is seriously defective, yet every parent-to-be incurs this risk. The conscientious man would like to have some idea of the magnitude of the risk before embarking on parenthood. How can he determine it? In part, by assaying his own and his wife's personal qualities; but only in part, because of the notorious "hiding" ability of recessive genes. It is necessary to look also at one's ancestors. When one does, one is sure, sooner or later, to discover undesirable characteristics. How undesirable must the characteristic be, to influence one's decision? And how near must the ancestry be to affect the risk significantly? These are questions to which only probable answers can be given, and to give them requires the considerable technical knowledge found only among a new breed of professional men known as "genetic counselors."

Genetic Counseling: A Rare Commodity

Few married couples seek genetic advice before they have any children at all. The impelling circumstance is usually the appearance of one defective child. At this point, the disturbed parents want to know if the defect is gene-caused, and what is the risk in producing another child. With these questions, they usually turn to the family physician for counsel. Unfortunately, he is all too often unable to help them at all. The trouble lies not merely in the fact that the young science of human genetics is still only poorly advanced, but also in the fact that many, probably the majority, of the medical doctors are largely unaware of the genetical knowledge that is already available—unaware of both the principles and the facts. An all-too-common reply of the family physician (as Sheldon Reed, 1955, has pointed out) is a reassurance of the parents with the old bromide, "Lightning never strikes twice in the same place." The doctor's intention in saying this is clearly laudable: to take some of the burden of anxiety from the parents' shoulders. But the advice flies in the face of the facts in two different ways. First, lightning *does* sometimes strike twice in the same place; or to take a more appropriate example, if I get a zero on one spin of the roulette wheel, the chance of my getting a zero on the next spin is uninfluenced by the fact that a zero has just turned up, for the roulette wheel (to paraphrase the mathematician Bertrand) has neither conscience nor memory. Secondly, the fact that lightning *has* struck once in an unfortunate family is an indication that it is *more* likely to strike again in the same family than it is in some other family selected at random from the same population. This unwelcome truth is shown over and over by a comparison of the two columns of figures in Table 1. The chance that a couple's first child will have a cleft palate is only 1 in 2,500; but if their child does have a cleft palate, the chance that the next child will also be so afflicted is 1 in 7, a very high chance, indeed. For clubfoot the risk figure rises from 1 in 1,000 to 1 in 30; for Mongolian idiocy, from 1 to 600 to 1 in 20; and so on. The physician who removes his patients' anxieties at the expense of the truth plays with fire. It is hard to get any human being to accept an unpleasant truth that is irrevocable, but in the last analysis there is no security in denying the decrees of fate. At the very least, the unwise physician endangers the good name of medicine.

It must surely seem odd to the layman that physicians generally should be ignorant of genetics. The explanation is actually very simple. Genetics is a new subject. The medical school curriculum has for over a hundred years been crammed full with essential studies. (There are few "electives" in medical school.) There are only three ways in which a new subject can get into an existing curriculum: by addition without increase in time, by addition with increase in time, or by displacement of an already existing topic. The first choice is repugnant because medical students already study extremely hard—their weekly hours of unpaid work are nearly twice those of a paid union laborer. The second choice—addition made by increasing the years of medical training—is also repugnant. The recent action of Johns Hopkins University in decreasing the total number of years in medical and premedical training was taken in the belief that we have already come close to adding the last straw to the camel's back. The third choice—displacing existing topics in the medical curriculum in favor of genetics—would, to a simply logical and dispassionate observer, seem the best solution; but to hope for it is politically naïve. There are undoubtedly topics of the present medical curriculum that are less valuable to a doctor than genetics, but such dispensable subjects are taught by flesh-and-blood professors, who are only human if they seek to protect their invested interests from the threatened encroachments of unvested new-comers. Medicine is based on science, which changes, but the profession of medicine is a human institution and therefore is highly resistant to change. It is hardly to be expected that the centenary of Mendel's publication (in 1866) will see medical genetics established as a required course in more than a handful of medical schools, at most. Human institutions don't change that fast.

What about the premedical curriculum? Most students prepare for medical school for four years, commonly taking a bachelor's degree in biological sciences; cannot genetics be made part of the premedical curriculum? It can, and in many institutions it has been (though, as of 1956, only two out of eighty-five United States medical schools required a knowledge of genetics for entrance). With the aid of such courses, the medical ignorance of successive crops of doctors is lessening. On the debit side of the ledger, however, it must be pointed out that the introductory course in genetics, which is usually all that the premedical student has time to take, includes almost nothing of the special technical methods needed to study the genetics of human beings.

There are a few dozen medical doctors in the United States who, by one means or another, have made themselves proficient in human genetics. Being so few, they are hard to find. Many of the best trained men in this field are not M.D.'s but Ph.D.'s. Since, however, such a degree has less prestige in the eyes of the patient, most Ph.D.'s specializing in human genetics work with medical colleagues, or give advice only through medical correspondents. Of departments or institutes specializing in human genetics and prepared to give genetic advice, Scheinfeld (in 1956) could find only eleven in the United States (*see* Table 4). For a nation in which each year some 60,000 married couples find themselves confronted with the anxiety-engendering fact of a defective child, this provision seems hardly adequate.

TABLE 4

Human Heredity Clinics. Taken from Scheinfeld, 1956, pp. 267–268. Where not otherwise specified, address inquiries to "Department of Human Genetics," at the institution named. It is best that contact with the institution be made by the patient's physician.

UNITED STATES

Bowman Gray School of Medicine, Winston-Salem, North Carolina
Department of Zoology, University of Chicago, Chicago 37, Illinois
Dight Institute, University of Minnesota, Minneapolis 14, Minnesota
University of Michigan, Ann Arbor, Michigan
New York Psychiatric Institute, New York 32, New York
Ohio State University, Columbus, Ohio
University of Oklahoma, Norman, Oklahoma
University of Texas, Austin, Texas
Tulane University Medical School, New Orleans, Louisiana
University of Utah, Salt Lake City, Utah
Medical College of Virginia, Richmond, Virginia

CANADA

Hospital for Sick Children, Toronto 2, Canada
McGill University, Toronto, Canada
Children's Memorial Hospital, Montreal, Canada

Counseling: How Can the Truth Be Accepted?

There is another side to the problem of genetic advice which we have not yet solved, but for different reasons. Given that the patient has found a competent adviser, and that his problem is one for which the facts are known, how does one advise him? (How, in fact, does one advise anyone about anything?) An actual case study will help make clear what the problem is. Sheldon C. Reed, of the Dight Institute for Human Genetics, was consulted about a couple who had produced a child suffering from *spina bifida* (incompletely formed spinal column) and hydrocephaly ("water on the brain"). The child was put into an institution. The mother was disturbed about not seeing her child and the parents wanted to know how serious was the risk of producing another defective offspring. After analyzing all the relevant facts, Reed wrote to the psychiatrist in charge (Reed, 1955, p. 62):

> *Reply.* "The chances are at least 1 in 10 and perhaps as high as 1 in 4 that the next conception will result in a malformation or a miscarriage. You, the psychiatrist, should convey this fact to the couple and make it clear that they must make the decision about another try."
>
> *Follow-up.* A few months later the psychiatrist reported, "The mother took the matter into her own hands and visited her defective child which gave her considerable relief and subsequent feeling of confidence. As a result of this, she and her husband were able to talk their problem through, and decided, despite greater risk than the average couple, but in the interest of having a family, that they would try once more."

Was the parents' decision *right?* Is a risk of 1 in 4 or 1 in 10 of bearing so grossly deformed a child low enough to justify producing more children? How can we decide? There is no accepted rationale for making such decisions. This lack is not confined to genetics, but is found wherever there is risk. Each American has about 1 chance in 5,000 of being killed by an automobile during any given year. Does this knowledge stop us from driving cars or walking across the street? Certainly not. Apparently we regard the advantages of using automobiles as sufficiently great recompense for the risk of being killed or injured by them. But suppose the risk were 1 in 500? Or 1 in 50? Or 1 in 5? It is evident that there must be some level at which we would say the risk is too great in comparison with the benefits. But at what level would we make this decision? We have no theory to tell us the correct answer.

This is one of the reasons why many genetic counselors believe they should not counsel at all, if "to counsel" means to advise the patient what he should do. "With rare exceptions," say Neel and Schull (1954), "we do *not* attempt to pass a judgment as to the advisability of parenthood. This is a decision to be reached by the family concerned." Professor Reed agrees. On the other hand, Dr. Franz J. Kallman, who is both a psychiatrist and a genetic counselor, strongly disagrees (1956). To tell a client cold-bloodedly that his chance of developing so fearful a nervous affliction as Huntington's chorea is 1 in 2, and that the chance that his child will have it is 1 in

4; and then to cast him adrift to make his own decision by himself—this, Kallman says, is the greatest psychological cruelty. He who has a genetic sword of Damocles hanging over his head is a disturbed human being; he needs psychological support and love—not statistics. (In passing, it should be noted that this need for human contact rules out advising by correspondence. The client who must find it in his heart to accept the decrees of fate will hardly do so unless the news is brought to him in face-to-face encounter. At this critical juncture of his life he requires warm human contact.)

The error of the "non-directive" genetic counselors is a simple one: they have failed to realize what it means to be a member of a *profession*. Ernest Greenwood has expressed the issues with especial clarity:

> A nonprofessional occupation has customers; a professional occupation has clients. What is the difference? A customer determines what services and/or commodities he wants, and he shops around until he finds them. His freedom of decision rests upon the premise that he has the capacity to appraise his own needs and to judge the potential of the service or of the commodity to satisfy them. The infallibility of his decisions is epitomized in the slogan: 'The customer is always right!' In a professional relationship, however, the professional dictates what is good or evil for the client, who has no choice but to accede to professional judgment. Here the premise is that, because he lacks the requisite theoretical background, the client cannot diagnose his own needs or discriminate among the range of possibilities for meeting them.

The client with a genetic problem is, in general, incompetent in two fields of knowledge: genetics and probability. The first needs no arguing. The second deficiency is not so obvious because many people are capable of making simple probability calculations, and of acting rationally on them when there is no psychological involvement. But when the individual is psychologically involved, his ability to make rational decisions may be seriously lessened. Many a young man has made a theoretical fortune playing the stock market *on paper,* only to discover that he can do nothing but lose money when he stakes a real fortune on his judgments and thus becomes emotionally involved. Some can pass the second, and real, test, but not many; the very existence of Las Vegas and Monte Carlo is evidence of the millions who are utterly unable to understand, *in their bones,* the meaning of probability. It is the professional duty of the genetic counselor to convey to his client the personal implications of a probability statistic. The counselor may, to secure acceptance of the truth, pretend to leave the decision up to the client, but this pretense is only tactical. The responsibility for really making the decision must rest on the shoulders of the professional.

Escape from Fate

To get married, to have children—healthy children—is considered the normal thing, almost a "right," in our society. Yet the odds against it, while small, are appreciable. In the United States, according to estimates of the National Research Council, 1 couple out of every 10 who desire children fails to produce them, try as they will. And of the children that are produced, 1 in 65 (nearly 2 percent) are defective at birth. The probabilities of being thwarted by fate are not negligible. And the use of the old-fashioned word "fate" is really justified, for all evidence points to the conclusion that the majority of the cases of infertility and of congenital deformity, as well as the majority of spontaneous abortions, are caused by genes, about which we can do nothing.

We must accept our genes; but there is more than one way of accepting them. The predestination of genetics is not one of a single track to which we are bound, but rather is that of a field with more or less clearly discerned boundaries within which we must work out our lives. The individual who learns that he harbors deleterious genes that will probably cause his children to be defective, is not thereby condemned to produce a succession of heart-rendingly deformed children. He has a number of other options, each with its own advantages and disadvantages.

For one thing, it is obvious that he can avoid having children entirely. This can most certainly be done by observing strict sexual continence—most certainly, but by no means most pleasantly. "I would that all men were even as I," said the apostle Paul, who was content to remain celibate; but he knew they were not, and added, "But if they cannot contain, let them marry: for it is better to marry than to burn" (I Corinthians, 7: 7, 9). A biologist's view of sexual ethics is utterly different: were all men like Paul, there would soon be no men to be concerned about. Only those animals that "burn" with sexual desire can perpetuate their genes (including the genes for "burning") into succeeding generations. Ethical principles must be designed for such as these. To the biologist, the Pauline ideal is, at best, trivial; at worst, it borders on the monstrous.

For the married couple who face possible genetic tragedy, various paths are open. If they elect to produce no children of their own, how shall they achieve infertility? Two ways are suggested. They can either make use of one of the various scientific techniques known, in which case their sexual intercourse can be almost completely spontaneous; this mode of contraception, which permits emotional spontaneity, is, by some, called "artificial" birth control. The other way involves the inhibition of strong natural impulses, with the restriction of intercourse to days that are decreed by the calendar rather than by the emotions. Those who call scientific contraception "artificial" call the repressive mode "natural." The logic of this position comes in an unbroken line of descent from Tertullian, a Roman ecclesiastical lawyer of the third century A.D. Tertullian defined as "unnatural," and hence as morally wrong, the practice of circumcision, acting in plays, shaving the face, and the wearing of *dyed* fabrics. The last proscription gives the show away. Did Tertullian suppose that *undyed* fabrics grew on trees? The only consistency in seventeen centuries of polemics against the "unnatural," is the identification of *recent* technological advances as unnatural. One suspects that there was a time in the prehistory of man when the milking of cows for human food was looked on as utterly abhorrent. Indeed: to those who have the imagination to see the entire sequence of acts as if it had never been seen before, there is something decidedly "unnatural" in a man's manipulating a cow's mammary glands and then drinking the exudate, which was undeniably intended by nature for a suckling calf, and not for a grown man. . . . But then, it is dangerous to think logically.

It is possible, of course, to have children even if one does not produce them. The practical discovery of this elementary fact is surprisingly recent. A century ago unwanted children (if they were lucky) were thrown into an orphan asylum, while unwillingly childless couples accepted their plight as an unmodifiable decree of fate. Now, so completely is the idea of adoption accepted that the supply-and-demand picture is completely changed: there simply are not enough orphaned babies to meet the requests of would-be adoptive parents.

Parents who have produced a defective child of their own and have decided to obtain future children only by adoption, will be chagrined to find that adoption agencies are very "choosy." They usually will not place a child in a home in which there is already a mentally retarded child, insisting that the atmosphere of the home first be made psychologically healthier by removing the defective child to an institution. Parents often find it hard to accept such an ultimatum: it seems cruel and unnatural to give up one's own child. But, in the long run, it is probably the kindest thing to do for the whole family, including the child. As Reed (pp. 92–93) points out, a mentally defective child in the family is

> . . . a source of embarrassment to its sibs and will cause them to go elsewhere for social contacts. The retarded child is an invitation to improper sexual exploitation by ill-mannered neighbors or others.
>
> Very frequently it will be the duty of the physician to convince the parents that the child would be better off in the state school than at home and to help with the procedures necessary to have the child admitted to the public institution. Even though the building may be old and crowded and the food scorned by Duncan Hines, the child will find himself among his equals and he will be able to compete with them, whereas in the home community he will be always either overprotected or cruelly rejected from social contacts. Children are more interested in satisfactory contacts with other children than they are in culinary fine points or the design of their bed spreads. To be sure, it is a little hard on the vanity of the parents to find that after a week or two their small retarded child no longer recognizes nor misses them, but it is fortunate that this does happen.

In the last few decades, yet another means has been employed to an increasing extent as a way of escaping a childless home, namely *semi-adoption.* If the parents are in some sense genetically incompatible, if the husband is sterile, or if the defective genes come from the male side, the married couple may decide that they would prefer to be half-parents, biologically speaking, rather than adoptive ones. For the wife to be fecundated by a man not her husband in order to produce a healthy family is a procedure that has probably been resorted to for thousands of years, to a small extent. Where it has involved deception, the results have probably often been as unhappy as they were for Eugene O'Neill's Nina Leeds, who indulged in a "Strange Interlude" to avoid perpetuating the insanity in her husband's family. But even when consent has been mutual, the procedure has been a psychologically risky one.

The avoidance of disruptive emotional involvements has been made possible by that greatest of all practical developments of the last two centuries, the discovery of the technical separability of copulation and procreation. Just as it is possible to have copulation without the production of children, so also is it possible for a woman to become pregnant without sexual intercourse. It is a comparatively simple matter to impregnate a woman with semen from a man whom she has never seen and who is completely unknown to her (and to her husband). The procedure is, in its essence, completely impersonal. It has been called by various names: *artificial insemination* (which term has the disadvantage of raising the hoary old "artificial" vs. "natural" bugaboo), *transemination* (on the analogy of transfusion of blood), *therapeutic insemination,* and *semi-adoption* (in recognition that one member of the couple is the biological parent, only the husband being an adoptive parent).

How many babies have been conceived by artificial insemination no one knows, but the number so produced in the United States undoubtedly runs into many thousands. The most common reason for resorting to the procedure is sterility; but desire to avoid transmitting hereditary "taints" also plays a small role. Whatever the motivation, the procedure follows a common pattern. The knowing doctor, faced with a request for a transemination, "drags his feet" for many weeks to make sure that the request springs from a deliberate and mature decision on the part of both husband and wife. We all of us imbibe from the mores of our society so much in the way of superstitions and irrational attitudes toward parenthood, honor, adultery and other high-level, high-voltage abstractions, that it is no easy matter to view involuntary sterility or defective heredity in a rational manner. Only married couples who are unusually mature are fit to become parents of a semi-adopted child. It takes time to conquer the evil in one's mind. Hence the delaying tactics of the wise physician.

Once the decision has been agreed upon by both parents and the family physician, the couple is generally referred to a specialist in sterility problems, who carries out the artificial insemination. For many reasons, the locus of such activities is usually a large city hospital. One of the reasons is the desire for secrecy. A couple who have themselves worked through to the stage of maturity required for this procedure may feel no personal need for secrecy; but they are part of a larger, less mature society that may include, for example, prospective grandparents, who have probably passed the period of emotional growth. To spare the feelings of such as these (and hence, reflexively, of any children produced) deceptive silence is usually the better part of wisdom.

A large hospital is also ideal for the preservation of the anonymity of the donor of the semen. In one room of the large building, he can produce the required sample, which can then be carried to another part where the recipient is waiting. Methods of cold storage are now available so that the insemination can even be made at a much later date. Personal identification, and hence the possibility of emotional involvement, is completely avoided.

The criteria for selecting donors are of great importance. A donor must, of course, be in good health, both physically and mentally. It is important to check his family pedigree as carefully as possible with regard to possible genetic defects. For social reasons, it is desirable to choose a donor who resembles the husband in coloration and general body type. This seldom is difficult; the cliché, "Why, he looks just like his father!" will usually spring readily to the lips of unknowing relatives and friends when they are confronted with the *fait accompli*. (That the mother's face shows a momentary resemblance to Mona Lisa's will probably escape their notice.) In practice, most semen donations are made by medical students, for good reasons. Because of rigorous selection, they are above the population average in intelligence, health and stability; they have no irrational prejudices against the procedure; and they are readily available.

Are babies produced by transemination legitimate? Probably not, some jurists warn; but no decisive cases have been tried. A Canadian court at one time expressed the gratuitous opinion (it was irrelevant to the case in hand) that (1) the production of children was the primary aim of the marriage bond; and that (2) therefore conception without copulation was adultery. This led an English wit to point out that same logic leads inevitably to the conclusion that copulation with contraceptives is not adultery, a view that not many courts are likely to accept. There the matter stands. The circumstances under which transemination is resorted to are such that it is not probable that a case requiring a decision will soon be brought before a court. Already the practice has been indulged in for more than half a century without significant litigation.

Attempts to pass legislative acts bringing the law into rational harmony with this new scientific development have so far failed. In the meantime, two different "gimmicks" have been proposed. Sometimes the parents adopt the child. This completely forestalls any possible charge of illegitimacy, but regional laws often make the procedure impossible or impracticable. Some districts require the consent of the biological parents; many require the naming of them. Both demands—which were devised before any legislator ever heard of transemination—make impossible the anonymity of the semen donor and the avoidance of publicity that are so desirable from a humane point of view. So the adoption procedure has been used very little. The other device is a procedural one. Most transeminations are performed because the husband is *believed* to be sterile; but since this is seldom a certainity, the attending physician can confound the legal quibblers by mixing semen from the husband with semen from the donor, and injecting the two together. Thus there is introduced a real doubt as to the paternity of the child. Scientifically, this procedure is rather ludicrous, but it has legal advantages. It may also have psychological advantages for the husband, who may not be completely reconciled to giving up the possibility of paternity. It takes only a very little wishful thinking to convince himself that he is the father after all. . . . Of course, where transemination is resorted to because of genetic defects on the husband's side, this mixed-semen procedure should not be used.

The medical jurist, Sidney B. Schatkin (1954), has predicted that the reaction of the law to artificial insemination will follow a pattern of evolution that has been shown in other legal adaptations to scientific advances, the stages being (successively): *perfect horror—skepticism—curiosity*—and, finally, *acceptance*. We should not, says Schatkin, become incensed at the inertia of the law; it is natural and proper that law should have its own mode of development.

The lag between medicine and the law is not only inevitable but desirable. Too often scientific theories and practices fail to fulfill their promise. Were medical discoveries immediately reflected in the law, we would have not medical progress, but chaos. Science with impunity may reverse itself repeatedly; the law hardly ever.

How long will it be before the final stage—acceptance of transemination—will be reached? There is no theory of legal kinetics to tell us the answer, but if the history of contraception is any guide, the year 2000 A.D. will certainly have come and gone before the majority of the states will have adopted satisfactory laws. In the meantime, many high-minded married couples will, each year, produce thousands of children, conceived in this extra-legal fashion with the connivance of equally high-minded physicians. No better course is open to those of humane and tender feelings.

Paternity: Words and Emotions

The law mirrors popular beliefs, if not of the present generation, at least of the preceding one; if not of both sexes, at least of the males, who make the laws and who often reveal their own insecurity in their legislation. Back of the opposition to transemination lie centuries-old attitudes toward paternity, attitudes that are embedded in language. A man may say, "This is my child," and no one questions the meaning because the language is traditional. But what does it mean, really, to say, "This is *my* child"? "My" is a possessive. What does it mean, to "possess" a child?

There was a time when possession of a child was complete—as complete as the possession of a chair or a cow. The father could do whatever he wished with his property. That time is now well past. The modern father's rights include little more than the right partially to determine the education of his child. His rights are more in the nature of privileges—the privilege of observing the growing up of a child, the privilege of maturing himself as he vicariously faces for a second time the trials he more or less failed to pass during his own youth and adolescence. "This is my child" means, "this is my right to further psychological development." For this right, literal biological parenthood is, of course, an irrelevancy. An adopted child is as legitimate a voucher as a natural one.

But still, in the male, there is a gnawing question: If I procreate a child with my own semen, is it not more *mine* than if I adopt one, or allow my wife to use another man's semen?

Let's see what the facts are. First, it is an error to think of the semen as the essential agent of reproduction. In the reproductive act, a man may deposit as much as one sixth of an ounce of semen in his wife's vagina, but of the millions of spermatozoa in this donation only one fertilizes the egg. One spermatozoan is not very big: it weighs about 0.00,000,000,000,02 of an ounce. The adult human weighs (say) 3,000 ounces. The maximum amount of substance that the father has contributed to his grown child is certainly less than one ten thousand million millionth of the total. In what sense, then, is the child *his* child?

There is, of course, a sense in which it is meaningful to say it is his child—it may look strikingly like him, and for good reason. Precious little of the substance of the child has come from the father, but that little is of critical importance. We should not, in fact, think in terms of substance, but rather in terms of *information*. The egg develops, through an incredibly complicated series of processes, into an adult that is distinguishable from all other adults. What determines the uniqueness of each human being? Genes, acting in conjunction with the environment. The fertilized egg has received half its genes from the mother, half from the father. Each gene can be thought of as a bit of information telling the zygote how to develop, whether to produce a long nose or a short nose, brown eyes or blue eyes, great intelligence or utter idiocy. What the father does contribute to his offspring is information, genetic information. And all this information, certainly 10,000 bits of it, and maybe as many as 100,000 bits, is packed into a tiny sperm's head which weighs not more than two hundred million millionths of an ounce. Great riches in a little room, indeed!

The father does, then, contribute significantly to the information that governs the development of the zygote. How unique is that information—how different is it from the information that might be contributed by another man chosen at random?

Every man has many genes—many bits of information. For most of the kinds of genes, a man is homozygous, that is, he has only one kind of allele. His genetic formula with respect to these genes we can represent as *AABBCCDDEE* . . . , the formula continuing through several *thousand* different letters of the genetic alphabet. With respect to the genes for which a man is homozygous, his spermatozoa will be a correct representation of the man himself, *ABCDE* . . . —"like father, like son"—or rather, *like father, like spermatozoa.*

With respect to other genes, however, a man will be heterozygous, say *HhIiJjKk*. . . . For how many genes will a man be heterozygous? We don't know. The number of heterozygous pairs will vary from man to man, but it is hardly conceivable that this number will ever be less than a hundred. With respect to such genes, it is never true that the spermatozoa are like the father. Each sperm has one and only one member of each pair of alleles; so, of the various sperm types, possible (*e.g., HiJK; hIjk;* etc.), *none* are like the father. Even if we grant complete dominance with each pair of alleles, it would take only ten sets to reduce to less than one in a thousand the probabilty that one spermatozoan would be truly representative of the father's phenotype. With only twenty heterozygous pairs, the probability is reduced to less than one in a million. And with as many as one hundred heterozygous pairs (a conservatively low figure) the probability of a spermatozoan being "like" the father is vanishingly small. Only by seizing upon a few out of an almost infinite number of human charactertistics can we persuade ourselves that a son is ever like his father. If one took the totality of differentia, without selection, the resemblance would be negligible indeed.

The genes possessed by a father are like a hand of cards. Each hand is unique. When it comes time for a father to pass genes on to his child, he does not pass on his whole hand, but only part of it. In this process chance plays a large role. Thus there is a not negligible probability that the hand that is passed on (the genes in the haploid spermatozoan) will be quite unrepresentative of the father's collection of cards. The haploid set of genes in a particular one of Mr. Jones's spermatozoa may, in fact, more nearly resemble what one would expect to find in a spermatozoan of Mr. Smith. If this spermatozoan reaches the egg first, the child may look more like the man next door than he does his own father, though his mother may have been as chaste as Susanna. Of all men, the true father is the one the child will most probably look like; but the chance that he will more nearly resemble an unrelated man in the same general population is almost as great.

As men come to appreciate the subtle principles underlying the fact of paternity, we can expect them to be less concerned with problems of "mine" and "thine" in the Fertilization Sweepstakes. Concern for the health and happiness of the children we are responsible for—morally responsible for, whether we are their biological fathers or not—may lead us to take steps to insure that the best possible spermatozoa are entered in the race, in utter disregard of emotionally charged possessive pronouns. It would be rash to assert that this trend, already slightly in evidence in our country, will necessarily increase, for that assumes that we will become ever more rational, which is certainly not self-evident. But if this does not come to pass in our own country, it very likely will in some other nation. The nation which behaves rationally will gain in strength. We will have to compete with it. Let us not forget that fact as we wrestle with the problems created by the conflict of tradition and rationality.

The Naturalist Biologists

The nineteenth-century naturalists John Muir and John Burroughs not only loved and studied individual aspects of nature, but like all true naturalists they were sensitively attuned to the overall quality of particular environments and worked diligently to help preserve all forms of life in a wild state for future generations to study and enjoy.

For too many years their messages were almost forgotten, and we ignored the preservation of our natural resources, allowing them to be exploited in the transitory interest of commerce. Many of the most ardent conservationists were single-mindedly absorbed in their own favorite projects, worrying about the disappearance of coyotes in the Southwest, warring against pollution of a beloved river, or crusading to preserve an ancient tree in a freeway path. The battle of conservation was being waged by many splintered forces.

In 1962, in one controversial book, Rachel L. Carson forced us to a total reevaluation of man's relationship with his environment. She was concerned—to paraphrase Keats—not only with the sedge withered on the lake but with the fact that birds no longer sing. *Silent Spring* stirred the interest of the general public and thousands of scientists in her attack on the mass application of chemical insecticides and their effects on wildlife, rivers, and vegetation. It touched off Congressional inquiries into the use of pesticides that led to formation of the Federal Committee on Pest Control and an increase in regulatory, educational, and enforcement procedures to provide proper safeguards against pesticide abuse.

It took considerable courage for Miss Carson to engage in the controversy which inevitably exploded. In some instances it became clear that because of a lack of sufficient data she had misinterpreted or overstated particular cases, and those in the employ of chemical companies or scientists with restricted views sought to employ such examples to destroy her primary message.

The result has been a dramatic shift in the past few years from concern with specific conservation problems to a broad approach that embraces the whole environment. Recognition of the fact that conservation should not be viewed, as Stewart Udall has noted, simply in terms of "mopping up the mess we have made" is indicated by the recent publication by the President's Advisory Committee of a report titled "Restoring the Quality of Our Environment."

The problem of preserving environmental quality—essentially a conflict between man's need for fibers, food, and energy and his desire to live in a world of natural beauty—will require continual vigilance and the coordinated efforts of the federal government, individual states, industry, and the public. Our parks and wilderness areas are already jammed during the summer months by millions of Americans as they make a mass exodus from their concrete, steel, and plastic environments.

The struggle to preserve existing facilities and meet the needs of the population influx of the future can be expected to tax our most ingenious minds. If we fail to develop an ecological approach in planning the future, our descendants may live in a drab, colorless tomorrow, a world of one endless urban blight.

JOHN STEINBECK

"Leave Taking from the Monterey Peninsula"

John Steinbeck is a native Californian and Nobel Prize winner in Literature. At the present time he is living in Sag Harbor, Long Island. His Log from the Sea of Cortez, The Grapes of Wrath, Cannery Row, East of Eden, *and* Tortilla Flat *are among the finest of his works. In* Log from the Sea of Cortez *Steinbeck and his marine biologist friend Ed Ricketts study marine invertebrates, philosophize, and enjoy living in close contact with their natural environment.*

The design of a book is the pattern of a reality controlled and shaped by the mind of the writer. This is completely understood about poetry or fiction, but it is too seldom realized about books of fact. And yet the impulse which drives a man to poetry will send another man into the tide pools and force him to try to report what he finds there. Why is an expedition to Tibet undertaken, or a sea bottom dredged? Why do men, sitting at the microscope, examine the calcareous plates of a sea-cucumber, and, finding a new arrangement and number, feel an exaltation and give the new species a name, and write about it possessively? It would be good to know the impulse truly, not to be confused by the "services to science" platitudes or the other little mazes into which we entice our minds so that they will not know what we are doing.

We have a book to write about the Gulf of California. We could

125

do one of several things about its design. But we have decided to let it form itself: its boundaries a boat and a sea; its duration a six weeks' charter time; its subject everything we could see and think and even imagine; its limits—our own without reservation.

We made a trip into the Gulf; sometimes we dignified it by calling it an expedition. Once it was called the Sea of Cortez, and that is a better-sounding and a more exciting name. We stopped in many little harbors and near barren coasts to collect and preserve the marine invertebrates of the littoral. One of the reasons we gave ourselves for this trip—and when we used this reason, we called the trip an expedition—was to observe the distribution of invertebrates, to see and to record their kinds and numbers, how they lived together, what they ate, and how they reproduced. That plan was simple, straight-forward, and only a part of the truth. But we did tell the truth to ourselves. We were curious. Our curiosity was not limited, but was as wide and horizonless as that of Darwin or Agassiz or Linnaeus or Pliny. We wanted to see everything our eyes would accommodate, to think what we could, and, out of our seeing and thinking, to build some kind of structure in modeled imitation of the observed reality. We knew that what we would see and record and construct would be warped, as all knowledge patterns are warped, first, by the collective pressure and stream of our time and race, second by the thrust of our individual personalities. But knowing this, we might not fall into too many holes—we might maintain some balance between our warp and the separate thing, the external reality. The oneness of these two might take its contribution from both. For example: the Mexican sierra has "XVII–15–IX" spines in the dorsal fin. These can easily be counted. But if the sierra strikes hard on the line so that our hands are burned, if the fish sounds and nearly escapes and finally comes in over the rail, his colors pulsing and his tail beating the air, a whole new relational externality has come into being—an entity which is more than the sum of the fish plus the fisherman. The only way to count the spines of the sierra unaffected by this second relational reality is to sit in a laboratory, open an evil-smelling jar, remove a stiff colorless fish from formalin solution, count the spines, and write the truth "D.

XVII–15–IX." There you have recorded a reality which cannot be assailed—probably the least important reality concerning either the fish or yourself.

It is good to know what you are doing. The man with his pickled fish has set down one truth and has recorded in his experience many lies. The fish is not that color, that texture, that dead, nor does he smell that way.

Such things we had considered in the months of planning our expedition and we were determined not to let a passion for unassailable little truths draw in the horizons and crowd the sky down on us. We knew that what seemed to us true could be only relatively true anyway. There is no other kind of observation. The man with his pickled fish has sacrificed a great observation about himself, the fish, and the focal point, which is his thought on both the sierra and himself.

We suppose this was the mental provisioning of our expedition. We said, "Let's go wide open. Let's see what we see, record what we find, and not fool ourselves with conventional scientific strictures. We could not observe a completely objective Sea of Cortez anyway, for in that lonely and uninhabited Gulf our boat and ourselves would change it the moment we entered. By going there, we would bring a new factor to the Gulf. Let us consider that factor and not be betrayed by this myth of permanent objective reality. If it exists at all, it is only available in pickled tatters or in distorted flashes. Let us go," we said, "into the Sea of Cortez, realizing that we become forever a part of it; that our rubber boots slogging through a flat of eelgrass, that the rocks we turn over in a tide pool, make us truly and permanently a factor in the ecology of the region. We shall take something away from it, but we shall leave something too." And if we seem a small factor in a huge pattern, nevertheless it is of relative importance. We take a tiny colony of soft corals from a rock in a little water world. And that isn't terribly important to the tide pool. Fifty miles away the Japanese shrimp boats are dredging with overlapping scoops, bringing up tons of shrimps, rapidly destroying the species so that it may never come back, and with the species destroying the ecological balance of the whole region. That isn't very important in the world. And thousands of miles away the great bombs are falling and the stars are not moved thereby. None of it is important or all of it is.

We determined to go doubly open so that in the end we could, if we wished, describe the sierra thus: "D. XVII–15–IX; A. II–15–IX," but also we could see the fish alive and swimming, feel it plunge against the lines, drag it threshing over the rail, and even finally eat it. And there is no reason why either approach should be inaccurate. Spine-count description need not suffer because another approach is also used. Perhaps out of the two approaches, we thought, there might emerge a picture more complete and even more accurate than either alone could produce. And so we went.

And so our boat was loaded, except for the fuel tanks, which we planned to fill at San Diego. Our crew entered the contests at the sardine fiesta—the skiff race, the greased-pole walk, the water-barrel tilt—and they did not win anything, but no one cared. And late in the night when the feast had died out we slept ashore for the last time, and our dreams were cluttered with things we might have forgotten. And the beer cans from the fiesta washed up and down the shore on the little brushing waves behind the breakwater.

We had planned to sail about ten o'clock on March 11, but so many people came to see us off and the leave-taking was so pleasant that it was afternoon before we could think of going. The moment or hour of leave-taking is one of the pleasantest times in human experience, for it has in it a warm sadness without loss. People who don't ordinarily like you very well are overcome with affection at leave-taking. We said good-by again and again and still could not bring ourselves to cast off the lines and start the engines. It would be good to live in a perpetual state of leave-taking, never to go nor to stay, but to remain suspended in that golden emotion of love and longing; to be missed without being gone; to be loved without satiety. How beautiful one is and how desirable; for in a few moments one will have ceased to exist. Wives and fiancées were there, melting and open. How beautiful they were too; and against the hull of the boat the beer cans from the fiesta of yesterday tapped lightly like little bells, and the sea-gulls flew around and around but did not land. There was no room for them—too many people were seeing us off. Even a few strangers were caught in the magic and came aboard and wrung our hands and went into the galley. If our medicine chest had held out we might truly never have sailed. But about twelve-thirty the last dose was prescribed and poured and taken. Only then did we realize that not only were *we* fortified against illness, but that fifty or sixty inhabitants of Monterey could look forward to a long period of good health.

The day of charter had arrived. That instrument said we would leave on the eleventh, and the master was an honest man. We ejected our guests, some forcibly. The lines were cast off. We backed and turned and wove our way out among the boats of the fishing fleet. In our rigging the streamers, the bunting, the serpentine still fluttered, and as the breakwater was cleared and the wind struck us, we seemed, to ourselves at least, a very brave and beautiful sight. The little bell buoy on the reef at Cabrillo Point was excited about it too, for the wind had freshened and the float rolled heavily and the four clappers struck the bell with a quick tempo. We stood on top of the deckhouse and watched the town of Pacific Grove slip by and dark pine-covered hills roll back on themselves as though they moved, not we.

We sat on a crate of oranges and thought what good men most biologists are, the tenors of the scientific world—temperamental, moody, lecherous, loud-laughing, and healthy. Once in a while one comes on the other kind—what used in the university to be called a "dry-ball"—but such men are not really biologists. They are the embalmers of the field, the picklers who see only the preserved form of life without any of its principle. Out of their own crusted minds they create a world wrinkled with formaldehyde. The true biologist deals with life, with teeming boisterous life, and learns something from it, learns that the first rule of life is living. The dry-balls cannot possibly learn a thing every starfish knows in the core of his soul and in the vesicles between his rays. He must, so know the starfish and the student biologist who sits at the feet of living things, proliferate in all directions. Having certain tendencies, he must move along their lines to the limit of their potentialities. And we have known biologists who did proliferate in all directions: one or two have had a little trouble about it. Your true biologist will sing you a song as loud and off-key as will a blacksmith, for he knows that morals are too often diagnostic of prostatitis and stomach ulcers. Sometimes he may proliferate a little too much in all directions, but he is as easy to kill as any other organism, and meanwhile he is very good company, and at least he does not confuse a low hormone productivity with moral ethics.

RACHEL L. CARSON

The Human Price

Rachel Carson's book Silent Spring *is termed "The most important chronicle of this century for the human race" by Supreme Court Justice William O. Douglas. In* Silent Spring *Miss Carson shows not only that she is an exacting scientist but also mounts an academic, forceful appeal to the people against the destructive forces of chemical warfare which are disrupting the delicately balanced scale of the natural world.*

As the tide of chemicals born of the Industrial Age has arisen to engulf our environment, a drastic change has come about in the nature of the most serious public health problems. Only yesterday mankind lived in fear of the scourges of smallpox, cholera, and plague that once swept nations before them. Now our major concern is no longer with the disease organisms that once were omnipresent; sanitation, better living conditions, and new drugs have given us a high degree of control over infectious disease. Today we are concerned with a different kind of hazard that lurks in our environment —a hazard we ourselves have introduced into our world as our modern way of life has evolved.

The new environmental health problems are multiple—created by radiation in all its forms, born of the neverending stream of chemicals of which pesticides are a part, chemicals now pervading the world in which we live, acting upon us directly and indirectly, separately and collectively. Their presence casts a shadow that is no less ominous because it is formless and obscure, no less frightening because it is simply impossible to predict the effects of lifetime exposure to chemical and physical agents that are not part of the biological experience of man.

"We all live under the haunting fear that something may corrupt the environment to the point where man joins the dinosaurs as an obsolete form of life," says Dr. David Price of the United States Public Health Service. "And what makes these thoughts all the more disturbing is the knowledge that our fate could perhaps be sealed twenty or more years before the development of symptoms."

Where do pesticides fit into the picture of environmental disease? We have seen that they now contaminate soil, water, and food, that they have the power to make our streams fishless and our gardens and woodlands silent and birdless. Man, however much he may like to pretend the contrary, is part of nature. Can he escape a pollution that is now so thoroughly distributed throughout our world?

We know that even single exposures to these chemicals, if the amount is large enough, can precipitate acute poisoning. But this is not the major problem. The sudden illness or death of farmers, spraymen, pilots, and others exposed to appreciable quantities of pesticides are tragic and should not occur. For the population as a whole, we must be more concerned with the delayed effects of absorbing small amounts of the pesticides that invisibly contaminate our world.

Responsible public health officials have pointed out that the biological effects of chemicals are cumulative over long periods of time, and that the hazard to the individual may depend on the sum of the exposures received throughout his lifetime. For these very reasons the danger is easily ignored. It is human nature to shrug off what may seem to us a vague threat of future disaster. "Men are naturally most impressed by diseases which have obvious manifestations," says a wise physician, Dr. René Dubos, "yet some of their worst enemies creep on them unobtrusively."

For each of us, as for the robin in Michigan or the salmon in the

Miramichi, this is a problem of ecology, of interrelationships, of interdependence. We poison the caddis flies in a stream and the salmon runs dwindle and die. We poison the gnats in a lake and the poison travels from link to link of the food chain and soon the birds of the lake margins become its victims. We spray our elms and the following springs are silent of robin song, not because we sprayed the robins directly but because the poison traveled, step by step, through the now familiar elm leaf-earthworm-robin cycle. These are matters of record, observable, part of the visible world around us. They reflect the web of life—or death—that scientists know as ecology.

But there is also an ecology of the world within our bodies. In this unseen world minute causes produce mighty effects; the effect, moreover, is often seemingly unrelated to the cause, appearing in a part of the body remote from the area where the original injury was sustained. "A change at one point, in one molecule even, may reverberate throughout the entire system to initiate changes in seemingly unrelated organs and tissues," says a recent summary of the present status of medical research. When one is concerned with the mysterious and wonderful functioning of the human body, cause and effect are seldom simple and easily demonstrated relationships. They may be widely separated both in space and time. To discover the agent of disease and death depends on a patient piecing together of many seemingly distinct and unrelated facts developed through a vast amount of research in widely separated fields.

We are accustomed to look for the gross and immediate effect and to ignore all else. Unless this appears promptly and in such obvious form that it cannot be ignored, we deny the existence of hazard. Even research men suffer from the handicap of inadequate methods of detecting the beginnings of injury. The lack of sufficiently delicate methods to detect injury before symptoms appear is one of the great unsolved problems in medicine.

"But," someone will object, "I have used dieldrin sprays on the lawn many times but I have never had convulsions like the World Health Organization spraymen—so it hasn't harmed me." It is not that simple. Despite the absence of sudden and dramatic symptoms, one who handles such materials is unquestionably storing up toxic materials in his body. Storage of the chlorinated hydrocarbons, as we have seen, is cumulative, beginning with the smallest intake. The toxic materials become lodged in all the fatty tissues of the body. When these reserves of fat are drawn upon the poison may then strike quickly. A New Zealand medical journal recently provided an example. A man under treatment for obesity suddenly developed symptoms of poisoning. On examination his fat was found to contain stored dieldrin, which had been metabolized as he lost weight. The same thing could happen with loss of weight in illness.

The results of storage, on the other hand, could be even less obvious. Several years ago the *Journal* of the American Medical Association warned strongly of the hazards of insecticide storage in adipose tissue, pointing out that drugs or chemicals that are cumulative require greater caution than those having no tendency to be stored in the tissues. The adipose tissue, we are warned, is not merely a place for the deposition of fat (which makes up about 18 per cent of the body weight), but has many important functions with which the stored poisons may interfere. Furthermore, fats are very widely distributed in the organs and tissues of the whole body, even being constituents of cell membranes. It is important to remember, therefore, that the fat-soluble insecticides become stored in individual cells, where they are in position to interfere with the most vital and necessary functions of oxidation and energy production. This important aspect of the problem will be taken up in the next chapter.

One of the most significant facts about the chlorinated hydrocarbon insecticides is their effect on the liver. Of all organs in the body the liver is most extraordinary. In its versatility and in the indispensable nature of its functions it has no equal. It presides over so many vital activities that even the slightest damage to it is fraught with serious consequences. Not only does it provide bile for the digestion of fats, but because of its location and the special circulatory pathways that converge upon it the liver receives blood directly from the digestive tract and is deeply involved in the metabolism of all the principal foodstuffs. It stores sugar in the form of glycogen and releases it as glucose in carefully measured quantities to keep the blood sugar at a normal level. It builds body proteins, including some essential elements of blood plasma concerned with blood-clotting. It maintains cholesterol at its proper level in the blood plasma, and inactivates the male and female hormones when they reach excessive levels. It is a storehouse of many vitamins, some of which in turn contribute to its own proper functioning.

Without a normally functioning liver the body would be disarmed—defenseless against the great variety of poisons that continually invade it. Some of these are normal by-products of metabolism, which the liver swiftly and efficiently makes harmless by withdrawing their nitrogen. But poisons that have no normal place in the body may also be detoxified. The "harmless" insecticides malathion and methoxychlor are less poisonous than their relatives only because a liver enzyme deals with them, altering their molecules in such a way that their capacity for harm is lessened. In similar ways the liver deals with the majority of the toxic materials to which we are exposed.

Our line of defense against invading poisons or poisons from within is now weakened and crumbling. A liver damaged by pesticides is not only incapable of protecting us from poisons, the whole wide range of its activities may be interfered with. Not only are the consequences far-reaching, but because of their variety and the fact that they may not immediately appear they may not be attributed to their true cause.

In connection with the nearly universal use of insecticides that are liver poisons, it is interesting to note the sharp rise in hepatitis that began during the 1950's and is continuing a fluctuating climb. Cirrhosis also is said to be increasing. While it is admittedly difficult, in dealing with human beings rather than laboratory animals, to "prove" that cause A produces effect B, plain common sense suggests that the relation between a soaring rate of liver disease and the prevalence of liver poisons in the environment is no coincidence. Whether or not the chlorinated hydrocarbons are the primary cause, it seems hardly sensible under the circumstances to expose ourselves to poisons that have a proven ability to damage the liver and so presumably to make it less resistant to disease.

Both major types of insecticides, the chlorinated hydrocarbons and the organic phosphates, directly affect the nervous system, although in somewhat different ways. This has been made clear by an infinite number of experiments on animals and by observations on human subjects as well. As for DDT, the first of the new organic insecticides to be widely used, its action is primarily on the central nervous system of man; the cerebellum and the higher motor cortex are thought to be the areas chiefly affected. Abnormal sensations as of prickling, burning, or itching, as well as tremors or even convulsions may follow exposure to appreciable amounts, according to a standard textbook of toxicology.

Our first knowledge of the symptoms of acute poisoning by DDT was furnished by several British investigators, who deliberately exposed themselves in order to learn the consequences. Two scientists at the British Royal Navy Physiological Laboratory invited absorption of DDT through the skin by direct contact with walls covered with a water-soluble paint containing 2 per cent DDT, overlaid with a thin film of oil. The direct effect on the nervous system is apparent in their eloquent description of their symptoms: "The tiredness, heaviness, and aching of limbs were very real things, and the mental state was also most distressing . . . [there was] extreme irritability . . . great distaste for work of any sort . . . a feeling of mental incompetence in tackling the simplest mental task. The joint pains were quite violent at times."

Another British experimenter who applied DDT in acetone solution to his skin reported heaviness and aching of limbs, muscular weakness, and "spasms of extreme nervous tension." He took a holiday and improved, but on return to work his condition deteriorated. He then spent three weeks in bed, made miserable by constant aching in limbs, insomnia, nervous tension, and feelings of acute anxiety. On occasion tremors shook his whole body—tremors of the sort now made all too familiar by the sight of birds poisoned by DDT. The experimenter lost 10 weeks from his work, and at the end of a year, when his case was reported in a British medical journal, recovery was not complete.

(Despite this evidence, several American investigators conducting an experiment with DDT on volunteer subjects dismissed the complaint of headache and "pain in every bone" as "obviously of psychoneurotic origin.")

There are now many cases on record in which both the symptoms and the whole course of the illness point to insecticides as the cause. Typically, such a victim has had a known exposure to one of the insecticides, his symptoms have subsided under treatment which included the exclusion of all insecticides from his environment, and most significantly *have returned with each renewed contact* with the offending chemicals. This sort of evidence—and no more—forms the basis of a vast amount of medical therapy in many other disorders. There is no reason why it should not serve as a warning that it is no longer sensible to take the "calculated risk" of saturating our environment with pesticides.

Why does not everyone handling and using insecticides develop the same symptoms? Here the matter of individual sensitivity enters in. There is some evidence that women are more susceptible than men, the very young more than adults, those who lead sedentary, indoor lives more than those leading a rugged life of work or exercise in the open. Beyond these differences are others that are no less real because they are intangible. What makes one person allergic to dust or pollen, sensitive to a poison, or susceptible to an infection whereas another is not is a medical mystery for which there is at present no explanation. The problem nevertheless exists and it affects significant numbers of the population. Some physicians estimate that a third or more of their patients show signs of some form of sensitivity, and that the number is growing. And unfortunately, sensitivity may suddenly develop in a person previously insensitive. In fact, some medical men believe that intermittent exposures to chemicals may produce just such sensitivity. If this is true, it may explain why some studies on men subjected to continuous occupational exposure find little evidence of toxic effects. By their constant contact with the chemicals these men keep themselves desensitized—as an allergist keeps his patients desensitized by repeated small injections of the allergen.

The whole problem of pesticide poisoning is enormously complicated by the fact that a human being, unlike a laboratory animal living under rigidly controlled conditions, is never exposed to one chemical alone. Between the major groups of insecticides, and between them and other chemicals, there are interactions that have serious potentials. Whether released into soil or water or a man's blood, these unrelated chemicals do not remain segregated; there are mysterious and unseen changes by which one alters the power of another for harm.

There is interaction even between the two major groups of insecticides usually thought to be completely distinct in their action. The power of the organic phosphates, those poisoners of the nerve-protective enzyme cholinesterase, may become greater if the body has first been exposed to a chlorinated hydrocarbon which injures the liver. This is because, when liver function is disturbed, the cholinesterase level drops below normal. The added depressive effect of the organic phosphate may then be enough to precipitate acute symptoms. And as we have seen, pairs of the organic phosphates themselves may interact in such a way as to increase their toxicity a hundredfold. Or the organic phosphates may interact with various drugs, or with synthetic materials, food additives—who can say what else of the infinite number of man-made substances that now pervade our world?

The effect of a chemical of supposedly innocuous nature can be drastically changed by the action of another; one of the best examples is a close relative of DDT called methoxychlor. (Actually, methoxychlor may not be as free from dangerous qualities as it is generally said to be, for recent work on experimental animals shows a direct action on the uterus and a blocking effect on some of the powerful pituitary hormones—reminding us again that these are chemicals with enormous biologic effect. Other work shows that methoxychlor has a potential ability to damage the kidneys.) Because it is not stored to any great extent when given alone, we are told that methoxychlor is a safe chemical. But this is not necessarily true. If the liver has been damaged by another agent, methoxychlor is stored in the body at *100 times* its normal rate, and will then imitate the effects of DDT with long-lasting effects on the nervous system. Yet the liver damage that brings this about might be so slight as to pass unnoticed. It might have been the result of any of a number of commonplace situations—using another insecticide, using a cleaning fluid containing carbon tetrachloride, or taking one of the so-called tranquilizing drugs, a number (but not all) of which are chlorinated hydrocarbons and possess power to damage the liver.

Damage to the nervous system is not confined to acute poisoning; there may also be delayed effects from exposure. Long-lasting damage to brain or nerves has been reported for methoxy-chlor and others. Dieldrin, besides its immediate consequences, can have long delayed effects ranging from "loss of memory, insomnia, and nightmares to mania." Lindane, according to medical findings, is stored in significant amounts in the brain and functioning liver tissue and may induce "profound and long lasting effects on the central nervous system." Yet this chemical, a form of benzene hexachloride, is much used in vaporizers, devices that pour a stream of volatilized insecticide vapor into homes, offices, restaurants.

The organic phosphates, usually considered only in relation to their more violent manifestations in acute poisoning, also have the power to produce lasting physical damage to nerve tissues and, according to recent findings, to induce mental disorders. Various cases of delayed paralysis have followed use of one or another of these insecticides. A bizarre happening in the United States during the prohibition era about 1930 was an omen of things to come. It was caused not by an insecticide but by a substance belonging chemically to the same group as the organic phosphate insecticides. During that period some medicinal substances were being pressed into service as substitutes for liquor, being exempt from the prohibition law. One of these was Jamaica ginger. But the *United States Pharmacopeia* product was expensive, and bootleggers conceived the idea of making a substitute Jamaica ginger. They succeeded so well that their spurious product responded to the appropriate chemical tests and deceived the government chemists. To give their false ginger the necessary tang they had introduced a chemical known as triorthocresyl phosphate. This chemical, like parathion and its relatives, destroys the protective enzyme cholinesterase. As a consequence of drinking the bootleggers' product some 15,000 people developed a permanently crippling type of paralysis of the leg muscles, a condition now called "ginger paralysis." The paralysis was accompanied by destruction of the nerve sheaths and by degeneration of the cells of the anterior horns of the spinal cord.

About two decades later various other organic phosphates came into use as insecticides, as we have seen, and soon cases reminiscent of the ginger paralysis episode began to occur. One was a greenhouse worker in Germany who became paralyzed several months after experiencing mild symptoms of poisoning on a few occasions after using parathion. Then a group of three chemical plant workers developed acute poisoning from exposure to other insecticides of this group. They recovered under treatment, but ten days later two of them developed muscular weakness in the legs. This persisted for 10 months in one; the other, a young woman chemist, was more severely affected, with paralysis in both legs and some involvement of the hands and arms. Two years later when her case was reported in a medical journal she was still unable to walk.

The insecticide responsible for these cases has been withdrawn from the market, but some of those now in use may be capable of like harm. Malathion (beloved of gardeners) has induced severe muscular weakness in experiments on chickens. This was attended (as in ginger paralysis) by destruction of the sheaths of the sciatic and spinal nerves.

All these consequences of organic phosphate poisoning, if survived, may be a prelude to worse. In view of the severe damage they inflict upon the nervous system, it was perhaps inevitable that these insecticides would eventually be linked with mental disease. That link has recently been supplied by investigators at the University of Melbourne and Prince Henry's Hospital in Melbourne, who reported on 16 cases of mental disease. All had a history of prolonged exposure to organic phosphorus insecticides. Three were scientists checking the efficacy of sprays; 8 worked in greenhouses; 5 were farm workers. Their symptoms ranged from impairment of memory to schizophrenic and depressive reactions. All had normal medical histories before the chemicals they were using boomeranged and struck them down.

Echoes of this sort of thing are to be found, as we have seen, widely scattered throughout medical literature, sometimes involving the chlorinated hydrocarbons, sometimes the organic phosphates. Confusion, delusions, loss of memory, mania—a heavy price to pay for the temporary destruction of a few insects, but a price that will continue to be exacted as long as we insist upon using chemicals that strike directly at the nervous system.

A Wind-Storm in the Forests

John Muir, Scottish-born American naturalist, worked chiefly in Yosemite Valley in California. He was an active and ardent campaigner for the establishment of forest reserves and national parks. His books include The Mountains of California, Our National Parks, *and* The Yosemite. *John Muir climbs to the top of a Douglas Spruce during a wind storm, and in* The Mountains of California *he describes what he sees in beautiful poetic prose.*

The mountain winds, like the dew and rain, sunshine and snow, are measured and bestowed with love on the forests to develop their strength and beauty. However restricted the scope of other forest influences, that of the winds is universal. The snow bends and trims the upper forests every winter, the lightning strikes a single tree here and there, while avalanches mow down thousands at a swoop as a gardener trims out a bed of flowers. But the winds go to every tree, fingering every leaf and branch and furrowed bole; not one is forgotten; the Mountain Pine towering with outstretched arms on the rugged buttresses of the icy peaks, the lowliest and most retiring tenant of the dells; they seek and find them all, caressing them tenderly, bending them in lusty exercise, stimulating their growth, plucking off a leaf or limb as required, or removing an entire tree or grove, now whispering and cooing through the branches like a sleepy child, now roaring like the ocean; the winds blessing the forests, the forests the winds, with ineffable beauty and harmony as the sure result.

After one has seen pines six feet in diameter bending like grasses before a mountain gale, and ever and anon some giant falling with a crash that shakes the hills, it seems astonishing that any, save the lowest thickset trees, could ever have found a period sufficiently stormless to establish themselves; or, once established, that they should not, sooner or later, have been blown down. But when the storm is over, and we behold the same forests tranquil again, towering fresh and unscathed in erect majesty, and consider what centuries of storms have fallen upon them since they were first planted,—hail, to break the tender seedlings; lightning, to scorch and shatter; snow, winds, and avalanches, to crush and overwhelm,—while the manifest result of all this wild storm-culture is the glorious perfection we behold; then faith in Nature's forestry is established, and we cease to deplore the violence of her most destructive gales, or of any other storm-implement whatsoever.

There are two trees in the Sierra forests that are never blown down, so long as they continue in sound health. These are the Juniper and the Dwarf Pine of the summit peaks. Their stiff, crooked roots grip the storm-beaten ledges like eagles' claws, while their lithe, cord-like branches bend round compliantly, offering but slight holds for winds, however violent. The other alpine conifers—the Needle Pine, Mountain Pine, Two-leaved Pine, and Hemlock Spruce—are never thinned out by this agent to any destructive extent, on account of their admirable toughness and the closeness of their growth. In general the same is true of the giants of the lower zones. The kingly Sugar Pine, towering aloft to a height of more than 200 feet, offers a fine mark to storm-winds; but it is not densely foliaged, and its long, horizontal arms swing round compliantly in the blast, like tresses of green, fluent algæ in a brook; while the Silver Firs in most places keep their ranks well together in united strength. The Yellow or Silver Pine is more frequently overturned than any other tree on the Sierra, because its leaves and branches form a larger mass in proportion to its height, while in many places it is planted sparsely, leaving open lanes through which storms may enter with full force. Furthermore, because it is distributed along the lower portion of the range, which was the first to be left bare on the breaking up of the ice-sheet at the close of the glacial winter, the soil it is growing upon has been longer exposed to post-glacial weathering, and consequently is in a more crumbling, decayed condition than the fresher soils farther up the range, and therefore offers a less secure anchorage for the roots.

While exploring the forest zones of Mount Shasta, I discovered the path of a hurricane strewn with thousands of pines of this species. Great and small had been uprooted or wrenched off by sheer force, making a clean gap, like that made by a snow avalanche. But hurricanes capable of doing this class of work are rare in the Sierra, and when we have explored the forests from one extremity of the range to the other, we are compelled to belive that they are the most beautiful on the face of the earth, however we may regard the agents that have made them so.

There is always something deeply exciting, not only in the sounds of winds in the woods, which exert more or less influence over every mind, but in their varied waterlike flow as manifested by the movements of the trees, especially those of the conifers. By no other trees are they rendered so extensively and impressively visible, not even by the lordly tropic palms or tree-ferns responsive to the gentlest breeze. The waving of a forest of the giant Sequoias is indescribably impressive and sublime, but the pines seem to me the best interpreters of winds. They are mighty waving goldenrods, ever in tune, singing and writing wind-music all their long century lives. Little, however, of this noble tree-waving and tree-music will you see or hear in the strictly alpine portion of the forests. The burly Juniper, whose girth sometimes more than equals its height, is about as rigid as the rocks on which it grows. The slender lash-like sprays of the Dwarf Pine stream out in wavering ripples, but the tallest and slenderest are far too unyielding to wave even in the heaviest gales. They only shake in quick, short vibrations. The Hemlock Spruce, however, and the Mountain Pine, and some of the tallest thickets of the Two-leaved species bow in storms with considerable scope and gracefulness. But it is only in the lower and middle zones that the meeting of winds and woods is to be seen in all its grandeur.

One of the most beautiful and exhilarating storms I ever enjoyed in the Sierra occurred in December, 1874, when I happened to be exploring one of the tributary valleys of the Yuba River. The sky and the ground and the trees had been thoroughly rain-washed and were dry again. The day was intensely pure, one of those incomparable bits of California winter, warm and balmy and full of white sparkling sunshine, redolent of all the purest influences of the spring, and at the same time enlivened with one of the most bracing wind-storms conceivable. Instead of camping out, as I usually do, I then chanced to be stopping at the house of a friend. But when the storm began to sound, I lost no time in pushing out into the woods to enjoy it. For on such occasions Nature has always something rare to show us, and the danger to life and limb is hardly greater than one would experience crouching deprecatingly beneath a roof.

It was still early morning when I found myself fairly adrift. Delicious sunshine came pouring over the hills, lighting the tops of the pines, and setting free a steam of summery fragrance that contrasted strangely with the wild tones of the storm. The air was mottled with pine-tassels and bright green plumes, that went flashing past in the sunlight like birds pursued. But there was not the slightest dustiness, nothing less pure than leaves, and ripe pollen, and flecks of withered bracken and moss. I heard trees falling for hours at the rate of one every two or three minutes; some uprooted, partly on account of the loose, water-soaked condition of the ground; others broken straight across, where some weakness caused by fire had determined the spot. The gestures of the various trees made a delightful study. Young Sugar Pines, light and feathery as squirrel-tails, were bowing almost to the ground; while the grand old patriarchs, whose massive boles had been tried in a hundred storms, waved solemnly above them, their long, arching branches streaming fluently on the gale, and every needle thrilling and ringing and shedding off keen lances of light like a diamond. The Douglas Spruces, with long sprays drawn out in level tresses, and needles massed in a gray, shimmering glow, presented a most striking appearance as they stood in bold relief along the hilltops. The madroños in the dells, with their red bark and large glossy leaves tilted every way, reflected the sunshine in throbbing spangles like those one so often sees on the rippled surface of a glacier lake. But the Silver Pines were now the most impressively beautiful of all. Colossal spires 200 feet in height waved like supple goldenrods chanting and bowing low as if in worship, while the whole mass of their long, tremulous foliage was kindled into one continuous blaze of white sun-fire. The force of the gale was such that the most steadfast monarch of them all rocked down to its roots with a motion plainly perceptible when one leaned against it. Nature was holding high festival, and every fiber of the most rigid giants thrilled with glad excitement.

I drifted on through the midst of this passionate music and motion, across many a glen, from ridge to ridge; often halting in the lee of a rock for shelter, or to gaze and listen. Even when the grand anthem had swelled to its highest pitch, I could distinctly hear the varying tones of individual trees,—Spruce, and Fir, and Pine, and leafless Oak,—and even the infinitely gentle rustle of the withered grasses at my feet. Each was expressing itself in its own way,—singing its own song, and making its own peculiar gestures,—manifesting a richness of variety to be found in no other forest I have yet seen. The coniferous woods of Canada, and the Carolinas, and Florida, are made up of trees that resemble one another about as nearly as blades of grass, and grow close together in much the same way. Coniferous trees, in general, seldom possess individual character, such as is manifest among Oaks and Elms. But the California forests are made up of a greater number of distinct species than any other in the world. And in them we find, not only a marked differentiation into special groups, but also a marked individuality in almost every tree, giving rise to storm effects indescribably glorious.

Toward midday, after a long, tingling scramble through copses of hazel and ceanothus, I gained the summit of the highest ridge in the neighborhood; and then it occurred to me that it would be a fine thing to climb one of the trees to obtain a wider outlook and get my ear close to the Æolian music of its topmost needles. But under the circumstances the choice of a tree was a serious matter. One whose instep was not very strong seemed in danger of being blown down, or of being struck by others in case they should fall; another was branchless to a considerable height above the ground, and at the same time too large to be grasped with arms and legs in climbing;

while others were not favorably situated for clear views. After cautiously casting about, I made choice of the tallest of a group of Douglas Spruces that were growing close together like a tuft of grass, no one of which seemed likely to fall unless all the rest fell with it. Though comparatively young, they were about 100 feet high, and their lithe, brushy tops were rocking and swirling in wild ecstasy. Being accustomed to climb trees in making botanical studies, I experienced no difficulty in reaching the top of this one, and never before did I enjoy so noble an exhilaration of motion. The slender tops fairly flapped and swished in the passionate torrent, bending and swirling backward and forward, round and round, tracing indescribable combinations of vertical and horizontal curves, while I clung with muscles firm braced, like a bobolink on a reed.

In its widest sweeps my tree-top described an arc of from twenty to thirty degrees, but I felt sure of its elastic temper, having seen others of the same species still more severly tried—bent almost to the ground indeed, in heavy snows—without breaking a fiber. I was therefore safe, and free to take the wind into my pulses and enjoy the excited forest from my superb outlook. The view from here must be extremely beautiful in any weather. Now my eye roved over the piny hills and dales as over fields of waving grain, and felt the light running in ripples and broad swelling undulations across the valleys from ridge to ridge, as the shining foliage was stirred by corresponding waves of air. Oftentimes these waves of reflected light would break up suddenly into a kind of beaten foam, and again, after chasing one another in regular order, they would seem to bend forward in concentric curves, and disappear on some hillside, like sea-waves on a shelving shore. The quantity of light reflected from the bent needles was so great as to make whole groves appear as if covered with snow, while the black shadows beneath the trees greatly enhanced the effect of the silvery splendor.

Excepting only the shadows there was nothing somber in all this wild sea of pines. On the contrary, notwithstanding this was the winter season, the colors were remarkably beautiful. The shafts of the pine and libocedrus were brown and purple, and most of the foliage was well tinged with yellow; the laurel groves, with the pale undersides of their leaves turned upward, made masses of gray; and then there was many a dash of chocolate color from clumps of manzanita, and jet of vivid crimson from the bark of the madroños, while the ground on the hillsides, appearing here and there through openings between the groves, displayed masses of pale purple and brown.

The sounds of the storm corresponded gloriously with this wild exuberance of light and motion. The profound bass of the naked branches and boles booming like waterfalls; the quick, tense vibrations of the pine-needles, now rising to a shrill, whistling hiss, now falling to a silky murmur; the rustling of laurel groves in the dells, and the keen metallic click of leaf on leaf—all this was heard in easy analysis when the attention was calmly bent.

The varied gestures of the multitude were seen to fine advantage, so that one could recognize the different species at a distance of several miles by this means alone, as well as by their forms and colors, and the way they reflected the light. All seemed strong and comfortable, as if really enjoying the storm, while responding to its most enthusiastic greetings. We hear much nowadays concerning the universal struggle for existence, but no struggle in the common meaning of the word was manifest here; no recognition of danger by any tree; no deprecation; but rather an invincible gladness as remote from exultation as from fear.

I kept my lofty perch for hours, frequently closing my eyes to enjoy the music by itself, or to feast quietly on the delicious fragrance that was streaming past. The fragrance of the woods was less marked than that produced during warm rain, when so many balsamic buds and leaves are steeped like tea; but, from the chafing of resiny branches against each other, and the incessant attrition of myriads of needles, the gale was spiced to a very tonic degree. And besides the fragrance from these local sources there were traces of scents brought from afar. For this wind came first from the sea, rubbing against its fresh, briny waves, then distilled through the redwoods, threading rich ferny gulches, and spreading itself in broad undulating currents over many a flower-enameled ridge of the coast mountains, then across the golden plains, up the purple foot-hills, and into these piny woods with the varied incense gathered by the way.

Winds are advertisements of all they touch; however much or little we may be able to read them; telling their wanderings even by their scents alone. Mariners detect the flowery perfume of land-winds far at sea, and sea-winds carry the fragrance of dulse and tangle far inland, where it is quickly recognized, though mingled with the scents of a thousand land-flowers. As an illustration of this, I may tell here that I breathed sea-air on the Firth of Forth, in Scotland, while a boy; then was taken to Wisconsin, where I remained nineteen years; then, without in all this time having breathed one breath of the sea, I walked quietly, alone, from the middle of the Mississippi Valley to the Gulf of Mexico, on a botanical excursion, and while in Florida, far from the coast, my attention wholly bent on the splendid tropical vegetation about me, I suddenly recognized a sea-breeze, as it came sifting through the palmettos and blooming vine-tangles, which at once awakened and set free a thousand dormant associations, and made me a boy again in Scotland, as if all the intervening years had been annihilated.

Most people like to look at mountain rivers, and bear them in mind; but few care to look at the winds, though far more beautiful and sublime, and though they become at times about as visible as flowing water. When the north winds in winter are making upward sweeps over the curving summits of the High Sierra, the fact is sometimes published with flying snow-banners a mile long. Those portions of the winds thus embodied can scarce be wholly invisible, even to the darkest imagination. And when we look around over an agitated forest, we may see something of the wind that stirs it, by its effects upon the trees. Yonder it descends in a rush of water-like ripples, and sweeps over the bending pines from hill to hill. Nearer, we see detached plumes and leaves, now speeding by on level currents, now whirling in eddies, or, escaping over the edges of the whirls, soaring aloft on grand, upswelling domes of air, or tossing on flame-like crests. Smooth, deep currents, cascades, falls, and swirling eddies, sing around every tree and leaf, and over all the varied topography of the region with telling changes of form, like mountain rivers conforming to the features of their channels.

After tracing the Sierra streams from their fountains to the plains, marking where they bloom white in falls, glide in crystal plumes, surge gray and foam-filled in boulder-choked gorges, and slip through the woods in long, tranquil reaches—after thus learning their language and forms in detail, we may at length hear them chanting all together in one grand anthem, and comprehend them all in clear inner vision, covering the range like lace. But even this spectacle is far less sublime and not a whit more substantial than what we may behold of these storm-streams of air in the mountain woods.

We all travel the milky way together, trees and men; but it never occurred to me until this storm-day, while swinging in the wind, that trees are travelers, in the ordinary sense. They make many journeys, not extensive ones, it is true; but our own little journeys, away and back again, are only little more than tree-wavings—many of them not so much.

When the storm began to abate, I dismounted and sauntered down through the calming woods. The storm-tones died away, and, turning toward the east, I beheld the countless hosts of the forests hushed and tranquil, towering above one another on the slopes of the hills like a devout audience. The setting sun filled them with amber light, and seemed to say, while they listened, "My peace I give unto you."

As I gazed on the impressive scene, all the so-called ruin of the storm was forgotten, and never before did these noble woods appear so fresh, so joyous, so immortal.

RACHEL L. CARSON

Journey to the Sea

Rachel Carson in Under the Sea Wind *brilliantly captures the struggle for survival which goes on along the seashore and in the dark depths of the sea with prose so beautifully executed that it is almost sheer poetry. No one has illuminated so much of the beauty and drama of nature as Rachel Carson.*

There is a pond that lies under a hill, where the threading roots of many trees—mountain ash, hickory, chestnut oak, and hemlock —hold the rains in a deep sponge of humus. The pond is fed by two streams that carry the runoff of higher ground to the west, coming down over rocky beds grooved in the hill. Cattails, bur reeds, spike rushes, and pickerel weeds stand rooted in the soft mud around its shores and, on the side under the hill, wade out halfway into its waters. Willows grow in the wet ground along the eastern shore of the pond, where the overflow seeps down a grass-lined spillway, seeking its passage to the sea.

The smooth surface of the pond is often ringed by spreading ripples made when shiners, dace, or other minnows push against the tough sheet between air and water, and the film is dimpled, too, by the hurrying feet of small water insects that live among the reeds and rushes. The pond is called Bittern Pond, because never a spring passes without a few of these shy herons nesting in its bordering reeds, and the strange, pumping cries of the birds that stand and sway in the cattails, hidden in the blend of lights and shadows, are thought by some who hear them to be the voice of an unseen spirit of the pond.

From Bittern Pond to the sea is two hundred miles as a fish swims. Thirty miles of the way is by narrow hill streams, seventy miles by a sluggish river crawling over the coastal plain, and a hundred miles through the brackish water of a shallow bay where the sea came in, millions of years ago, and drowned the estuary of a river.

Every spring a number of small creatures come up the grassy spillway and enter Bittern Pond, having made the two-hundred-mile journey from the sea. They are curiously formed, like pieces of slender glass rods shorter than a man's finger. They are young eels, or elvers, that were born in the deep sea. Some of the eels go higher into the hills but a few remain in the pond, where they live on crayfish and water beetles and catch frogs and small fishes and grow to adulthood.

Now it was autumn and the end of the year. From the moon's quarter to its half, rains had fallen, and all the hill streams ran in flood. The water of the two feeder streams of the pond was deep and swift and jostled the rocks of the stream beds as it hurried to the sea. The pond was deeply stirred by the inrush of water, which swept through its weed forests and swirled through its crayfish holes and crept up six inches on the trunks of its bordering willows.

The wind had sprung up at dusk. At first it had been a gentle breeze, stroking the surface of the pond to velvet smoothness. At midnight it had grown to a half gale that set all the rushes to swaying wildly and rattled the dead seed heads of the weeds and plowed deep furrows in the surface waters of the pond. The wind roared down from the hills, over forests of oak and beech and hickory and pine. It blew toward the east, toward the sea two hundred miles away.

Anguilla, the eel, nosed into the swift water that raced toward the overflow from the pond. With her keen senses she savored the strange tastes and smells in the water. They were the bitter tastes and smells of dead and rain-soaked autumn leaves, the tastes of forest moss and lichen and root-held humus. Such was the water that hurried past the eel, on its way to the sea.

Anguilla had entered Bittern Pond as a finger-long elver ten years before. She had lived in the pond through its summers and autumns and winters and springs, hiding in its weed beds by day and prowling through its waters by night, for like all eels she was a lover of darkness. She knew every crayfish burrow that ran in honeycombing furrows through the mudbank under the hill. She knew her way among the swaying, rubbery stems of spatterdock, where frogs sat on the thick leaves; and she knew where to find the spring peepers clinging to grass blades, bubbling shrilly, where in spring the pond overflowed its grassy northern shore. She could find the banks where the water rats ran and squeaked in play or tusseled in anger, so that sometimes they fell with a splash into the water—easy prey for a lurking eel. She knew the soft mud beds deep in the bottom of the pond, where in winter she could lie buried, secure against the cold—for like all eels she was a lover of warmth.

Now it was autumn again, and the water was chilling to the cold rains shed off the hard backbones of the hills. A strange restiveness was growing in Anguilla the eel. For the first time in her adult life, the food hunger was forgotten. In its place was a strange, new hunger, formless and ill-defined. Its dimly perceived object was a place of warmth and darkness—darker than the blackest night over Bittern Pond. She had known such a place once—in the dim beginnings of life, before memory began. She could not know that the way to it lay beyond the pond outlet over which she had clambered ten years before. But many times that night, as the wind and the rain tore at the surface film of the pond, Anguilla was drawn irresistibly toward the outlet over which the water was spilling on its journey to the sea. When the cocks were crowing in the farmyard over the hill, saluting the third hour of the new day, Anguilla slipped into the channel spilling down to the stream below and followed the moving water.

Even in flood, the hill stream was shallow, and its voice was the noisy voice of a young stream, full of gurglings and tricklings and the sound of water striking stone and of stone rubbing against stone. Anguilla followed the stream, feeling her way by the changing pressure of the swift water currents. She was a creature of night and darkness, and so the black water path neither confused nor frightened her.

In five miles the stream dropped a hundred feet over a rough and boulder-strewn bed. At the end of the fifth mile it slipped between two hills, following along a deep gap made by another and larger stream years before. The hills were clothed with oak and beech and hickory, and the stream ran under their interlacing branches.

At daybreak Anguilla came to a bright, shallow riffle where the stream chattered sharply over gravel and small rubble. The water moved with a sudden acceleration, draining swiftly toward the brink of a ten-foot fall where it spilled over a sheer rock face into a basin below. The rush of water carried Anguilla with it, down the steep, thin slant of white water and into the pool. The basin was deep and still and cool, having been rounded out of the rock by centuries of falling water. Dark water mosses grew on its sides and stoneworts were rooted in its silt, thriving on the lime which they took from the stones and incorporated in their round, brittle stems. Anguilla hid among the stoneworts of the pool, seeking a shelter from light and sun, for now the bright shallows of the stream repelled her.

Before she had lain in the pool for an hour another eel came over the falls and sought the darkness of the deep leaf beds. The second eel had come from higher up in the hills, and her body was lacerated in many places from the rocks of the thin upland streams she had decended. The newcomer was a larger and more powerful eel than Anguilla, for she had spent two more years in fresh water before coming to maturity.

Anguilla, who had been the largest eel in Bittern Pond for more than a year, dived down through the stoneworts at sight of the strange eel. Her passage swayed the stiff, limy stems of the chara and disturbed three water boatmen that were clinging to the chara stems, each holding its position by the grip of a jointed leg, set with rows of bristles. The insects were browsing on the film of desmids and diatoms that coated the stems of the stoneworts. The boatmen were clothed in glistening blankets of air which they had carried down with them when they dived through the surface film, and when the passing of the eel dislodged them from their quiet anchorage they rose like air bubbles, for they were lighter than water.

An insect with a body like a fragment of twig supported by six jointed legs was walking over the floating leaves and skating on the surface of the water, on which it moved as on strong silk. Its feet depressed the film into six dimples, but did not break it, so light was its body. The insect's name meant "a marsh treader," for its kind often lived in the deep sphagnum moss of bogs. The marsh treader was foraging, watching for creatures like mosquito larvae or small crustaceans to move up to the surface from the pool below. When one of the water boatmen suddenly broke through the film at the feet of the marsh treader, the twiglike insect speared it with the sharp stilettos projecting beyond its mouth and sucked the little body dry.

When Anguilla felt the strange eel pushing into the thick mat of dead leaves on the floor of the pool, she moved back into the dark recess behind the waterfall. Above her the steep face of the rock was green with the soft fronds of mosses that grew where their leaves escaped the flow of water, yet were always wet with fine spray from the falls. In spring the midges came there to lay their eggs, spinning them in thin, white skeins on the wet rocks. Later when the eggs hatched and the gauzy-winged insects began to emerge from the falls in swarms, they were watched for by bright-eyed little birds who sat on overhanging branches and darted open-mouthed into the clouds of midges. Now the midges were gone, but other small animals lived in the green, water-soaked thickets of the moss. They were the larvae of beetles and soldier flies and crane flies. They were smooth-bodied creatures, lacking the grappling hooks and suckers and the flattened, stream-molded bodies that enabled their relatives to live in the swift currents draining to the brink of the falls overhead or a dozen feet away where the pool spilled its water into the stream bed. Although they lived only a few inches from the veil of water that dropped sheer to the pool, they knew nothing of swift water and its dangers; their peaceful world was of water seeping slow through green forests of moss.

The beginning of the great leaf fall had come with the rains of the past fortnight. Throughout the day, from the roof of the forest to its floor, there was a continuous downdrift of leaves. The leaves fell so silently that the rustle of their settling to the ground was no louder than the thin scratching of the feet of mice and moles moving through their passages in the leaf mold.

All day flights of broad-winged hawks passed down along the ridges of the hills, going south. They moved with scarcely a beat of their outspread wings, for they were riding on the updrafts of air made as the west wind struck the hills and leaped upward to pass over them. The hawks were fall migrants from Canada that had followed down along the Appalachians for the sake of the air currents that made the flight easier.

At dusk, as the owls began to hoot in the woods, Anguilla left the pool and traveled downstream alone. Soon the stream flowed through rolling farm country. Twice during the night it dropped over small milldams that were white in the thin moonlight. In the stretch below the second dam, Anguilla lay for a time under an overhanging bank, where the swift currents were undercutting the heavy, grassy turf. The sharp hiss of the water over the slanting boards of the dam had frightened her. As she lay under the bank the eel that had rested with her in the pool of the waterfall came over the milldam and passed on downstream. Anguilla followed, letting the current take her bumping and jolting over the shallow riffles and gliding swiftly through the deeper stretches. Often she was aware of dark forms moving in the water near her. They were other eels, come from many of the upland feeder creeks of the main stream. Like Anguilla, the other long, slender fishes yielded to the hurrying water and let the currents speed their passage. All of the migrants were roe eels, for only the females ascend far into the fresh-water streams, beyond all reminders of the sea.

The eels were almost the only creatures that were moving in the stream that night. Once, in a copse of beech, the stream made a sharp bend and scoured out a deeper bed. As Anguilla swam into this rounded basin, several frogs dived down from the soft mud bank where they had been sitting half out of water and hid on the bottom close to the bole of a fallen tree. The frogs had been startled by the approach of a furred animal that left prints like those of human feet in the soft mud and whose small black mask and black-ringed tail showed in the faint moonlight. The raccoon lived in a hole high up in one of the beeches near by and often caught frogs and crayfish in the stream. He was not disconcerted by the series of splashes that greeted his approach, for he knew where the foolish frogs would hide. He walked out on the fallen tree and lay down flat on its trunk. He took a firm grip on its bark with the claws of his hind feet and left forepaw. The right paw he dipped into the water, reaching down as far as he could and exploring with busy, sensitive fingers the leaves and mud under the trunk. The frogs tried to burrow deeper into the litter of leaves and sticks and other stream debris. The patient fingers felt into every hole and crevice, pushed away leaves and probed the mud. Soon the coon felt a small, firm body beneath his fingers—felt the sudden movement as the frog tried to escape. The coon's grip tightened and he drew the frog quickly up onto the log. There he killed it, washed it carefully by dipping it into the stream, and ate it. As he was finishing his meal, three small black masks moved into a patch of moonlight at the edge of the stream. They belonged to the coon's mate and their two cubs, who had come down the tree to prowl for their night's food.

From force of habit, the eel thrust her snout inquisitively into the leaf litter under the log, adding to the terror of the frogs, but she did not molest them as she would have done in the pond, for hunger was forgotten in the stronger instinct that made her a part of the moving stream. When Anguilla slipped into the central current of water that swept past the end of the log, the two young coons and their mother had walked out onto the trunk and four black-masked faces were peering into the water, preparing to fish the pool for frogs.

By morning the stream had broadened and deepened. Now it fell silent and mirrored an open woods of sycamore, oak, and dogwood. Passing through the woods, it carried a freight of brightly colored leaves—bright-red, crackling leaves from the oaks, mottled green and yellow leaves from the sycamores, dull-red, leathery leaves from the dogwoods. In the great wind the dogwoods had lost their leaves, but they held their scarlet berries. Yesterday robins had gathered in flocks in the dogwoods, eating the berries; today the robins were gone south and in their place flurries of starlings swept from tree to tree, chattering and rattling and whistling to one another as they stripped the branches of berries. The starlings were in bright new fall plumage, with every breast feather spear-tipped with white.

Anguilla came to a shallow pool formed when an oak had been uprooted in a great autumn storm ten years before and had fallen across the stream. Oak dam and pool were new in the stream since Anguilla had ascended it as an elver in the spring of that year. Now a great mat of weeds, silt, sticks, dead branches, and other debris was

packed around the massive trunk, plastering all the crevices, so that
the water was backed up into a pool two feet deep. During the period
of the full moon the eels lay in the oak-dam pool, fearing to travel in
the moon-white water of the stream almost as much as they feared
the sunlight.

In the mud of the pool were many burrowing, worm-like
larvae—the young of lamprey eels. They were not true eels, but
fishlike creatures whose skeleton was gristle instead of bone, with
round, tooth-studded mouths that were always open because there
were no jaws. Some of the young lampreys had hatched from eggs
spawned in the pool as much as four years before and had spent most
of their life buried in the mud flats of the shallow stream, blind and
toothless. These older larvae, grown nearly twice the length of a
man's finger, had this fall been transformed into the adult shape, and
for the first time they had eyes to see the water world in which they
lived. Now like the true eels, they felt in the gentle flow of water to
the sea something that urged them to follow, to descend to salt water
for an interval of sea life. There they would prey semi-parastically
on cod, haddock, mackerel, salmon, and many other fishes and in
time would return to the river, like their parents, to spawn and die. A
few of the young lampreys slipped away over the log dam every day
and on a cloudy night, when the rain had fallen and white mist lay in
the stream valley, the eels followed.

The next night the eels came to a place where the stream
diverged around an island grown thickly with willows. The eels
followed the south channel around the island, where there were
broad mud flats. The island had been formed over centuries of time
as the stream had dropped part of its silt load before it joined the
main river. Grass seeds had taken root; seeds of trees had been
brought by the water and by birds; willow shoots had sprung from
broken twigs and branches carried down in flood waters; an island
had been born.

The water of the main river was gray with approaching day
when the eels entered it. The river channel was twelve feet deep and
its water was turbid because of the inpouring of many tributary
streams swollen with autumn rains. The eels did not fear the gloomy
channel water by day as they had feared the bright shallows of the
hill streams, and so this day they did not rest but pushed on

downstream. There were many other eels in the river—migrants from other tributaries. With the increase in their numbers the excitement of the eels grew, and as the days passed they rested less often, pressing on downstream with fevered haste.

As the river widened and deepened, a strange taste came into the water. It was a slightly bitter taste, and at certain hours of the day and night it grew stronger in the water that the eels drew into their mouths and passed over their gills. With the bitter taste came unfamiliar movements of the water—a period of pressure against the downflow of the river currents followed by slow release and then swift acceleration of the current.

Now groups of slender posts stood at intervals in the river, marking out funnel shapes from which straight rows of posts ran slanting toward the shore. Blackened netting, coated with slimy algae, was run from post to post and showed several feet above the water. Gulls were often sitting on the pound nets, waiting for men to come and fish the nets so that they could pick up any fish that might be thrown away or lost. The posts were coated with barnacles and with small oysters, for now there was enough salt in the water for these shellfish to grow.

Sometimes the sandspits of the river were dotted with small shore birds standing at rest or probing at the water's edge for snails, small shrimps, worms, or other food. The shore birds were of the sea's edge, and their presence in numbers hinted of the nearness of the sea.

The strange, bitter taste grew in the water and the pulse of the tides beat stronger. On one of the ebb tides a group of small eels—none more than two feet long—came out of a brackish-water marsh and joined the migrants from the hill streams. They were males, who had never ascended the rivers but had remained within the zone of tides and brackish water.

In all of the migrants striking changes in appearance were taking place. Gradually the river garb of olive brown was changing to a glistening black, with underparts of silver. These were the colors worn only by mature eels about to undertake a far sea journey. Their bodies were firm and rounded with fat—stored energy that would be needed before the journey's end. Already in many of the migrants the snouts were becoming higher and more compressed, as though from some sharpening of the sense of smell. Their eyes were enlarged to twice their normal size, perhaps in preparation for a descent along darkening sea lanes.

Where the river broadened out to its estuary, it flowed past a high clay cliff on its southern bank. Buried in the cliff were thousands of teeth of ancient sharks, vertebrae of whales, and shells of mollusks that had been dead when the first eels had come in from the sea, eons ago. The teeth, bones, and shells were relics of the time when a warm sea had overlain all the coastal plain and the hard remains of its creatures had settled down into its bottom oozes. Buried millions of years in darkness, they were washed out of the clay by every storm to lie exposed, warmed by sunshine and bathed by rain.

The eels spent a week descending the bay, hurrying through water of increasing saltiness. The currents moved with a rhythm that was of neither river nor sea, being governed by eddies at the mouths of the many rivers that emptied into the bay and by holes in the muddy bottom thirty or forty feet beneath. The ebb tides ran stronger than the floods, because the strong outflow of the rivers resisted the press of water from the sea.

At last Anguilla neared the mouth of the bay. With her were thousands of eels, come down, like the water that brought them, from all the hills and uplands of thousands of square miles, from every stream and river that drained away to the sea by the bay. The eels followed a deep channel that hugged the eastern shore of the bay and came to where the land passed into a great salt marsh. Beyond the marsh, and between it and the sea, was a vast shallow arm of the bay, studded with islands of green marsh grass. The eels gathered in the marsh, waiting for the moment when they should pass to the sea.

The next night a strong southeast wind blew in from the sea, and when the tide began to rise the wind was behind the water, pushing it into the bay and out into the marshes. That night the bitterness of brine was tasted by fish, birds, crabs, shellfish, and all the other water creatures of the marsh. The eels lay deep under water, savoring the salt that grew stronger hour by hour as the wind-driven wall of sea water advanced into the bay. The salt was of the sea. The eels were ready for the sea—for the deep sea and all it held for them. Their years of river life were ended.

The wind was stronger than the forces of moon and sun, and, when the tide turned an hour after midnight, the salt water continued to pile up in the marsh, being blown upstream in a deep surface layer while the underlying water ebbed to the sea.

Soon after the tide turn, the seaward movement of the eels began. In the large and strange rhythms of a great water which each had known in the beginning of life, but each had long since forgotten, the eels at first moved hesitantly in the ebbing tide. The water carried them through an inlet between two islands. It took them under a fleet of oyster boats riding at anchor, waiting for daybreak. When morning came, the eels would be far away. It carried them past leaning spar buoys that marked the inlet channel and past several whistle and bell buoys anchored on shoals of sand or rock. The tide took them close under the lee shore of the larger island, from which a lighthouse flashed a long beam of light toward the sea.

From a sandy spit of the island came the cries of shore birds that were feeding in darkness on the ebb tide. Cry of shore bird and crash of surf were the sounds of the edge of the land—the edge of the sea.

The eels struggled through the line of breakers, where foam seething over black water caught the gleam of the lighthouse beacon and frothed whitely. Once beyond the wind-driven breakers they found the sea gentler, and as they followed out over the shelving sand they sank into deeper water, unrocked by violence of wind and wave.

As long as the tide ebbed, eels were leaving the marshes and running out to sea. Thousands passed the lighthouse that night, on the first lap of a far sea journey—all the silver eels, in fact, that the marsh contained. And as they passed through the surf and out to sea, so also they passed from human sight and almost from human knowledge.

JOHN BURROUGHS

Bird-Songs

John Burroughs was one of America's great naturalists and essayists on nature study. His books include Wake-Robin, Birds and Poets, Locusts and Wild Honey, The Ways of Nature, Squirrels and Other Fur-Bearers, The Breath of Life, *and* Accepting the Universe. *He was greatly influenced by Ralph Waldo Emerson and Henry David Thoreau and was a personal friend of Walt Whitman. His writings, while scientifically accurate, are characterized by lovely poetic prose.*

I suspect it requires a special gift of grace to enable one to hear the bird-songs; some new power must be added to the ear, or some obstruction removed. There are not only scales upon our eyes so that we do not see, there are scales upon our ears so that we do not hear. A city woman who had spent much of her time in the country once asked a well-known ornithologist to take her where she could hear the bluebird. "What, never heard the bluebird!" said he. "I have not," said the woman. "Then you will never hear it," said the bird-lover; never hear it with that inward ear that gives beauty and meaning to the note. He could probably have taken her in a few minutes where she could have heard the call or warble of the bluebird; but it would have fallen upon unresponsive ears—upon ears that were not sensitized by love for the birds or associations with them. Bird-songs are not music, properly speaking, but only suggestions of music. A great many people whose attention would be quickly arrested by the same volume of sound made by a musical instrument or by artificial means never hear them at all. The sound of a boy's penny whistle there in the grove or the meadow would separate itself more from the background of nature, and be a greater challenge to the ear, than is the strain of the thrush or the song of the sparrow. There is something elusive, indefinite, neutral, about bird-songs that makes them strike obliquely, as it were, upon the ear; and we are very apt to miss them. They are a part of nature, the Nature that lies about us, entirely occupied with her own affairs, and quite regardless of our presence. Hence it is with bird-songs as it is with so many other things in nature—they are what we make them; the ear that hears them must be half creative. I am always disturbed when persons not especially observant of birds ask me to take them where they can hear a particular bird, in whose song they have become interested through a description in some book. As I listen with them, I feel like apologizing for the bird: it has a bad cold, or has just heard some depressing news; it will not let itself out. The song seems so casual and minor when you make a dead set at it. I have taken persons to hear the hermit thrush, and I have fancied that they were all the time saying to themselves, "Is that all?" But should one hear the bird in his walk, when the mind is attuned to simple things and is open and receptive, when expectation is not aroused and the song comes as a surprise out of the dusky silence of the woods, then one feels that it merits all the fine things that can be said of it.

One of our popular writers and lecturers upon birds told me this incident: He had engaged to take two city girls out for a walk in the country, to teach them the names of the birds they might see and hear. Before they started, he read to them. Henry van Dyke's poem on the song sparrow,—one of our best bird-poems,—telling them that the song sparrow was one of the first birds they were likely to hear. As they proceeded with their walk, sure enough, there by the roadside was a sparrow in song. The bird man called the attention of his companions to it. It was some time before the unpracticed ears of the girls could make it out; them one of them said (the poem she had

From *The Ways of Nature* by John Burroughs. Reprinted by permission of the Houghton Mifflin Co.

just heard, I suppose, still ringing in her ears), "What! that little squeaky thing?" The sparrow's song meant nothing to her at all, and how could she share the enthusiasm of the poet? Probably the warble of the robin, or the call of the meadowlark or of the highhole, if they chanced to hear them, meant no more to these girls. If we have no associations with these sounds, they will mean very little to us. Their merit as musical performances is very slight. It is as signs of joy and love in nature, as heralds of spring, and as the spirit of the woods and fields made audible, that they appeal to us. The drumming of the woodpeckers and of the ruffed grouse give great pleasure to a countryman, though these sounds have not the quality of real music. It is the same with the call of the migrating geese or the voice of any wild thing: our pleasure in them is entirely apart from any considerations of music. Why does the wild flower, as we chance upon it in the woods or bogs, give us more pleasure than the more elaborate flower of the garden or lawn? Because it comes as a surprise, offers a greater contrast with its surroundings, and suggests a spirit in wild nature that seems to take thought of itself and to aspire to beautiful forms.

The songs of caged birds are always disappointing, because such birds have nothing but their musical qualities to recommend them to us. We have separated them from that which gives quality and meaning to their songs. One recalls Emerson's lines:—

> I thought the sparrow's note from heaven,
>   Singing at dawn on the alder bough;
> I brought him home, in his nest, at even;
>   He sings the song, but it cheers not now,
> For I did not bring home the river and sky;—
> He sang to my ear,—they sang to my eye.

I have never yet seen a caged bird that I wanted,—at least, not on account of its song,—nor a wild flower that I wished to transfer to my garden. A caged skylark will sing its song sitting on a bit of turf in the bottom of the cage; but you want to stop your ears, it is so harsh and sibilant and penetrating. But up there against the morning sky, and above the wide expanse of fields, what delight we have in it! It is not the concord of sweet sounds: it is the soaring spirit of gladness and ecstasy raining down upon us from "heaven's gate."

Then, if to the time and the place one could only add the association, or hear the bird through the vista of the years, the song touched with the magic of youthful memories! One season a friend in England sent me a score of skylarks in a cage. I gave them their liberty in a field near my place. They drifted away, and I never heard them or saw them again. But one Sunday a Scotchman from a neighboring city called upon me, and declared with visible excitement that on his way along the road he had heard a skylark. He was not dreaming; he knew it was a skylark, though he had not heard one since he had left the banks of the Doon, a quarter of a century or more before. What pleasure it gave him! How much more the song meant to him than it would have meant to me! For the moment he was on his native heath again. Then I told him about the larks I had liberated, and he seemed to enjoy it all over again with renewed appreciation.

Many years ago some skylarks were liberated on Long Island, and they became established there, and may now occasionally be heard in certain localities. One summer day a friend of mine was out there observing them; a lark was soaring and singing in the sky above him. An old Irishman came along, and suddenly stopped as if transfixed to the spot; a look of mingled delight and incredulity came into his face. Was he indeed hearing the bird of his youth? He took off his hat, turned his face skyward, and with moving lips and streaming eyes stood a long time regarding the bird. "Ah," my friend thought, "if I could only hear that song with his ears!" How it brought back his youth and all those long-gone days on his native hills!

The power of bird-songs over us is so much a matter of association that every traveler to other countries finds the feathered songsters of less merit than those he left behind. The stranger does not hear the birds in the same receptive, uncritical frame of mind as does the native; they are not in the same way the voices of the place and the season. What music can there be in that long, piercing, far-heard note of the first meadowlark in spring to any but a native, or in the "o-ka-lee" of the red-shouldered starling as he rests upon the willows in March? A stranger would probably recognize melody and a wild woodsy quality in the flutings of the veery thrush; but how much more they would mean to him after he had spent many

successive Junes threading our northern trout-streams and encamp-
ing on their banks! The veery will come early in the morning, and
again at sundown, and perch above your tent, and blow his soft,
reverberant note for many minutes at a time. The strain repeats the
echoes of the limpid stream in the halls and corridors of the leafy
woods.

While in England in 1882, I rushed about two or three
counties in late June and early July, bent on hearing the song of the
nightingale, but missed it by a few days, and in some cases, as it
seemed, only by a few hours. The nightingale seems to be wound up
to go only so long, or till about the middle of June, and it is only by a
rare chance that you hear one after that date. Then I came home to
hear a nightingale in song one winter morning in a friend's house in
the city. It was a curious let-down to my enthusiasm. A caged song in
a city chamber in broad daylight, in lieu of the wild, free song in the
gloaming of an English landscape! I closed my eyes, abstracted
myself from my surroundings, and tried my best to fancy myself
listening to the strain back there amid the scenes I had haunted
about Haslemere and Godalming, but with poor success, I suspect.
The nightingale's song, like the lark's, needs vista, needs all the
accessories of time and place. The song is not all in the singing, any
more than the wit is all in the saying. It is in the occasion, the
surroundings, the spirit of which it is the expression. My friend said
that the bird did not fully let itself out. Its song was a brilliant medley
of notes,—no theme that I could detect,—like the lark's song in this
respect; all the notes of the field and forest appeared to be the gift of
this bird, but what tone! what accent! like that of a great poet!

Nearly every May I am seized with an impulse to go back to the
scenes of my youth, and hear the bobolinks in the home meadows
once more. I am sure they sing there better than anywhere else. They
probably drink nothing but dew, and the dew distilled in those high
pastoral regions has surprising virtues. It gives a clear, full, vibrant
quality to the birds' voices that I have never heard elsewhere. The
night of my arrival, I leave my southern window open, so that the
meadow chorus may come pouring in before I am up in the morning.
How it does transport me athwart the years, and make me a boy
again, sheltered by the paternal wing. On one occasion, the third
morning after my arrival, a bobolink appeared with a new note in his

song. The note sounded like the word "baby" uttered with a peculiar, tender resonance: but it was clearly an interpolation; it did not belong there; it had no relation to the rest of the song. Yet the bird never failed to utter it with the same joy and confidence as the rest of his song. Maybe it was the beginning of a variation that will in time result in an entirely new bobolink song.

On my last spring visit to my native hills, my attention was attracted to another songster not seen or heard there in my youth, namely, the prairie horned lark. Flocks of these birds used to be seen in some of the Northern States in the late fall during their southern migrations; but within the last twenty years they have become regular summer residents in the hilly parts of many sections of New York and New England. They are genuine skylarks, and lack only the powers of song to make them as attractive as their famous cousins of Europe.

The larks are ground-birds when they perch, and sky-birds when they sing; from the turf to the clouds—nothing between. Our horned lark mounts upward on quivering wing in the true lark fashion, and, spread out against the sky at an altitude of two or three hundred feet, hovers and sings. The watcher and listener below holds him in his eye, but the ear catches only a faint, broken, half-inarticulate note now and then—mere splinters, as it were, of the song of the skylark. The song of the latter is continuous, and is loud and humming; it is a fountain of jubilant song up there in the sky: but our lark sings in snatches; at each repetition of its notes it dips forward and downward a few feet, and then rises again. One day I kept my eye upon one until it had repeated its song one hundred and three times; then it closed its wings, and dropped toward the earth like a plummet, as does its European congener. While I was watching the bird, a bobolink flew over my head, between me and the lark, and poured out his voluble and copious strain. "What a contrast," I thought, "between the voice of the spluttering, tongue-tied lark, and the free, liquid, and varied song of the bobolink!"

I have heard of a curious fact in the life-histories of these larks in the West. A Michigan woman once wrote me that her brother, who was an engineer on an express train that made daily trips between two Western cities, reported that many birds were struck by the engine every day, and killed—often as many as thirty on a trip of sixty miles. Birds of many kinds were killed, but the most common was a bird that went in flocks, the description of which answered to the horned lark. Since then I have read in a Minnesota newspaper that many horned larks are killed by railroad locomotives in that State. It was thought that the birds sat behind the rails to get out of the wind, and on starting up in front of the advancing train, were struck down by the engine. The Michigan engineer referred to thought that the birds gathered upon the track to earth their wings, or else to pick up the grain that leaks out of the wheat-trains, and sows the track from Dakota to the seaboard. Probably the wind which they might have to face in getting up was the prime cause of their being struck. One does not think of the locomotive as a bird-destroyer, though it is well known that many of the smaller mammals often fall beneath it.

A very interesting feature of our bird-songs is the wing-song, or song of ecstasy. It is not the gift of many of our birds. Indeed, less than a dozen species are known to me as ever singing on the wing. It seems to spring from more intense excitement and self-abandonment than the ordinary song delivered from the perch. When its joy reaches the point of rapture, the bird is literally carried off its feet, and up it goes into the air, pouring out its song as a rocket pours out its sparks. The skylark and the bobolink habitually do this, while a few others of our birds do it only on occasions. One summer, up in the Catskills, I added another name to my list of ecstatic singers—that of the vesper sparrow. Several times I heard a new song in the air, and caught a glimpse of the bird as it dropped back to the earth. My attention would be attracted by a succession of hurried, chirping notes, followed by a brief burst of song, then by the vanishing form of the bird. One day I was lucky enough to see the bird as it was rising to its climax in the air, and to identify it as the vesper sparrow. The burst of song that crowned the upward flight of seventy-five or one hundred feet was brief; but it was brilliant and striking, and entirely unlike the leisurely chant of the bird while upon the ground. It suggested a lark, but was less buzzing or humming. The preliminary chirping notes, uttered faster and faster as the bird mounted in the air, were like the trail of sparks which a rocket emits before its grand burst of color at the top of its flight.

It is interesting to note that this bird is quite lark-like in its color and markings, having the two lateral white quills in the tail, and it has the habit of elevating the feathers on the top of the head so as to suggest a crest. The solitary skylark that I discovered several years ago in a field near me was seen on several occasions paying his addresses to one of these birds, but the vesper-bird was shy, and eluded all his advances.

Probably the perch-songster among our ordinary birds that is most regularly seized with the fit of ecstasy that results in this lyric burst in the air, as I described in my first book, "Wake Robin," over thirty years ago, is the oven-bird, or wood-accentor—the golden-crowned thrush of the old ornithologists. Every loiterer about the woods knows this pretty, speckled-breasted, olive-backed little bird, which walks along over the dry leaves a few yards from him, moving its head as it walks, like a miniature domestic fowl. Most birds are very stiff-necked, like the robin, and as they run or hop upon the ground, carry the head as if it were riveted to the body. Not so the oven-bird, or the other birds that walk, as the cow-bunting, or the quail, or the crow. They move the head forward with the movement of the feet. The sharp, reiterated, almost screeching song of the oven-bird, as it perches on a limb a few feet from the ground, like the words, "preacher, preacher, preacher," or "teacher, teacher, teacher," uttered louder and louder, and repeated six or seven times, is also familiar to most ears; but its wild, ringing, rapturous burst of song in the air high above the tree-tops is not so well known. From a very prosy, tiresome, unmelodious singer, it is suddenly transformed for a brief moment into a lyric poet of great power. It is a great surprise. The bird undergoes a complete transformation. Ordinarily it is a very quiet, demure sort of bird. It walks about over the leaves, moving its head like a little hen; then perches on a limb a few feet from the ground and sends forth its shrill, rather prosy, unmusical chant. Surely it is an ordinary, commonplace bird. But wait till the inspiration of its flightsong is upon it. What a change! Up it goes through the branches of the trees, leaping from limb to limb, faster and faster, till it shoots from the tree-tops fifty or more feet into the air above them, and bursts into an ecstasy of song, rapid, ringing, lyrical; no more like its habitual performance than a match is like a rocket; brief but thrilling; emphatic but musical. Having reached its climax of flight and song, the bird closes its wings and drops nearly perpendicularly downward like the skylark. If its song were more prolonged, it would rival the song of that famous bird. The bird does this many times a day during early June, but oftenest at twilight. The song in quality and general cast is like that of its congener, the water-accentor, which, however, I believe is never delivered on the wing. From its habit of singing at twilight, and from the swift, darting motions of the bird, I am inclined to think that in it we have solved the mystery of Thoreau's "night-warbler," that puzzled and eluded him for years. Emerson told him he must beware of finding and booking it, lest life should have nothing more to show him. The older ornithologists must have heard this song many times, but they never seem to have suspected the identity of the singer.

Other birds that sing on the wing are the meadowlark, goldfinch, purple finch, indigo-bird, Maryland yellow-throat, and woodcock. The flight-song of the woodcock I have heard but twice in my life. The first time was in the evening twilight about the middle of April. The bird was calling in the dusk "yeap, yeap," or "seap, seap," from the ground,—a peculiar reedy call. Then, by and by, it started upward on an easy slant, that peculiar whistling of its wings alone heard; then, at an altitude of one hundred feet or more, it began to float about in wide circles and broke out in an ecstatic chipper, almost a warble at times, with a peculiar smacking musical quality; then, in a minute or so, it dropped back to the ground again, not straight down like the lark, but more spirally, and continued its call as before. In less than five minutes it was up again. The next time, a few years later, I heard the song in company with a friend, Dr. Clara Barrus. Let me give the woman's impression of the song as she afterward wrote it up for a popular journal.

"The sunset light was flooding all this May loveliness of field and farm and distant wood; song sparrows were blithely pouring out happiness by the throatful; peepers were piping and toads trilling, and we thought it no hardship to wait in such a place till the dusk should gather, and the wary woodcock announce his presence. But hark! while yet 'tis light, only a few rods distant, I hear that welcome 'seap . . . seap,' and lo! a chipper and a chirr, and past us he flies, —a direct, slanting upward flight, somewhat labored,—his bill showing long against the reddened sky. 'He has something in his mouth,' I start to say, when I bethink me what a long bill he has.

Around, above us he flies in wide ambitious circles, the while we are enveloped, as it were, in that hurried chippering sound—fine, elusive, now near, now distant. How rapid is the flight! Now it sounds faster and faster, 'like a whiplash flashed through the air,' said my friend; up, up he soars, till he becomes lost to sight at the instant that his song ends in that last mad ecstasy that just precedes his alighting."

The meadowlark sings in a level flight, half hovering in the air, giving voice to a rapid medley of lark-like notes. The goldfinch also sings in a level flight, beating the air slowly with its wings broadly open, and pouring out its jubilant, ecstatic strain. I think it indulges in this wing-song only in the early season. After the mother bird has begun sitting, the male circles about within earshot of her, in that curious undulating flight, uttering his "per-chic-o-pee, per-chic-o-pee," while the female calls back to him in the tenderest tones, "Yes, lovie; I hear you." The indigo-bird and the purple finch, when their happiness becomes too full and buoyant for them longer to control it, launch into the air, and sing briefly, ecstatically, in a tremulous, hovering flight. The air-song of these birds does not differ essentially from the song delivered from the perch, except that it betrays more excitement, and hence is a more complete lyrical rapture.

The purple finch is our finest songster among the finches. Its strain is so soft and melodious, and touched with such a childlike gayety and plaintiveness, that I think it might sound well even in a cage inside a room, if the bird would only sing with the same joyous abandonment, which, of course, it would not do.

It is not generally known that individual birds of the same species show different degrees of musical ability. This is often noticed in caged birds, among which the principle of variation seems more active; but an attentive observer notes the same fact in wild birds. Occasionally he hears one that in powers of song surpasses all its fellows. I have heard a sparrow, an oriole, and a wood thrush, each of which had a song of its own that far exceeded any other. I stood one day by a trout-stream, and suspended my fishing for several minutes to watch a song sparrow that was singing on a dry limb before me. He had five distinct songs, each as markedly different from the others as any human songs, which he repeated one after the other. He may have had a sixth or a seventh, but he bethought himself of some business in the next field, and flew away before he had exhausted his repertory. I once had a letter from Robert Louis Stevenson, who said he had read an account I had written of the song of the English blackbird. He said I might as well talk of the song of man; that every blackbird had its own song; and then he told me of a remarkable singer he used to hear somewhere amid the Scottish hills. But his singer was, of course, an exception; twenty-four blackbirds out of every twenty-five probably sing the same song, with no appreciable variations: but the twenty-fifth may show extraordinary powers. I told Stevenson that his famous singer had probably been to school to some nightingale on the Continent or in southern England. I might have told him of the robin I once heard here that sang with great spirit and accuracy the song of the brown thrasher, or of another that had the note of the whip-poor-will interpolated in the regular robin song, or of still another that had the call of the quail. In each case the bird had probably heard the song and learned it while very young. In the Trossachs, in Scotland, I followed a song thrush about for a long time, attracted by its peculiar song. It repeated over and over again three or four notes of a well-known air, which it might have caught from some shepherd boy whistling to his flock or to his cow.

The songless birds—why has Nature denied them this gift? But they nearly all have some musical call or impulse that serves them very well. The quail has his whistle, the woodpecker his drum, the pewee his plaintive cry, the chickadee his exquisitely sweet call, the highhole his long, repeated "wick, wick, wick," one of the most welcome sounds of spring, the jay his musical gurgle, the hawk his scream, the crow his sturdy caw. Only one of our pretty birds of the orchard is reduced to an all but inaudible note, and that is the cedar-bird.

JOHN BURROUGHS

The Pastoral Bees

John Burroughs in The Pastoral Bees *exhibits the keen eye of the trained observer, and yet the golden thread of the aesthetic values continuously manifest themselves. Mr. Burroughs states "It is a homely old stanza current among bee folk":*

> A swarm of bees in May
> Is worth a load of hay;
> A swarm of bees in June
> Is worth a silver spoon;
> But a swarm in July
> Is not worth a fly.

The honey-bee goes forth from the hive in spring like the dove from Noah's ark, and it is not till after many days that she brings back the olive leaf, which in this case is a pellet of golden pollen upon each hip, usually obtained from the alder or the swamp willow. In a country where maple sugar is made the bees get their first taste of sweet from the sap as it flows from the spiles, or as it dries and is condensed upon the sides of the buckets. They will sometimes, in their eagerness, come about the boiling-place and be overwhelmed by the steam and the smoke. But bees appear to be more eager for bread in the spring than for honey: their supply of this article, perhaps, does not keep as well as their stores of the latter; hence fresh bread, in the shape of new pollen, is diligently sought for. My bees get their first supplies from the catkins of the willows. How quickly they find them out! If but one catkin opens anywhere within range, a bee is on hand that very hour to rifle it, and it is a most pleasing experience to stand near the hive some mild April day and see them come pouring in with their little baskets packed with this first fruitage of the spring. They will have new bread now; they have been to mill in good earnest; see their dusty coats, and the golden grist they bring home with them.

When a bee brings pollen into the hive he advances to the cell in which it is to be deposited and kicks it off, as one might his overalls or rubber boots, making one foot help the other; then he walks off without ever looking behind him; another bee, one of the indoor hands, comes along and rams it down with his head and packs it into the cell, as the dairymaid packs butter into a firkin with a ladle.

The first spring wild-flowers, whose shy faces among the dry leaves and rocks are so welcome, are rarely frequented by the bee. The anemone, the hepatica, the bloodroot, the arbutus, the numerous violets, the spring beauty, the corydalis, etc., woo all lovers of nature, but seldom woo the honey-loving bee. The arbutus, lying low and keeping green all winter, attains to perfume and honey, but only once have I seen it frequented by bees.

The first honey is perhaps obtained from the flowers of the red maple and the golden willow. The latter sends forth a wild, delicious perfume. The sugar maple blooms a little later, and from its silken tassels a rich nectar is gathered. My bees will not label these different varieties for me, as I really wish they would. Honey from the maple, a tree so clean and wholesome, and full of such virtues every way, would be something to put one's tongue to. Or that from the blossoms of the apple, the peach, the cherry, the quince, the currant,—one would like a card of each of these varieties to note their peculiar qualities. The apple-blossom is very important to the bees. A single swarm has been know to gain twenty pounds in weight during its continuance. Bees love the ripened fruit, too, and in August and September will suck themselves tipsy upon varieties such as the sops-of-wine.

The interval between the blooming of the fruittrees and that of the clover and the raspberry is bridged over in many localities by the

From *Locusts and Wild Honey* by John Burroughs. Reprinted by permission of the Houghton Mifflin Co.

honey locust. What a delightful summer murmur these trees send forth at this season! I know nothing about the quality of the honey, but it ought to keep well. But when the red raspberry blooms, the fountains of plenty are unsealed indeed; what a commotion about the hives then, especially in localities where it is extensively cultivated, as in places along the Hudson! The delicate white clover, which begins to bloom about the same time, is neglected; even honey itself is passed by for this modest, colorless, all but odorless flower. A field of these berries in June sends forth a continuous murmur like that of an enormous hive. The honey is not so white as that obtained from clover, but it is easier gathered; it is in shallow cups, while that of the clover is in deep tubes. The bees are up and at it before sunrise, and it takes a brisk shower to drive them in. But the clover blooms later and blooms everywhere, and is the staple source of supply of the finest quality of honey. The red clover yields up its stores only to the longer proboscis of the bumblebee, else the bee pasturage of our agricultural districts would be unequaled. I do not know from what the famous honey of Chamouni in the Alps is made, but it can hardly surpass our best products. The snow-white honey of Anatolia in Asiatic Turkey, which is regularly sent to Constantinople for the use of the grand seignior and the ladies of his seraglio, is obtained from the cotton plant, which makes me think that the white clover does not flourish there. The white clover is indigenous with us: its seeds seem latent in the ground, and the application of certain stimulants to the soil, such as wood ashes, causes them to germinate and spring up.

The rose, with all its beauty and perfume, yields no honey to the bee, unless the wild species be sought by the bumblebee.

Among the humbler plants let me not forget the dandelion that so early dots the sunny slopes, and upon which the bee languidly grazes, wallowing to his knees in the golden but not over-succulent pasturage. From the blooming rye and wheat the bee gathers pollen, also from the obscure blossoms of Indian corn. Among weeds, catnip is the great favorite. It lasts nearly the whole season and yields richly. It could no doubt be profitably cultivated in some localities, and catnip honey would be a novelty in the market. It would probably partake of the aromatic properties of the plant from which it was derived.

Among your stores of honey gathered before mid-summer you may chance upon a card, or mayhap only a square inch or two of comb, in which the liquid is as transparent as water, of a delicious quality, with a slight flavor of mint. This is the product of the linden or basswood, of all the trees in our forest the one most beloved by the bees. Melissa, the goddess of honey, has placed her seal upon this tree. The wild swarms in the woods frequently reap a choice harvest from it. I have seen a mountain-side thickly studded with it, its straight, tall, smooth, light gray shaft carrying its deep green crown far aloft, like the tulip-tree or the maple.

In some of the Northwestern States there are large forests of it, and the amount of honey reported stored by strong swarms in this section during the time the tree is in bloom is quite incredible. As a shade and ornamental tree the linden is fully equal to the maple, and, if it were as extensively planted and cared for, our supplies of virgin honey would be greatly increased. The famous honey of Lithuania in Russia is the product of the linden.

It is a homely old stanza current among bee folk that

> *A swarm of bees in May*
> *Is worth a load of hay;*
> *A swarm of bees in June*
> *Is worth a silver spoon*
> *But a swarm in July*
> *Is not worth a fly.*

A swarm in May is indeed a treasure; it is, like an April baby, sure to thrive, and will very likely itself send out a swarm a month or two later: but a swarm in July is not to be despised; it will store no clover or linden honey for the "grand seignior and the ladies of his seraglio," but plenty of the rank and wholesome poor man's nectar, the sun-tanned product of the plebeian buckwheat. Buckwheat honey is the black sheep in this white flock, but there is spirit and character in it. It lays hold of the taste in no equivocal manner, especially when at a winter breakfast it meets its fellow, the russet buckwheat cake. Bread with honey to cover it from the same stalk is double good fortune. It is not black, either, but nut-brown, and belongs to the same class of goods as Herrick's Nut-brown mirth and russet wit. How the bees love it, and they bring the delicious door of the blooming plant to the hive with them, so that in the moist warm twilight the apiary is redolent with the perfume of buckwheat.

Yet evidently it is not the perfume of any flower that attracts the bees; they pay no attention to the sweet-scented lilac, or to heliotrope, but work upon sumach, silkweed, and the hateful snapdragon. In September they are hard pressed, and do well if they pick up enough sweet to pay the running expenses of their establishment. The purple asters and the goldenrod are about all that remain to them.

Bees will go three or four miles in quest of honey, but it is a great advantage to move the hive near the good pasturage, as has been the custom from the earliest times in the Old World. Some enterprising person, taking a hint perhaps from the ancient Egyptians, who had floating apiaries on the Nile, has tried the experiment of floating several hundred colonies north on the Mississippi, starting from New Orleans and following the opening season up, thus realizing a sort of perpetual May or June, the chief attraction being the blossoms of the river willow, which yield honey of rare excellence. Some of the bees were no doubt left behind, but the amount of virgin honey secured must have been very great. In September they should have begun the return trip, following the retreating summer south.

It is the making of wax that costs with the bee. As with the poet, the form, the receptacle, gives him more trouble than the sweet that fills it, though, to be sure, there is always more or less empty comb in both cases. The honey he can have for the gathering, but the wax he must make himself,—must evolve from his own inner consciousness. When wax is to be made, the wax-makers fill themselves with honey and retire into their chamber for private meditation; it is like some solemn religious rite: they take hold of hands, or hook themselves together in long lines that hang in festoons from the top of the hive, and wait for the miracle to transpire. After about twenty-four hours their patience is rewarded, the honey is turned into wax, minute scales of which are secreted from between the rings of the abdomen of each bee; this is taken off and from it the comb is built up. It is calculated that about twenty-five pounds of honey are used in elaborating one pound of comb, to say nothing of the time that is lost. Hence the importance, in an economical point of view, of a recent device by which the honey is extracted and the comb returned intact to the bees. But honey without the comb is the perfume without the rose,—it is sweet merely, and soon degenerates into candy. Half the delectableness is in breaking down these frail and exquisite walls yourself, and tasting the nectar before it has lost its freshness by contact with the air. Then the comb is a sort of shield or foil that prevents the tongue from being overwhelmed by the first shock of the sweet.

The drones have the least enviable time of it. Their foothold in the hive is very precarious. They look like the giants, the lords of the swarm, but they are really the tools. Their loud, threatening hum has no sting to back it up, and their size and noise make them only the more conspicuous marks for the birds. They are all candidates for the favors of the queen, a fatal felicity that is vouchsafed to but one. Fatal, I say, for it is a singular fact in the history of bees that the fecundation of the queen costs the male his life. Yet day after day the drones go forth, threading the mazes of the air in hopes of meeting her whom to meet is death. The queen only leaves the hive once, except when she leads away the swarm, and as she makes no appointment with the male, but wanders here and there, drones enough are provided to meet all the contingencies of the case.

One advantage, at least, results from this system of things: there is no incontinence among the males in this republic!

Toward the close of the season, say in July or August, the fiat goes forth that the drones must die; there is no further use for them. Then the poor creatures, how they are huddled and hustled about, trying to hide in corners and byways! There is no loud, defiant humming now, but abject fear seizes them. They cower like hunted criminals. I have seen a dozen or more of them wedge themselves into a small space between the glass and the comb, where the bees could not get hold of them, or where they seemed to be overlooked in the general slaughter. They will also crawl outside and hide under the edges of the hive. But sooner or later they are all killed or kicked out. The drone makes no resistance, except to pull back and try to get away; but (putting yourself in his place) with one bee a-hold of your collar or the hair of your head, and another a-hold of each arm or leg, and still another feeling for your waistbands with his sting, the odds are greatly against you.

Is is a singular fact, also, that the queen is made, not born. If the entire population of Spain or Great Britain were the offspring of one mother, it might be found necessary to hit upon some device by which a royal baby could be manufactured out of an ordinary one, or else give up the fashion of royalty. All the bees in the hive have a common parentage, and the queen and the worker are the same in the egg and in the chick; the patent of royalty is in the cell and in the food; the cell being much larger, and the food a peculiar stimulating kind of jelly. In certain contingencies, such as the loss of the queen with no eggs in the royal cells, the workers take the larva of an ordinary bee, enlarge the cell by taking in the two adjoining ones, and nurse it and stuff it and coddle it, till at the end of sixteen days it comes out a queen. But ordinarily, in the natural course of events, the young queen is kept a prisoner in her cell till the old queen has left with the swarm. Later on, the unhatched queen is guarded against the reigning queen, who only wants an opportunity to murder every royal scion in the hive. At this time both the queens, the one a prisoner and the other at large, pipe defiance at each other, a shrill, fine, trumpet-like note that any ear will at once recognize. This challenge, not being allowed to be accepted by either party, is followed, in a day or two, by the abdication of the reigning queen; she leads out the swarm, and her successor is liberated by her keepers, who, in her time, abdicates in favor of the next younger. When the bees have decided that no more swarms can issue, the reigning queen is allowed to use her stiletto upon her unhatched sisters. Cases have been known where two queens issued at the same time, when a mortal combat ensued, encouraged by the workers, who formed a ring about them, but showed no preference, and recognized the victor as the lawful sovereign. For these and many other curious facts we are indebted to the blind Huber.

It is worthy of note that the position of the queen cells is always vertical, while that of the drones and workers is horizontal; majesty stands on its head, which fact may be a part of the secret.

The notion has always very generally prevailed that the queen of the bees is an absolute ruler, and issues her royal orders to willing subjects. Hence Napoleon the First sprinkled the symbolic bees over the imperial mantle that bore the arms of his dynasty; and in the country of the Pharaohs the bee was used as the emblem of a people sweetly submissive to the orders of its king. But the fact is, a swarm of bees is an absolute democracy, and kings and despots can find no warrant in their example. The power and authority are entirely vested in the great mass, the workers. They furnish all the brains and foresight of the colony, and administer its affairs. Their word is law, and both king and queen must obey. They regulate the swarming, and give the signal for the swarm to issue from the hive; they select and make ready the tree in the woods and conduct the queen to it.

The peculiar office and sacredness of the queen consists in the fact that she is the mother of the swarm, and the bees love and cherish her as a mother and not as a sovereign. She is the sole female bee in the hive, and the swarm clings to her because she is their life. Deprived of their queen, and of all brood from which to rear one, the swarm loses all heart and soon dies, though there be an abundance of honey in the hive.

The common bees will never use their sting upon the queen; if she is to be disposed of, they starve her to death; and the queen herself will sting nothing but royalty,—nothing but a rival queen.

The queen, I say, is the mother bee; it is undoubtedly complimenting her to call her a queen and invest her with regal authority, yet she is a superb creature, and looks every inch a queen. It is an event to distinguish her amid the mass of bees when the swarm alights; it awakens a thrill. Before you have seen a queen, you wonder if this or that bee, which seems a little larger than its fellows, is not she, but when you once really set eyes upon her you do not doubt for a moment. You know *that* is the queen. That long, elegant, shining, feminine-looking creature can be none less than royalty. How beautifully her body tapers, how distinguished she looks, how deliberate her movements! The bees do not fall down before her, but caress her and touch her person. The drones, or males, are large bees, too, but coarse, blunt, broad-shouldered, masculine-looking. There is but one fact or incident in the life of the queen that looks imperial and authoritative: Huber relates that when the old queen is restrained in her movements by the workers, and prevented from destroying the young queens in their cells, she assumes a peculiar attitude and utters a note that stikes every bee motionless and makes every head bow; while this sound lasts, not a bee stirs, but all look abashed and humbled: yet whether the emotion is one of fear, or reverence, or of sympathy with the distress of the queen mother, is hard to determine. The moment it ceases and she advances again toward the royal cells, the bees bite and pull and insult her as before.

I always feel that I have missed some good fortune if I am away from home when my bees swarm. What a delightful summer sound it is! how they come pouring out of the hive, twenty or thirty thousand bees, each striving to get out first! It is as when the dam gives way and lets the waters loose; it is a flood of bees which breaks upward into the air, and becomes a maze of whirling black lines to the eye, and a soft chorus of myriad musical sounds to the ear. This way and that way they drift, now contracting, now expanding, rising, sinking, growing thick about some branch or bush, then dispersing and massing at some other point, till finally they begin to alight in earnest, when in a few moments the whole swarm is collected upon the branch, forming a bunch perhaps as large as a two-gallon measure. Here they will hang from one to three or four hours or until a suitable tree in the woods is looked up, when, if they have not been offered a hive in the mean time, they are up and off. In hiving them, if any accident happens to the queen the enterprise miscarries at once. One day I shook a swarm from a small pear-tree into a tin pan, set the pan down on a shawl spread beneath the tree, and put the hive over it. The bees presently all crawled up into it, and all seemed to go well for ten or fifteen minutes, when I observed that something was wrong; the bees began to buzz excitedly and to rush about in a bewildered manner, then they took to the wing and all returned to the parent stock. On lifting up the pan, I found beneath it the queen with three or four other bees. She had been one of the first to fall, had missed the pan in her descent, and I had set it upon her. I conveyed her tenderly back to the hive, but either the accident terminated fatally with her, or else the young queen had been liberated in the interim, and one of them had fallen in combat, for it was ten days before the swarm issued a second time.

No one, to my knowledge, has ever seen the bees house-hunting in the woods. Yet there can be no doubtt that they look up new quarters either before or on the day the swarm issues. For all bees are wild bees and incapable of domestication; that is, the instinct to go back to nature and take up again their wild abodes in the trees is never eradicated. Years upon years of life in the apiary seem to have no appreciable effect towards their final, permanent domestication. That every new swarm contemplates migrating to the woods, seems confirmed by the fact that they will only come out when the weather is favorable to such an enterprise, and that a passing cloud, or a sudden wind, after the bees are in the air, will usually drive them back into the parent hive. Or an attack upon them with sand or gravel, or loose earth or water, will quickly cause them to change their plans. I would not even say but that, when the bees are going off, the apparently absurd practice, now entirely discredited by regular bee keepers but still resorted to by unscientific folk, of beating upon tin pans, blowing horns, and creating an uproar generally, might not be without good results. Certainly not be drowning the "orders" of the queen, but by impressing the bees, as with some unusual commotion in nature. Bees are easily alarmed and disconcerted, and I have known runaway swarms to be brought down by a farmer plowing in the field who showered them with handfuls of loose soil.

I love to see a swarm go off—if it is not mine, and, if mine must go, I want to be on hand to see the fun. It is a return to first principles again by a very direct route. The past season I witnessed two such escapes. One swarm had come out the day before, and, without alighting, had returned to the parent hive,—some hitch in the plan, perhaps, or may be the queen had found her wings too weak. The next day they came out again and were hived. But something offended them, or else the tree in the woods—perhaps some royal old maple or birch, holding its head high above all others, with snug, spacious, irregular chambers and galleries—had too many attractions; for they were presently discovered filling the air over the garden, and whirling excitedly around. Gradually they began to drift over the street; a moment more, and they had become separated from the other bees, and, drawing together in a more compact mass or cloud, away they went, a humming, flying vortex of bees, the queen in the centre, and the swarm revolving around her as a pivot,—over meadows, across creeks and swamps, straight for the heart of the mountain, about a mile distant,—slow at first, so that the youth who gave chase kept up with them, but increasing their speed till only a foxhound could have kept them in sight. I saw their pursuer laboring up the side of the mountain; saw his white shirtsleeves gleam as he entered the woods; but he returned a few hours afterward without any clue as to the particular tree in which they had taken refuge out of the ten thousand that covered the side of the mountain.

The other swarm came out about one o'clock of a hot July day, and at once showed symptoms that alarmed the keeper, who, however, threw neither dirt nor water. The house was situated on a steep side-hill. Behind it the ground rose, for a hundred rods or so, at an angle of nearly forty-five degrees, and the prospect of having to chase them up this hill, if chase them we should, promised a good trial of wind at least; for it soon became evident that their course lay in this direction. Determined to have a hand, or rather a foot, in the chase, I threw off my coat and hurried on, before the swarm was yet fairly organized and under way. The route soon led me into a field of standing rye, every spear of which held its head above my own. Plunging recklessly forward, my course marked to those watching from below by the agitated and wriggling grain, I emerged from the miniature forest just in time to see the runaways disappearing over the top of the hill, some fifty rods in advance of me. Lining them as well as I could, I soon reached the hilltop, my breath utterly gone and the perspiration streaming from every pore of my skin. On the other side the country opened deep and wide. A large valley swept around to the north, heavily wooded at its head and on its sides. It became evident at once that the bees had made good their escape, and that whether they had stopped on one side of the valley or the other, or had indeed cleared the opposite mountain and gone into some unknown forest beyond, was entirely problematical. I turned back, therefore, thinking of the honey-laden tree that some of these forests would hold before the falling of the leaf.

I heard of a youth in the neighborhood more lucky than myself on a like occasion. It seems that he had got well in advance of the swarm, whose route lay over a hill, as in my case, and as he neared the summit, hat in hand, the bees had just come up and were all about him. Presently he noticed them hovering about his straw hat, and alighting on his arm; and in almost as brief a time as it takes to relate it, the whole swarm had followed the queen into his hat. Being near a stone wall, he coolly deposited his prize upon it, quickly disengaged himself from the accommodating bees, and returned for a hive. The explanation of this singular circumstance no doubt is, that the queen, unused to such long and heavy flights, was obliged to alight from very exhaustion. It is not very unusual for swarms to be thus found in remote fields, collected upon a bush or branch of a tree.

When a swarm migrates to the woods in this manner, the individual bees, as I have intimated, do not move in right lines or straight forward, like a flock of birds, but round and round, like chaff in a whirlwind. Unitedly they form a humming, revolving, nebulous mass, ten or fifteen feet across, which keeps just high enough to clear all obstacles, except in crossing deep valleys, when, of course, it may be very high. The swarm seems to be guided by a line of couriers, which may be seen (at least at the outset) constantly going and coming. As they take a direct course, there is always some chance of following them to the tree, unless they go a long distance, and some obstruction, like a wood or a swamp or a high hill, intervenes,— enough chance, at any rate, to stimulate the lookers-on to give vigorous chase as long as their wind holds out. If the bees are successfully followed to their retreat, two plans are feasible,—either to fell the tree at once, and seek to hive them, perhaps bring them home in the section of the tree that contains the cavity; or to leave the tree till fall, then invite your neighbors and go and cut it, and see the ground flow with honey. The former course is more business-like; but the later is the one usually recommended by one's friends and neighbors.

Perhaps nearly one third of all the runaway swarms leave when no one is about, and hence are unseen and unheard, save, perchance, by some distant laborers in the field, or by some youth plowing on the side of the mountain, who hears an unusual humming noise, and sees the swarm dimly whirling by overhead, and, maybe, gives chase; or he may simply catch the sound, when he pauses, looks quickly around, but sees nothing. When he comes in at night he tells how he heard or saw a swarm of bees go over; and perhaps from beneath one of the hives in the garden a black mass of bees has disappeared during the day.

They are not partial as to the kind of tree,—pine, hemlock, elm, birch, maple, hickory,—any tree with a good cavity high up or low down. A swarm of mine ran away from the new patent hive I gave them, and took up their quarters in the hollow trunk of an old apple-tree across an adjoining field. The entrance was a mouse-hole near the ground.

Another swarm in the neighborhood deserted their keeper, and went into the cornice of an outhouse that stood amid evergreens in the rear of a large mansion. But there is no accounting for the taste of bees, as Samson found when he discovered the swarm in the carcass, or more probably the skeleton, of the lion he had slain.

In any given locality, especially in the more wooded and mountainous districts, the number of swarms that thus assert their independence forms quite a large per cent. In the Northern States these swarms very often perish before spring; but in such a country as Florida they seem to multiply, till bee-trees are very common. In the West, also, wild honey is often gathered in large quantities. I noticed, not long since, that some wood-choppers on the west slope of the Coast Range felled a tree that had several pailfuls in it.

One night on the Potomac a party of us unwittingly made our camp near the foot of a bee-tree, which next day the winds of heaven blew down, for our special delectation, at least so we read the sign. Another time, while sitting by a waterfall in the leafless April woods, I discovered a swarm in the top of a large hickory. I had the season before remarked the tree as a likely place for bees, but the screen of leaves concealed them from me. This time my former presentiment occurred to me, and, looking sharply, sure enough there were the bees, going out and in a large, irregular opening. In June a violent tempest of wind and rain demolished the tree, and the honey was all lost in the creek into which it fell. I happened along that way two or three days after the tornado, when I saw a remnant of the swarm, those, doubtless, that escaped the flood and those that were away when the disaster came, hanging in a small black mass to a branch high up near where their home used to be. They looked forlorn enough. If the queen was saved, the remnant probably sought another tree; otherwise the bees soon died.

I have seen bees desert their hive in the spring when it was infested with worms, or when the honey was exhausted; at such times the swarm seems to wander aimlessly, alighting here and there, and perhaps in the end uniting with some other colony. In case of such union, it would be curious to know if negotiations were first opened between the parties, and if the houseless bees are admitted at once to all the rights and franchises of their benefactors. It would be very like the bees to have some preliminary plan and understanding about the matter on both sides.

Bees will accommodate themselves to almost any quarters, yet no hive seems to please them so well as a section of a hollow tree,—"gums," as they are called in the South and West where the sweet gum grows. In some European countries the hive is always made from the trunk of a tree, a suitable cavity being formed by boring. The old-fashioned straw hive is picturesque, and a great favorite with the bees also.

The life of a swarm of bees is like an active and hazardous campaign of an army; the ranks are being continually depleted, and continually recruited. What adventures they have by flood and field, and what hairbreadth escapes! A strong swarm during the honey season loses, on an average, about four or five thousand a month, or one hundred and fifty a day. They are overwhelmed by wind and rain, caught by spiders, benumbed by cold, crushed by cattle, drowned in rivers and ponds, and in many nameless ways cut off or disabled. In the spring the principal mortality is from the cold. As the sun declines they get chilled before they can reach home. Many fall down outside the hive, unable to get in with their burden. One may see them come utterly spent and drop hopelessly into the grass in front of their very doors. Before they can rest the cold has stiffened them. I go out in April and May and pick them up by the handfuls, their baskets loaded with pollen, and warm them in the sun or in the house, or by the simple warmth of my hand, until they can crawl into the hive. Heat is their life, and an apparently lifeless bee may be revived by warming him. I have also picked them up while rowing on the river and seen them safely to shore. It is amusing to see them come hurrying home when there is a thunder-storm approaching. They come piling in till the rain is upon them. Those that are overtaken by the storm doubtless weather it as best they can in the sheltering trees or grass. It is not probable that a bee ever gets lost by wandering into strange and unknown parts. With their myriad eyes they see everything; and then their sense of locality is very acute, is, indeed, one of their ruling traits. When a bee marks the place of his hive, or of a bit of good pasturage in the fields or swamps, or of the beehunter's box of honey on the hills or in the woods, he returns to it as unerringly as fate.

Honey was a much more important article of food with the ancients than it is with us. As they appear to have been unacquainted with sugar, honey, no doubt, stood them instead. It is too rank and pungent for the modern taste; it soon cloys upon the palate. It demands the appetite of youth, and the strong, robust digestion of people who live much in the open air. It is a more wholesome food than sugar, and modern confectionery is poison beside it. Besides grape sugar, honey contains manna, mucilage, pollen, acid, and other vegetable odoriferous substances and juices. It is a sugar with a kind of wild natural bread added. The manna of itself is both food and medicine, and the pungent vegetable extracts have rare virtues. Honey promotes the excretions, and dissolves the glutinous and starchy impedimenta of the system.

Hence it is not without reason that with the ancients a land flowing with milk and honey should mean a land abounding in all good things; and the queen in the nursery rhyme, who lingered in the kitchen to eat "bread and honey" while the "king was in the parlor counting out his money," was doing a very sensible thing. Epaminondas is said to have rarely eaten anything but bread and honey. The Emperor Augustus one day inquired of a centenarian how he had kept his vigor of mind and body so long; to which the veteran replied that it was by "oil without and honey within." Cicero, in his "Old Age," classes honey with meat and milk and cheese as among the staple articles with which a well-kept farmhouse will be supplied.

Italy and Greece, in fact all the Mediterranean countries, appear to have been famous lands for honey. Mount Hymettus, Mount Hybla, and Mount Ida produced what may be called the classic honey of antiquity, an article doubtless in no wise superior to our best products. Leigh Hunt's "Jar of Honey" is mainly distilled from Sicilian history and literature, Theocritus furnishing the best yield. Sicily has always been rich in bees. Swinburne (the traveler of a hundred years ago, says the woods on this island abounded in wild honey, and that the people also had many hives near their houses.

The idyls of Theocritus are native to the island in this respect, and
abound in bees—"flat-nosed bees," as he calls them in the Seventh
Idyl—and comparisons in which comb-honey is the standard of the
most delectable of this world's goods. His goatherds can think of no
greater bliss than that the mouth be filled with honey-combs, or to be
inclosed in a chest like Daphnis and fed on the comb of bees; and
among the delectables with which Arsinoë cherishes Adonis are
"honeycakes," and other tidbits made of "sweet honey." In the
country of Theocritus this custom is said still to prevail: when a
couple are married, the attendants place honey in their mouths, by
which they would symbolize the hope that their love may be as sweet
to their souls as honey to the palate.

It was fabled that Homer was suckled by a priestess whose
breasts distilled honey; and that once, when Pindar lay asleep, the
bees dropped honey upon his lips. In the Old Testament the food of
the promised Immanuel was to be butter and honey (there is much
doubt about the butter in the original), that he might know good
from evil; and Johathan's eyes were enlightened by partaking of
some wood or wild honey: "See, I pray you, how mine eyes have
been enlightened, because I tasted a little of this honey." So far as
this part of his diet was concerned, therefore, John the Baptist,
during his sojourn in the wilderness, his divinity-school days in the
mountains and plains of Judea, fared extremely well. About the
other part, the locusts, or, not to put too fine a point on it, the
grasshoppers, as much cannot be said, though they were among the
creeping and leaping things the children of Israel were permitted to
eat. They were probably not eaten raw, but roasted in that most
primitive of ovens, a hole in the ground made hot by building a fire
in it. The locusts and honey may have been served together, as the
Bedas of Ceylon are said to season their meat with honey. At any
rate, as the locust is often a great plague in Palestine, the prophet in
eating them found his account in the general weal, and in the profit
of the pastoral bees; the fewer locusts, the more flowers. Owing to its
numerous wild-flowers, and flowering shrubs, Palestine has always been a famous country for bees. They deposit their honey in
hollow trees, as our bees do when they escape from the hive, and in
holes in the rocks, as ours do not. In a tropical or semi-tropical
climate, bees are quite apt to take refuge in the rocks; but where ice

and snow prevail, as with us, they are much safer high up in the trunk of a forest tree.

The best honey is the product of the milder parts of the temperate zone. There are too many rank and poisonous plants in the tropics. Honey from certain districts of Turkey produces headache and vomiting, and that from Brazil is used chiefly as medicine. The honey of Mount Hymettus owes its fine quality to wild thyme. The best honey in Persia and in Florida is collected from the orange blossom. The celebrated honey of Narbonne in the south of France is obtained from a species of rosemary. In Scotland good honey is made from the blossoming heather.

RACHEL L. CARSON

The Birth of An Island

Rachel L. Carson's The Sea Around Us *was the National Book Award winner in 1951. In it she captures the beginnings of the earth and seas, the power of the wind, waves, and never ending tides, and the birth of an island. Scientifically accurate, her description still leaves a gossamer of mystery.*

> *Many a green isle needs must be*
> *in the deep, wide sea . . .*
> —SHELLEY

Millions of years ago, a volcano built a mountain on the floor of the Atlantic. In eruption after eruption, it pushed up a great pile of volcanic rock, until it had accumulated a mass a hundred miles across at its base, reaching upward toward the surface of the sea. Finally its cone emerged as an island with an area of about 200 square miles. Thousands of years passed, and thousands of thousands. Eventually the waves of the Atlantic cut down the cone and reduced it to a shoal—all of it, that is, but a small fragment which remained above water. This fragment we know as Bermuda.

With variations, the life story of Bermuda has been repeated by almost every one of the islands that interrupt the watery expanses of the oceans far from land. For these isolated islands in the sea are fundamentally different from the continents. The major land masses and the ocean basins are today much as they have been throughout the greater part of geologic time. But islands are ephemeral, created today, destroyed tomorrow. With few exceptions, they are the result of the violent, explosive, earth-shaking eruptions of submarine volcanoes, working perhaps for millions of years to achieve their end. It is one of the paradoxes in the ways of earth and sea that a process seemingly so destructive, so catastrophic in nature, can result in an act of creation.

Islands have always fascinated the human mind. Perhaps it is the instinctive response of man, the land animal, welcoming a brief intrusion of earth in the vast, overwhelming expanse of sea. Here in a great ocean basin, a thousand miles from the nearest continent, with miles of water under our vessel, we come upon an island. Our imaginations can follow its slopes down through darkening waters to where it rests on the sea floor. We wonder why and how it arose here in the midst of the ocean.

The birth of a volcanic island is an event marked by prolonged and violent travail: the forces of the earth striving to create, and all the forces of the sea opposing. The sea floor, where an island begins, is probably nowhere more than about fifty miles thick—a thin covering over the vast bulk of the earth. In it are deep cracks and fissures, the results of unequal cooling and shrinkage in past ages. Along such lines of weakness the molten lava from the earth's interior presses up and finally bursts forth into the sea. But a submarine volcano is different from a terrestrial eruption, where the lava, molten rocks, gases, and other ejecta are hurled into the air through an open crater. Here on the bottom of the ocean the volcano has resisting it all the weight of the ocean water above it. Despite the immense pressure of, it may be, two or three miles of sea water, the new volcanic cone builds upward toward the surface, in flow after flow of lava. Once within reach of the waves, its soft ash and tuff are violently attacked, and for a long period the potential island may remain a shoal, unable to emerge. But, eventually, in new eruptions, the cone is pushed up into the air and a rampart against the attacks of the waves is built of hardened lava.

Navigators' charts are marked with numerous, recently

discovered submarine mountains. Many of these are the submerged remnants of the islands of a geologic yesterday. The same charts show islands that emerged from the sea at least fifty million years ago, and others that arose within our own memory. Among the undersea mountains marked on the charts may be the islands of tomorrow, which at this moment are forming, unseen, on the floor of the ocean and are growing upward toward its surface.

For the sea is by no means done with submarine eruptions; they occur fairly commonly, sometimes detected only by instruments, sometimes obvious to the most casual observer. Ships in volcanic zones may suddenly find themselves in violently disturbed water. There are heavy discharges of steam. The sea appears to bubble or boil in a furious turbulence. Fountains spring from its surface. Floating up from the deep, hidden places of the actual eruption come the bodies of fishes and other deep-sea creatures, and quantities of volcanic ash and pumice.

One of the youngest of the large volcanic islands of the world is Ascension in the South Atlantic. During the Second World War the American airmen sang

If we don't find Ascension
Our wives will get a pension

this island being the only piece of dry land between the hump of Brazil and the bulge of Africa. It is a forbidding mass of cinders, in which the vents of no less than forty extinct volcanoes can be counted. It has not always been so barren, for its slopes have yielded the fossil remains of trees. What happened to the forests no one knows; the first men to explore the island, about the year 1500, found it treeless, and today it has no natural greenness except on its highest peak, known as Green Mountain.

In modern times we have never seen the birth of an island as large as Ascension. But now and then there is a report of a small island appearing where none was before. Perhaps a month, a year, five years later, the island has disappeared into the sea again. These are the little, stillborn islands, doomed to only a brief emergence above the sea.

About 1830 such an island suddenly appeared in the Mediterranean between Sicily and the coast of Africa, rising from

100-fathom depths after there had been signs of volcanic activity in the area. It was little more than a black cinder pile, perhaps 200 feet high. Waves, wind, and rain attacked it. Its soft and porous materials were easily eroded; its substance was rapidly eaten away and it sank beneath the sea. Now it is a shoal, marked on the charts as Graham's Reef.

Falcon Island, the tip of a volcano projecting above the Pacific nearly two thousand miles east of Australia, suddenly disappeared in 1913. Thirteen years later, after violent eruptions in the vicinity, it as suddenly rose again above the surface and remained as a physical bit of the British Empire until 1949. Then it was reported by the Colonial Under Secretary to be missing again.

Almost from the moment of its creation, a volcanic island is foredoomed to destruction. It has in itself the seeds of its own dissolution, for new explosions, or landslides of the soft soil, may violently accelerate its disintegration. Whether the destruction of an island comes quickly or only after long ages of geologic time may also depend on external forces: the rains that wear away the loftiest of land mountains, the sea, and even man himself.

South Trinidad, or in the Portuguese spelling, 'Ilha Trinidade,' is an example of an island that has been sculptured into bizarre forms through centuries of weathering—an island in which the signs of dissolution are clearly apparent. This group of volcanic peaks lies in the open Atlantic, about a thousand miles northeast of Rio de Janeiro. E. F. Knight wrote in 1907 that Trinidad 'is rotten throughout, its substance has been disintegrated by volcanic fires and by the action of water, so that it is everywhere tumbling to pieces.' During an interval of nine years between Knight's visits, a whole mountainside had collapsed in a great landslide of broken rocks and volcanic debris.

Sometimes the disintegration takes abrupt and violent form. The greatest explosion of historic time was the literal evisceration of the island of Krakatoa. In 1680 there had been a premonitory eruption on this small island in Sunda Strait, between Java and Sumatra in the Netherlands Indies. Two hundred years later there had been a series of earthquakes. In the spring of 1883, smoke and steam began to ascend from fissures in the volcanic cone. The ground became noticeably warm, and warning rumblings and hissings came from the volcano. Then, on 27 August, Krakatoa literally exploded. In an appalling series of eruptions, that lasted two days, the whole northern half of the cone was carried away. The sudden inrush of ocean water added the fury of superheated steam to the cauldron. When the inferno of white-hot lava, molten rock, steam, and smoke had finally subsided, the island that had stood 1400 feet above the sea had become a cavity a thousand feet below sea level. Only along one edge of the former crater did a remnant of the island remain.

Krakatoa, in its destruction, became known to the entire world. The eruption gave rise to a hundred-foot wave that wiped out villages along the Strait and killed people by tens of thousands. The wave was felt on the shores of the Indian Ocean and at Cape Horn; rounding the Cape into the Atlantic, it sped northward and retained its identity even as far as the English Channel. The sound of the explosions was heard in the Philippine Islands, in Australia, and on the Island of Madagascar, nearly 3000 miles away. And clouds of volcanic dust, the pulverized rock that had been torn from the heart of Krakatoa, ascended into the stratosphere and were carried around the globe to give rise to a series of spectacular sunsets in every country of the world for nearly a year.

Although Krakatoa's dramatic passing was the most violent eruption that modern man has witnessed, Krakatoa itself seems to have been the product of an even greater one. There is evidence that an immense volcano once stood where the waters of Sunda Strait now lie. In some remote period a titanic explosion blew it away, leaving only its base represented by a broken ring of islands. The largest of these was Krakatoa, which, in its own demise, carried away what was left of the original crater ring. But in 1929 a new volcanic island arose in this place—Anak Krakatoa, Child of Krakatoa.

Subterranean fires and deep unrest disturb the whole area occupied by the Aleutians. The islands themselves are the peaks of a thousand-mile chain of undersea mountains, of which volcanic action was the chief architect. The geologic structure of the ridge is little known, but it rises abruptly from oceanic depths of about a mile on one side and two miles on the other. Apparently this long narrow ridge indicates a deep fracture of the earth's crust. On many of the islands volcanoes are now active, or only temporarily quiescent. In the short history of modern navigation in this region, it has often happened that a new island has been reported but perhaps only the following year could not be found.

The small island of Bogoslof, since it was first observed in 1796, has altered its shape and position several times and has even disappeared completely, only to emerge again. The original island was a mass of black rock, sculptured into fantastic, towerlike shapes. Explorers and sealers coming upon it in the fog were reminded of a castle and named it Castle Rock. At the present time there remain only one or two pinnacles of the castle, a long spit of black rocks where sea lions haul out, and a cluster of higher rocks resounding with the cries of thousands of sea birds. Each time the parent volcano erupts, as it has done at least half a dozen times since men have been observing it, new masses of steaming rocks emerge from the heated waters, some to reach heights of several hundred feet before they are destroyed in fresh explosions. Each new cone that appears is, as described by the volcanologist Jaggar, "the live crest, equivalent to a crater, of a great submarine heap of lava six thousand feet high, piled above the floor of Bering Sea where the Aleutian mountains fall off to the deep sea."

One of the few exceptions to the almost universal rule that oceanic islands have a volcanic origin seems to be the remarkable and fascinating group of islets knows as the Rocks of St. Paul. Lying in the open Atlantic between Brazil and Africa, St. Paul's Rocks are an obstruction thrust up from the floor of the ocean into the midst of the racing Equatorial Current, a mass against which the seas, which have rolled a thousand miles unhindered, break in sudden violence. The entire cluster of rocks covers not more than a quarter of a mile, running in a curved line like a horseshoe. The highest rock is no more than sixty feet above the sea; spray wets it to the summit. Abruptly the rocks dip under water and slope steeply down into great depths. Geologists since the time of Darwin have puzzled over the origin of these black, wavewashed islets. Most of them agree that they are composed of material like that of the sea floor itself. In some remote period, inconceivable stresses in the earth's crust must have pushed a solid rock mass upward more than two miles.

So bare and desolate that not even a lichen grows on them, St.

Paul's Rocks would seem one of the most unpromising places in the world to look for a spider, spinning its web in archnidan hope of snaring passing insects. Yet Darwin found spiders when he visited the Rocks in 1833, anf forty years later the naturalists of H.M.S. *Challenger* also reported them, busy at their web-spinning. A few insects are there, too, some as parasites on the sea birds, three species of which nest on the Rocks. One of the insects is a small brown moth that lives on feathers. This very nearly completes the inventory of the inhabitants of St. Paul's Rocks, except for the grotesque crabs that swarm over the islets, living chiefly on the flying fish brought by the birds to their young.

St. Paul's Rocks are not alone in having an extraordinary assortment of inhabitants, for the faunas and floras of oceanic islands are amazingly different from those of the continents. The pattern of island life is peculiar and significant. Aside from forms recently introduced by man, islands remote from the continents are never inhabited by any land mammals, except sometimes the one mammal that has learned to fly—the bat. There are never any frogs, sala- manders, or other amphibians. Of reptiles, there may be a few snakes, lizards, and turtles, but the more remote the island from a major land mass, the fewer reptiles there are, and the really isolated islands have none. There are usually a few species of land birds, some insects, and some spiders. So remote an island as Tristan da Cunha in the South Atlantic, 1500 miles from the nearest continent, has no land animals but these: three species of land birds, a few insects, and several small snails.

With so selective a list, it is hard to see how, as some biologists believe, the islands could have been colonized by migration across land bridges, even if there were good evidence for the existence of the bridges. The very animals missing from the islands are the ones that would have had to come dry-shod, over the hypothetical bridges. The plants and animals that we find on oceanic islands, on the other hand, are the ones that could have come by wind or water. As an alternative, then, we must suppose that the stocking of the islands has been accomplished by the strangest migration in earth's history—a migration that began long before man appeared on earth and is still continuing, a migration that seems more like a series of cosmic accidents than an orderly process of nature.

We can only guess how long after its emergence from the sea an oceanic island may lie uninhabited. Certainly in its original state it is a land bare, harsh, and repelling beyond human experience. No living thing moves over the slopes of its volcanic hills; no plants cover its naked lava fields. But little by little, riding on the winds, drifting on the currents, or rafting in on logs, floating brush, or trees, the plants and animals that are to colonize it arrive from the distant continents.

So deliberate, so unhurried, so inexorable are the ways of nature that the stocking of an island may require thousands or millions of years. It may be that no more than half a dozen times in all these eons does a particular from, such as a tortoise, make a successful landing upon its shores. To wonder impatiently why man is not a constant witness of such arrivals is to fail to understand the majestic pace of the process.

Yet we have occasional glimpses of the method. Natural rafts of uprooted trees and matted vegetation have frequently been seen adrift at sea, more than a thousand miles off the mouths of such great tropical rivers as the Congo, the Ganges, the Amazon, and the Orinoco. Such rafts could easily carry an assortment of insect, reptile, or mollusk passengers. Some of the involuntary passengers might be able to withstand long weeks at sea; others would die during the first stages of the journey. Probably the ones best adapted for travel by raft are the wood-boring insects, which, of all the insect tribe, are most commonly found on oceanic islands. The poorest raft travelers must be the mammals. But even a mammal might cover short interisland distances. A few days after the explosion of Krakatoa, a small monkey was rescued from some drifting timber in Sundra Strait. She had been terribly burned, but survived the experience.

No less than the water, the winds and the air currents play their part in bringing habitants to the islands. The upper atmosphere, even during the ages before man entered it in his machines, was a place of congested traffic. Thousands of feet above the earth, the air is crowded with living creatures, drifting, flying, gliding, ballooning, or involuntarily swirling along on the high winds. Discovery of this rich aerial plankton had to wait until man himself had found means to make physical invasion of these regions. With special nets and traps, scientists have now collected from the upper atmosphere many of the forms that inhabit oceanic islands. Spiders, whose almost invariable presence on these islands is a fascinating problem, have been captured nearly three miles above the earth's surface. Airmen have passed through great numbers of the white, silken filaments of spiders' 'parachutes' at heights of two to three miles. At altitudes of 6000 to 16,000 feet, and with wind velocities reaching 45 miles an hour, many living insects have been taken. At such heights and on such strong winds, they might well have been carried hundreds of miles. Seeds have been collected at altitudes up to 5000 feet. Among those commonly taken are members of the Composite family, especially the so-called "thistle-down" typical of oceanic islands.

An interesting point about transport of living plants and animals by wind is the fact that in the upper layers of the earth's atmosphere the winds do not necessarily blow in the same direction as at the earth's surface. The trade winds are notably shallow, so that a man standing on the cliffs of St. Helena, a thousand feet above the sea is above the wind, which blows with great force below him. Once drawn into the upper air, insects, and the like can easily be carried in a direction contrary to that of the winds prevailing at island level.

The wide-ranging birds that visit islands of the ocean in migration may also have a good deal to do with the distribution of plants, and perhaps even of some insects and minute land shells. From a ball of mud taken from a bird's plumage, Charles Darwin raised eighty-two separate plants, belonging to five distinct species! Many plant seeds have hooks or prickles, ideal for attachment to feathers. Such birds as the Pacific golden plover, which annually flies from the mainland of Alaska to the Hawaiian Islands and even beyond, probably figure in many riddles of plant distribution.

The catastrophe of Krakatoa gave naturalists a perfect opportunity to observe the colonization of an island. With most of the island itself destroyed, and the remnant covered with a deep layer of lava and ash that remained hot for weeks, Krakatoa after the explosive eruptions of 1883 was, from a biological standpoint, a new volcanic island. As soon as it was possible to visit it, scientists searched for signs of life, although it was hard to imagine how any living thing could have survived. Not a single plant or animal could be found. It was not until nine months after the eruption that the naturalist Cotteau was able to report: "I only discovered one microscopic spider—only one. This strange pioneer of the renovation was busy spinning its web." Since there were no insects on the island, the web-spinning of the bold little spider was presumably in vain, and except for a few blades of grass, practically nothing lived on Krakatoa for a quarter of a century. Then the colonists began to arrive—a few mammals in 1908; a number of birds, lizards, and snakes; various mollusks, insects, and earthworms. Ninety per cent of Krakatoa's new inhabitants, Dutch scientists found, were forms that could have arrived by air.

Isolated from the great mass of life on the continents, with no opportunity for the crossbreeding that tends to preserve the average and to eliminate the new and unusual, island life has developed in a remarkable manner. On these remote bits of earth, nature has excelled in the creation of strange and wonderful forms. As though to prove her incredible versatility, almost every island has developed species that are endemic—that is, they are peculiar to it alone and are duplicated nowhere else on earth.

It was from the pages of earth's history written on the lava fields of the Galapagos that young Charles Darwin got his first inkling of the great truths of the origin of species. Observing the strange plants and animals—giant tortoises, black, amazing lizards that hunted their food in the surf, sea lions, birds in extraordinary variety—Darwin was struck by their vague similarity to mainland species of South and Central America, yet was haunted by the differences, differences that distinguish them not only from the mainland species but from those on other islands of the archipelago. Years later he was to write in reminiscence: "Both in space and time, we seem to be brought somewhat near to that great fact—that mystery of mysteries—the first appearance of new beings on earth."

Of the "new beings" evolved on islands, some of the most striking examples have been birds. In some remote age before there were men, a small, pigeonlike bird found its way to the island of Mauritius, in the Indian Ocean. By processes of change at which we can only guess, this bird lost the power of flight, developed short, stout legs, and grew larger until it reached the size of a modern turkey. Such was the origin of the fabulous dodo, which did not long survive the advent of man on Mauritius. New Zealand was the sole home of the moas. One species of these ostrich-like birds stood twelve feet high. Moas had roamed New Zealand from the early part of the Tertiary; those that remained when the Maoris arrived soon died out.

Other island forms besides the dodo and the moas have tended to become large. Perhaps the Galapagos tortoise became a giant after its arrival on the islands, although fossil remains on the continents cast doubt on this. The loss of wing use and even of the wings themselves (the moas had none) are common results of insular life. Insects on small, wind-swept islands tend to lose the power of flight—those that retain it are in danger of being blown out to sea. The Galapagos Islands have a flightless cormorant. There have been at least fourteen species of flightless rails on the islands of the Pacific alone.

One of the most interesting and engaging characteristics of island species is their extraordinary tameness—a lack of sophistication in dealings with the human race, which even the bitter teachings of experience do not quickly alter. When Robert Cushman Murphy visited the island of South Trinidad in 1913 with a party from the brig *Daisy,* terns alighted on the heads of the men in the whaleboat and peered inquiringly into their faces. Albatrosses on Laysan, whose habits include wonderful ceremonial dances, allowed naturalists to walk among their colonies and responded with a grave bow to similar polite greetings from the visitors. When the British ornithologist David Lack visited the Galapagos Islands, a century after Darwin, he found that the hawks allowed themselves to be touched, and the flycatchers tried to remove hair from the heads of the men for nesting material. "It is a curious pleasure," he wrote, "to have the birds of the wilderness settling upon one's shoulders, and the pleasure could be much less rare were man less destructive."

But man, unhappily, has written one of his blackest records as a destroyer on the oceanic islands. He has seldom set foot on an island that he has not brought about disastrous changes. He has destroyed environments by cutting, clearing, and burning; he has brought with him as a chance associate the nefarious rat; and almost invariably he has turned loose upon the islands a whole Noah's Ark of goats, hogs, cattle, dogs, cats, and other non-native animals as well as plants. Upon species after species of island life, the black night of extinction has fallen.

In all the world of living things, it is doubtful whether there is a more delicately balanced relationship than that of island life to its environment. This environment is a remarkably uniform one. In the midst of a great ocean, ruled by currents and winds that rarely shift their course, climate changes little. There are few natural enemies, perhaps none at all. The harsh struggle for existence that is the normal lot of continental life is softened on the islands. When this gentle pattern of life is abruptly changed, the island creatures have little ability to make the adjustments necessary for survival.

Ernst Mayr tells of a steamer wrecked off Lord Howe Island east of Australia in 1918. Its rats swam ashore. In two years they had so nearly exterminated the native birds that an islander wrote, "This paradise of birds has become a wilderness, and the quietness of death reigns where all was melody."

On Tristan da Cunha almost all of the unique land birds that had evolved there in the course of the ages were exterminated by hogs and rats. The native fauna of the island of Tahiti is losing ground against the horde of alien species that man has introduced. The Hawaiian Islands, which have lost their native plants and animals faster than almost any other area in the world, are a classic example of the results of interfering with natural balances. Certain relations of animal to plant, and of plant to soil, had grown up through the centuries. When man came in and rudely disturbed this balance, he set off a whole series of chain reactions.

Vancouver brought cattle and goats to the Hawaiian Islands, and the resulting damage to forests and other vegetation was enormous. Many plant introductions were as bad. A plant known as the pamakani was brought in many years ago, according to report, by a Captain Makee for his beautiful gardens on the island of Maui. The pamakani, which has light, wind-borne seeds, quickly escaped from the captain's gardens, ruined the pasture lands on Maui, and proceeded to hop from island to island. The CCC boys were at one time put to work to clear it out of the Honouliuli Forest Reserve, but as fast as they destroyed it, the seeds of new plants arrived on the wind. Lantana was another plant brought in as an ornamental species. Now it covers thousands of acres with a thorny, scrambling growth—despite large sums of money spent to import parasitic insects to control it.

There was once a society in Hawaii for the special purpose of introducing exotic birds. Today when you go to the islands, you see, instead of the exquisite native birds that greeted Captain Cook, mynas from India, cardinals from the United States or Brazil, doves from Asia, weavers from Australia, skylarks from Europe, and titmice from Japan. Most of the original bird life has been wiped out, and to find its fugitive remnants you would have to search assiduously in the most remote hills.

Some of the island species have, at best, the most tenuous hold on life. The Laysan teal is found nowhere in the world but on the one small island of Laysan. Even on this island it occurs only on one end, where there is a seepage of fresh water. Probably the total population of this species does not exceed fifty individuals. Destruction of the small swampy bit of land that is its home, or the introduction of a hostile or competing species, could easily snap the slender thread of life.

Most of man's habitual tampering with nature's balance by introducing exotic species has been done in ignorance of the fatal chain of events that would follow. But in modern times, at least, we might profit by history. About the year 1513, the Portuguese introduced goats onto the recently discovered island of St. Helena, which had devoloped a magnificent forest of gumwood, ebony, and brazilwood. By 1560 or thereabouts, the goats had so multiplied that they wandered over the island by the thousand, in flocks a mile long. They trampled the young trees and ate the seedlings. By this time the colonists had begun to cut and burn the forests, so that it is hard to say whether men or goats were the more responsible for the destruction. But of the result there was no doubt. By the early 1800's the forests were gone, and the naturalist Alfred Wallace later described this once beautiful, forest-clad volcanic island as a 'rocky desert,' in which the remnants of the original flora persisted only in the most inaccessible peaks and crater ridges.

When the astronomer Halley visited the islands of the Atlantic about 1700, he put a few goats ashore on South Trinidad. This time, without the further aid of man, the work of deforestation proceeded so rapidly that it was nearly completed within the century. Today

Trinidad's slopes are the place of a ghost forest, strewn with the fallen and decaying trunks of long-dead trees; its soft volcanic soils, no longer held by the interlacing roots, are sliding away into the sea.

One of the most interesting of the Pacific islands was Laysan, a tiny scrap of soil which is a far outrider of the Hawaiian chain. It once supported a forest of sandalwood and fanleaf palms and had five land birds, all peculiar to Laysan alone. One of them was the Laysan rail, a charming, gnomelike creature no more than six inches high, with wings that seemed too small (and were never used as wings), and feet that seemed too large, and a voice like distant, tinkling bells. About 1887, the captain of a visiting ship moved some of the rails to Midway, about 300 miles to the west, establishing a second colony. It seemed a fortunate move, for soon thereafter rabbits were introduced on Laysan. Within a quarter of a century, the rabbits had killed off the vegetation of the tiny island, reduced it to a sandy desert, and all but exterminated themselves. As for the rails, the devastation of their island was fatal, and the last rail died about 1924.

Perhaps the Laysan colony could later have been restored from the Midway group had not tragedy struck there also. During the war in the Pacific, rats went ashore to island after island from ships and landing craft. They invaded Midway in 1943. The adult rails were slaughtered. The eggs were eaten, and the young birds killed. The world's last Laysan rail was seen in 1944.

The tragedy of the oceanic islands lies in the uniqueness, the irreplaceability of the species they have developed by the slow processes of the ages. In a reasonable world men would have treated these islands as precious possessions, as natural museums filled with beautiful and curious works of creation, valuable beyond price because nowhere in the world are they duplicated. W. H. Hudson's lament for the birds of the Argentine pampas might even more truly have been spoken of the islands: "The beautiful has vanished and returns not."

HENRY DAVID THOREAU

Winter Animals

Henry David Thoreau's Walden *describes his Robinson Crusoe existence at a pond in Concord, Massachusetts, bare of creature comforts but enriched by the study and contemplation of nature.*

When the ponds were firmly frozen, they afforded not only new and shorter routes to many points, but new views from their surfaces of the familiar landscape around them. When I crossed Flint's Pond, after it was covered with snow, though I had often paddled about and skated over it, it was so unexpectedly wide and so strange that I could think of nothing but Baffin's Bay. The Lincoln hills rose up around me at the extremity of a snowy plain, in which I did not remember to have stood before; and the fishermen, at an indeterminable distance over the ice, moving slowly about with their wolfish dogs, passed for sealers or Esquimaux, or in misty weather loomed like fabulous creatures, and I did not know whether they were giants or pygmies. I took this course when I went to lecture in Lincoln in the evening, traveling in no road and passing no house between my own hut and the lecture room. In Goose Pond, which lay in my way, a colony of muskrats dwelt, and raised their cabins high above the ice, though none could be seen abroad when I crossed it. Walden, being like the rest usually bare of snow, or with only shallow and interrupted drifts on it, was my yard where I could walk freely when the snow was nearly two feet deep on a level elsewhere and the villagers were confined to their streets. There, far from the village street, and except at very long intervals, from the jingle of sleigh-bells, I slid and skated, as in a vast mooseyard well trodden, overhung by oak woods and solemn pines bent down with snow or bristling with icicles.

For sounds in winter nights, and often in winter days, I heard the forlorn but melodious note of a hooting owl indefinitely far; such a sound as the frozen earth would yield if struck with a suitable plectrum, the very *lingua vernacula* of Walden Wood, and quite familiar to me at last, though I never saw the bird while it was making it. I seldom opened my door in a winter evening without hearing it; *Hoo hoo hoo, hooer hoo,* sounded sonorously, and the first three syllables accented somewhat like *how der do*; or sometimes *hoo hoo* only. One night in the beginning of winter, before the pond froze over, about nine o'clock, I was startled by the loud honking of a goose, and, stepping to the door, heard the sound of their wings like a tempest in the woods as they flew low over my house. They passed over the pond toward Fair Haven, seemingly deterred from settling by my light, their commodore honking all the while with a regular beat. Suddenly an unmistakable cat owl from very near me, with the most harsh and tremendous voice I ever heard from any inhabitant of the woods, responded at regular intervals to the goose, as if determined to expose and disgrace this intruder from Hudson's Bay by exhibiting a greater compass and volume of voice in a native, and *boo-hoo* him out of Concord horizon. What do you mean by alarming the citadel at this time of night consecrated to me? Do you think I am ever caught napping at such an hour, and that I have not got lungs and a larynx as well as yourself? *Boo-hoo, boo-hoo, boo-hoo!* It was one of the most thrilling discords I ever heard. And yet, if you had a discriminating ear, there were in it the elements of a concord such as these plains never saw nor heard.

I also heard the whooping of the ice in the pond, my great bed-fellow in that part of Concord, as if it were restless in its bed and would fain turn over, were troubled with flatulency and bad dreams; or I was waked by the cracking of the ground by the frost, as if some one had driven a team against my door, and in the morning would

find a crack in the earth a quarter of a mile long and a third of an inch
wide.

Sometimes I heard the foxes as they ranged over the snow-crust,
in moonlight nights, in search of a partridge or other game, barking
raggedly and demoniacally like forest dogs, as if laboring with some
anxiety, or seeking expression, struggling for light and to be dogs
outright and run freely in the streets; for it we take the ages into our
account, may there not be a civilization going on among brutes as
well as men? They seemed to me to be rudimental, burrowing men,
still standing on their defence, awaiting their transformation.
Sometimes one came near to my window, attracted by my light,
barked a vulpine curse at me, and then retreated.

Usually the red squirrel (*Sciurus Hudsonius*) waked me in the
dawn, coursing over the roof and up and down the sides of the house,
as if sent out of the woods for this purpose. In the course of the
winter I threw out half a bushel of ears of sweet corn, which had not
got ripe, on to the snow-crust by my door, and was amused by
watching the motions of the various animals which were baited by it.
In the twilight and the night the rabbits came regularly and made a
hearty meal. All day long the red squirrels came and went, and
afforded me much entertainment by their manœuvres. One would
approach at first warily through the shrub oaks, running over the
snow-crust by fits and starts like a leaf blown by the wind, now a few
paces this way, with wonderful speed and waste of energy, making
inconceivable haste with his "trotters," as if it were for a wager, and
now as many paces that way, but never getting on more than half a
rod at a time; and then suddenly pausing with a ludicrous expression
and a gratuitous somerset, as if all the eyes in the universe were fixed
on him,—for all the motions of a squirrel, even in the most solitary
recesses of the forest, imply spectators as much as those of a dancing
girl,—wasting more time in delay and circumspection than would
have sufficed to walk the whole distance,—I never saw one walk,—
and then suddenly, before you could say Jack Robinson, he would be
in the top of a young pitch pine, winding up his clock and chiding all
imaginary spectators, soliloquizing and talking to all the universe at
the same time,—for no reason that I could ever detect, or he himself
was aware of, I suspect. At length he would reach the corn, and
selecting a suitable ear, frisk about in the same uncertain

trigonometrical way to the topmost stick of my woodpile, before my window, where he looked me in the face, and there sit for hours, supplying himself with a new ear from time to time, nibbling at first voraciously and throwing the half-naked cobs about; till at length he grew more dainty still and played with his food, tasting only the inside of the kernel, and the ear, which was held balanced over the stick by one paw, slipped from his careless grasp and fell to the ground, when he would look over at it with a ludicrous expression of uncertainty, as if suspecting that it had life, with a mind not made up whether to get it again, or a new one, or be off; now thinking of corn, then listening to hear what was in the wind. So the little impudent fellow would waste many an ear in a forenoon; till at last, seizing some longer and plumper one, considerably bigger than himself, and skillfully balancing it, he would set out with it to the woods, like a tiger with a buffalo, by the same zigzag course and frequent pauses, scratching along with it as if it were too heavy for him and falling all the while, making its fall a diagonal between a perpendicular and horizontal, being determined to put it through at any rate;—a singularly frivolous and whimsical fellow;—and so he would get off with it to where he lived, perhaps carry it to the top of a pine tree forty or fifty rods distant, and I would afterwards find the cobs strewn about the woods in various directions.

At length the jays arrive, whose discordant screams were heard long before, as they were warily making their approach an eighth of a mile off, and in a stealthy and sneaking manner they flit from tree to tree, nearer and nearer, and pick up the kernels which the squirrels have dropped. Then, sitting on a pitch pine bough, they attempt to swallow in their haste a kernel which is too big for their throats and chokes them; and after great labor they disgorge it, and spend an hour in the endeavor to crack it by repeated blows with their bills. They were manifestly thieves, and I had not much respect for them; but the squirrels, though at first shy, went to work as if they were taking what was their own.

Meanwhile also came the chickadees in flocks, which, picking up the crumbs the squirrels had dropped, flew to the nearest twig, and, placing them under their claws, hammered away at them with their little bills, as if it were an insect in the bark, till they were sufficiently reduced for their slender throats. A little flock of these titmice came daily to pick a dinner out of my wood-pile, or the crumbs at my door, with faint flitting lisping notes, like the tinkling of icicles in the grass, or else with sprightly *day day day,* or more rarely, in springlike days, a wiry summery *phe-be* from the woodside. They were so familiar that at length one alighted on an armful of wood which I was carrying in, and pecked at the sticks without fear. I once had a sparrow alight upon my shoulder for a moment while I was hoeing in a village garden, and I felt that I was more distinguished by that circumstance than I should have been by any epaulet I could have worn. The squirrels also grew at last to be quite familiar, and occasionally stepped upon my shoe, when that was the nearest way.

When the ground was not yet quite covered, and again near the end of winter, when the snow was melted on my south hillside and about my wood-pile, the partridges came out of the woods morning and evening to feed there. Which ever side you walk in the woods the partridge bursts away on whirring wings, jarring the snow from the dry leaves and twigs on high, which comes sifting down in the sunbeams like golden dust, for this brave bird is not to be scared by winter. It is frequently covered up by drifts, and, it is said, "sometimes plunges from on wing into the soft snow, where it remains concealed for a day or two." I used to start them in the open land also, where they had come out of the woods at sunset to "bud" the wild apple trees. They will come regularly every evening to particular trees, where the cunning sportsman lies in wait for them, and the distant orchards next the woods suffer thus not a little. I am glad that the partridge gets fed, at any rate. It is Nature's own bird which lives on buds and diet-drink.

In dark winter mornings, or in short winter afternoons, I sometimes heard a pack of hounds threading all the woods with hounding cry and yelp, unable to resist the instinct of the chase, and the note of the hunting-horn at intervals, proving that man was in the rear. The woods ring again, and yet no fox bursts forth on to the open level of the pond, nor following pack pursuing their Actæon. And perhaps at evening I see the hunters returning with a single brush trailing from their sleigh for a trophy, seeking their inn. They tell me that if the fox would remain in the bosom of the frozen earth he would be safe, or if he would run in a straight line away no foxhound could overtake him; but, having left his pursuers far behind, he stops to rest and listen till they come up, and when he runs he circles round to his old haunts, where the hunters await him. Sometimes, however, he will run upon a wall many rods, and then leap off far to one side, and he appears to know that water will not retain his scent. A hunter told me that he once saw a fox pursued by hounds burst out on to Walden when the ice was covered with shallow puddles, run part way across, and then return to the same shore. Ere long the hounds arrived, but here they lost the scent. Sometimes a pack hunting by themselves would pass my door, and circle round my house, and yelp and hound without regarding me, as if afflicted by a species of madness, so that nothing could divert them from the pursuit. Thus they circle until they fall upon the recent trail of a fox, for a wise hound will forsake everything else for this. One day a man came to my hut from Lexington to inquire after his hound that made a large track, and had been hunting for a week by himself. But I fear that he was not the wiser for all I told him, for every time I attempted to answer his questions he interrupted me by asking, "What do you do here?" He had lost a dog, but found a man.

One old hunter who has a dry tongue, who used to come to bathe in Walden once every year when the water was warmest, and at such times looked in upon me, told me that many years ago he took his gun one afternoon and went out for a cruise in Walden Wood; and as he walked the Wayland road he heard the cry of hounds approaching, and ere long a fox leaped the wall into the road, and as quick as thought leaped the other wall out of the road, and his swift bullet had not touched him. Some way behind came an old hound and her three pups in full pursuit, hunting on their own account, and disappeared again in the woods. Late in the afternoon, as he was resting in the thick woods south of Walden, he heard the voice of the hounds far over toward Fair Haven still pursuing the fox; and on they came, their hounding cry which made all the woods ring sounding nearer and nearer, now from Well Meadow, now from the Baker Farm. For a long time he stood still and listened to their music, so sweet to a hunter's ear, when suddenly the fox appeared, threading the solemn aisles with an easy coursing pace, whose sound was concealed by a sympathetic rustle of the leaves, swift and still, keeping the ground, leaving his pursuers far behind; and leaping upon a rock amid the woods, he sat erect and listening, with his back to the hunter. For a moment compassion restrained the latter's arm; but that was a short-lived mood, and as quick as thought can follow thought his piece was levelled, and *whang!*—the fox, rolling over the rock, lay dead on the ground. The hunter still kept his place and listened to the hounds. Still on they came, and now the near woods resounded through all their aisles with their demoniac cry. At length the old hound burst into view with muzzle to the ground, and snapping the air as if possessed, and ran directly to the rock; but, spying the dead fox, she suddenly ceased her hounding, as if struck dumb with amazement, and walked round and round him in silence; and one by one her pups arrived, and, like their mother, were sobered into silence by the mystery. Then the hunter came forward and stood in their midst, and the mystery was solved. They waited in silence while he skinned the fox, then followed the brush a while, and at length turned off into the woods again. That evening a Weston squire came to the Concord hunter's cottage to inquire for his hounds, and told how for a week they had been hunting on their own account from Weston woods. The Concord hunter told him what he knew and offered him the skin; but the other declined it and departed. He did not find his hounds that night, but the next day learned that they had crossed the river and put up at a farmhouse for the night, whence, having been well fed, they took their departure early in the morning.

The hunter who told me this could remember one Sam Nutting, who used to hunt bears on Fair Haven Ledges, and exchange their skins for rum in Concord village; who told him, even, that he had seen a moose there. Nutting had a famous foxhound named Burgoyne,—he pronounced it Bugine,—which my informant used to borrow. In the "Wast Book" of an old trader of this town, who was also a captain, town-clerk, and representative. I find the following entry. Jan. 18th, 1742-3, "John Melven Cr. by 1 Grey Fox 0—2—3;" they are not now found here; and in his ledger, Feb. 7th, 1743, Hezekiah Stratton has credit "by ½ a Catt skin 0—1—4½;" of course, a wild-cat, for Stratton was a sergeant in the old French war, and would not have got credit for hunting less noble game. Credit is given for deerskins also, and they were daily sold. One man still preserves the horns of the last deer that was killed in this vicinity, and another has told me the particulars of the hunt in which his uncle was engaged. The hunters were formerly a numerous and merry crew here. I remember well one gaunt Nimrod who would catch up a leaf by the roadside and play a strain on it wilder and more melodious, if my memory serves me, than any hunting-horn.

At midnight, when there was a moon, I sometimes met with hounds in my path prowling about the woods, which would skulk out of my way, as if afraid, and stand silent amid the bushes till I had passed.

Squirrels and wild mice disputed for my store of nuts. There were scores of pitch pines around my house, from one to four inches in diameter, which had been gnawed by mice the previous winter,—a Norwegian winter for them, for the snow lay long and deep, and they were obliged to mix a large proportion of pine bark with their other diet. These trees were alive and apparently flourishing at mid-summer, and many of them had grown a foot, though completely girdled; but after another winter such were without exception dead. It is remarkable that a single mouse should thus be allowed a whole pine tree for its dinner, gnawing round instead of up and down it; but perhaps it is necessary in order to thin these trees, which are wont to grow up densely.

The hares (*Lepus Americanus*) were very familiar. One had her form under my house all winter, separated from me only by the flooring, and she startled me each morning by her hasty departure when I began to stir,—thump, thump, thump, striking her head against the floor timbers in her hurry. They used to come round my door at dusk to nibble the potato parings which I had thrown out, and were so nearly the color of the ground that they could hardly be distinguished when still. Sometimes in the twilight I alternately lost and recovered sight of one sitting motionless under my window. When I opened my door in the evening, off they would go with a squeak and a bounce. Near at hand they only excited my pity. One evening one sat by my door two paces from me, at first trembling with fear, yet unwilling to move; a poor wee thing, lean and bony, with ragged ears and sharp nose, scant tail and slender paws. It looked as if Nature no longer contained the breed of nobler bloods, but stood on her last toes. Its large eyes appeared young and unhealthy, almost dropsical. I took a step, and lo, away it scud with an elastic spring over the snow-crust, straightening its body and its limbs into graceful length, and soon put the forest between me and itself,—the wild free venison, asserting its vigor and the dignity of Nature. Not without reason was its slenderness. Such then was its nature. (*Lepus, levipes,* lightfoot, some think.)

What is a country without rabbits and partridges? They are among the most simple and indigenous animal products; ancient and venerable families known to antiquity as to modern times; of the very hue and substance of Nature, nearest allied to leaves and to the ground,—and to one another; it is either winged or it is legged. It is hardly as if you had seen a wild creature when a rabbit or a partridge bursts away, only a natural one, as much to be expected as rustling leaves. The partridge and the rabbit are still sure to thrive, like true natives of the soil, whatever revolutions occur. If the forest is cut off, the sprouts and bushes which spring up afford them concealment, and they become more numerous than ever. That must be a poor country indeed that does not support a hare. Our woods teem with them both, and around every swamp may be seen the partridge or rabbit walk, beset with twiggy fences and horse-hair snares, which some cow-boy tends.

SECTION III

Animal Behavior

Recently, I observed a brightly-colored male bluejay who lives in my front yard engaged in some unusual and to me informative behavior. He was shadow-boxing with his own reflection, which he had chanced to see in one of my car's shiny chrome hubcaps while foraging for food. After vainly attempting to frighten this invader by shows of strength, he then backed up and charged headlong into his mirrored twin. Futile attack followed futile attack, until he became dazed and I, feeling sorry for him, drove my car with the imagined intruder into the street. Protection of territory as exhibited by my front yard bluejay typifies most birds, reptiles, social insects, and a vast number of mammalian species from squirrels to man.

A. S. Pearse, in his paper on "Habits of Fiddler Crabs," records some amazing behavioral research on those pugnacious shoreline crabs that dig burrows in sand or mud and retreat into them to pull their trap doors shut when the tide is high. Each male fiddler crab has one small chela, or claw, to hold prey, while the other chela—huge by comparison—is employed to hammer food or an enemy into insensibility. Each crab lives near his burrow, which he cleans and will defend against enemies. Pearse established that the burrow constitutes the crab's territory, and while he will graze up to twelve yards from that burrow, he will not defend the grazing range. Fiddler crabs removed from their sandy homesteads for any distance rush madly back to it. If they cross some defended territory of another fiddler, they almost without exception do battle with him.

213

Konrad Lorenz, describing the behavior of his tiny fish-friend, the stickleback, employs poetic imagery: "Who could reproduce in words, what artist in colour, that glowing red that makes the sides of the male stickleback glassy and transparent, the iridescent blue-green of its back whose colour and brilliance can only be compared with the illuminating power of neon lighting, or finally, the brilliant emerald green of its eyes?" The poet would stop at that point, but Lorenz, the scientist, went on to observe that the stickleback, at mating time, glows whenever it sees an opponent or a female, and "does so as long as it is in the vicinity of its nest, in its chosen territory." From this discovery, Lorenz made the following conclusion about the stickleback: "The basic principle of his fighting is 'my home is my castle'."

Similar observations of a territorial instinct are reported by zoologist Helmut K. Buechner on the Uganda kob, a strikingly graceful antelope of the African savannahs. The dominant males among these antelopes succeed in establishing their priority to a certain area on a common stamping ground. The female kob shows absolutely no interest in any male who has not succeeded in acquiring his own piece of real estate.

The socio-sexual territorial behavior of the fiddler crab, the European stickleback, and the Uganda kob can be multiplied by several hundred other examples of animal behavior centering around territorial rights. A rare exception to exclusive territorial control was found by George Schaller in his studies of wild African gorillas. Until Schaller's investigations, it had been thought that each monkey and ape group lived in a territory whose boundaries it defended against all other members of the same species. Schaller, living among gorillas in the forest, was able to observe peaceful interactions among different groups when they met. He concluded that "the gorilla certainly shares its range and its abundant food resources with others of its kind, disdaining all claims to a plot of land of its own."

While there are such exceptions as the gorilla, Professor Buechner was able to summarize certain behavioral traits relating to territory that many vertebrates possess in common: (1) males compete for property rights, never for the female of the species; (2) territorial dominance gives the owner a psychological advantage over an intruder, so that the owner usually wins most battles on his property; and (3) fighting, if it occurs, is usually restricted to individual territories and does not take place in the general grazing range. Buechner points out that courtship, mating, and nest building rarely occur outside the individual's territory.

Man, like the fiddler crab and thousands of other animals, fiercely defends his territory. The territorial brand is stamped on all of us city dwellers who buy postage stamp lots, build houses, and then shut ourselves off from our neighbors by high fences that keep intruders out of our territories. Many of us have dogs that will protect our concept of home territory. Even on that territory which we view as our own, there are others we may scarcely notice in passing who have staked their claims on the property to which we hold the deed. In the trees around my house, jays, mockingbirds, and golden-crowned sparrows have the audacity to assert their sovereignty. And as I walk about the yard, I note that territorial warfare has broken out between two ant colonies.

We may either cheer or view with dismay the chauvinistic politicians of our city, state, or nation when they seek to arouse hostile emotions against foreigners. Such emotions are deeply embedded in our biological heritage, however, and few of us are not affected by the flags, national anthems, diverse languages, and some of the host of symbols that man has evolved to stimulate him in the defense of his homeland. When the Germans almost destroyed London in their bombing raids in World War II, they found the resistance of the English people unweakened. Instead, they encountered a people welded together who were able to fight harder. The same unyielding tenacity of people fighting for their native soil drove Napoleon's armies back after the near destruction of Moscow.

The animal behaviorists have provided us with hundreds of studies establishing that from mice to men the essential drive is acquisition and protection of territory. Their discoveries have recently been summed up and elaborated upon in a remarkable book titled *The Territorial Imperative* (1966) by Robert Ardrey, who tends to view the territorial drive as an instinct that makes war inevitable among mankind.

Ardrey may possibly be correct in his pessimistic theories, yet in reading the animal behaviorists, we must always avoid the fallacy of many of the early pioneers in this discipline who had a habit of generalizing from animal experiments to complex human behavior. The excessive enthusiasm of many of the earliest animal behaviorists, men such as George J. Romanes, who worked with fishes, cats, and dogs, and the Russian physiologist Pavlov, who discovered the conditioned reflex in dogs, led to their tendency to interpret human motivations in terms of animal responses. Animal behavior study lapsed into ill repute for several decades.

Unlike animals, man throughout his history has in his many aspects shown a remarkable ability to modify his environment and adapt to changing circumstances. Man's hope in this nuclear age may lie in his ability to surmount his genetic inheritances. While we must view efforts to overgeneralize from animals to man with caution, we should recognize that it is perhaps desirable that generalists such as Ardrey occasionally attempt to survey the sciences broadly and draw conclusions. By injecting some controversy into research and rustling the leaves of the academic ivy, we can often prod scientists into realizing that research can never be compartmentalized and that new ideas are stimulated periodically by subjecting the findings of researchers in diverse areas to fresh scrutiny.

KONRAD Z. LORENZ

The Taming of the Shrew

Konrad Z. Lorenz's King Solomon's Ring *is one of the most delightful and accurate books ever written on animal behavior. The entire book is tissued with humor, affection and human interest. This book by its obvious merit is a classic that is guaranteed to give equal satisfaction to the student of natural history as well as to the ordinary reader. Sir Julian Huxley calls Dr. Lorenz "one of the most outstanding naturalists of our day."*

All shrews are particularly difficult to keep; this is not because, as we are led proverbially to believe, they are hard to tame, but because the metabolism of these smallest of mammals is so very fast that they will die of hunger within two or three hours if the food supply fails. Since they feed exclusively on small, living animals, mostly insects, and demand, of these, considerably more than their own weight every day, they are most exacting charges. At the time of which I am writing, I had never succeeded in keeping any of the terrestrial shrews alive for any length of time; most of those that I happened to obtain had probably only been caught because they were already ill and they died almost at once. I had never succeeded in procuring a healthy specimen. Now the order Insectivora is very low in the genealogical hierarchy of mammals and is, therefore, of particular interest to the comparative ethologist. Of the whole group, there was only one representative with whose behaviour I was tolerably familiar, namely the hedgehog, an extremely interesting animal of whose ethology Professor Herter of Berlin has made a very thorough study. Of the behaviour of all other members of the family practically nothing is known. Since they are nocturnal and partly subterranean animals, it is nearly impossible to approach them in field observation, and the difficulty of keeping them in captivity had hitherto precluded their study in the laboratory. So the Insectivores were officially placed on my programme.

First I tried to keep the common mole. It was easy to procure a healthy specimen, caught to order in the nursery gardens of my father-in-law, and I found no difficulty in keeping it alive. Immediately on its arrival, it devoured an almost incredible quantity of earthworms which, from the very first moment, it took from my hand. But, as an object of behaviour study, it proved most disappointing. Certainly, it was interesting to watch its method of disappearing in the space of a few seconds under the surface of the ground, to study its astoundingly efficient use of its strong, spade-shaped fore-paws, and to feel their amazing strength when one held the little beast in one's hand. And again, it was remarkable with what surprising exactitude it located, by smell, from underground, the earthworms which I put on the surface of the soil in its terrarium. But these observations were the only benefits I derived from it. It never became any tamer and it never remained above ground any longer than it took to devour its prey; after this, it sank into the earth as a submarine sinks into the water. I soon grew tired of procuring the immense quantities of living food it required and, after a few weeks, I set it free in the garden.

It was years afterwards, on an excursion to that extraordinary lake, the Neusiedlersee, which lies on the Hungarian border of Austria, that I again thought of keeping an insectivore. This large stretch of water, though not thirty miles from Vienna, is an example of the peculiar type of lake found in the open steppes of Eastern Europe and Asia. More than thirty miles long and half as broad, its deepest parts are only about five feet deep and it is much shallower on the average. Nearly half its surface is overgrown with reeds which form an ideal habitat for all kinds of water-birds. Great colonies of white, purple, and grey heron and spoonbills live among the reeds and, until a short while ago, glossy ibis were still to be found here. Greylag geese breed here in great numbers and, on the eastern, reedless shore, avocets and many other rare waders can regularly be found. On the occasion of which I am speaking, we, a dozen tired zoologists, under the experienced guidance of my friend Otto Koenig, were wending our way, slowly and painfully, through the forest of reeds. We were walking in single file, Koenig first, I second, with a few students in our wake. We literally left a wake, an inky-black one in pale grey water. In the reed-forests of Lake Neusiedel, you walk knee deep in slimy, black ooze, wonderfully perfumed by sulphuretted-hydrogen-producing bacteria. This mud clings tenaciously and only releases its hold on your foot with a loud, protesting plop at every step.

After a few hours of this kind of wading you discover aching muscles whose very existence you had never suspected. From the knees to the hips you are immersed in the milky, clay-colored water characteristic of the lake, which, among the reeds, is populated by myriads of extremely hungry leeches conforming to the old pharmaceutical recipe, "Hirudines medicinales maxime affamati". The rest of your person inhabits the upper air, which here consists of clouds of tiny mosquitoes whose bloodthirsty attacks are all the more exasperating because you require both your hands to part the dense reeds in front of you and can only slap your face at intervals. The British ornithologist who may perhaps have envied us some of our rare specimens will perceive that bird-watching on Lake Neusiedel is not, after all, an entirely enviable occupation.

We were thus wending our painful way through the rushes when suddenly Koenig stopped and pointed mutely towards a pond, free from reeds, that stretched in front of us. At first, I could only see whitish water, dark blue sky and green reeds, the standard colours of Lake Neusiedel. Then, suddenly, like a cork popping up on to the surface, there appeared, in the middle of the pool, a tiny black animal, hardly bigger than a man's thumb. And for a moment I was in the rare position of a zoologist who sees a specimen and is not able to classify it, in the literal sense of the word: I did not know to which class of vertebrates the object of my gaze belonged. For the first fraction of a second I took it for the young of some diving bird of a species unknown to me. It appeared to have a beak and it swam on the water like a bird, not in it as a mammal. It swam about in narrow curves and circles, very much like a whirligig beetle, creating an extensive wedge-shaped wake, quite out of proportion to the tiny animal's size. Then a second little beast popped up from below, chased the first one with a shrill, bat-like twitter, then both dived and were gone. The whole episode had not lasted five seconds.

I stood open-mouthed, my mind racing. Koenig turned round with a broad grin, calmly detached a leech that was sticking like a leech to his wrist, wiped away the trickle of blood from the wound, slapped his cheek, thereby killing thirty-five mosquitoes, and asked, in the tone of an examiner, "What was that?" I answered as calmly as I could, "water-shrews", thanking, in my heart, the leech and the mosquitoes for the respite they had given me to collect my thoughts. But my mind was racing on: water-shrews ate fishes and frogs which were easy to procure in any quantity; water-shrews were less subterranean than most other insectivores; they were the very insectivores to keep in captivity. "That's an animal I must catch and keep"; I said to my friend. "That is easy", he responded. "There is a nest with young under the floor mat of my tent." I had slept that night in this tent and Koenig had not thought it worth while to tell me of the shrews; such things are, to him, as much a matter of course as wild little spotted crakes feeding out of his hand, or as any other wonders of his queer kingdom in the reeds.

On our return to the tent that evening, he showed me the nest. It contained eight young which, compared with their mother, who rushed away as we lifted the mat, were of enormous size. They were considerably more than half her length and must each have weighed well between a fourth and a third of their dam: that is to say, the whole litter weighed, at a very modest estimate, twice as much as the old shrew. Yet they were still quite blind and the tips of their teeth were only just visible in their rosy mouths. And two days later when I took them under my care, they were still quite unable to eat even the soft abdomens of grasshoppers, and in spite of evident greed, they chewed interminably on a soft piece of frog's meat without succeeding in detaching a morsel from it. On our journey home, I fed them on the squeezed-out insides of grasshoppers and finely minced frog's meat, a diet on which they obviously throve. Arrived home in Altenberg, I improved on this diet by preparing a food from the squeezed-out insides of mealworm larvae, with some finely chopped small, fresh fishes, worked into a sort of gravy with a little milk. They consumed large quantities of this food, and their little nest-box looked quite small in comparison with the big china bowl whose contents they emptied three times a day. All these observations raise the problem of how the female water-shrew succeeds in feeding her gigantic litter. It is absolutely impossible that she should do so on milk alone. Even on a more concentrated diet my young shrews devoured the equivalent of their own weight daily and this meant nearly twice the weight of a grown shrew. Yet, at that time of their lives, young shrews could not possibly engulf a frog or a fish brought whole to them by their mother, as my charges indisputably proved. I can only think that the mother feeds her young by regurgitation of chewed food. Even thus, it is little short of miraculous that the adult female should be able to obtain enough meat to sustain herself and her voracious progeny.

When I brought them home, my young water-shrews were still blind. They had not suffered from the journey and were as sleek and fat as one could wish. Their black, glossy coats were reminiscent of moles, but the white colour of their underside, as well as the round, streamlined contours of their bodies reminded me distinctly of penguins, and not, indeed, without justification: both the stream-lined form and the light underside are adaptations to a life in the water. Many free-swimming animals, mammals, birds, amphibians and fishes, are silvery-white below in order to be invisible to enemies swimming in the depths. Seen from below, the shining white belly blends perfectly with the reflecting surface film of the water. It is very characteristic of these water animals that the dark dorsal and the white ventral colours do not merge gradually into each other as is the case in "counter-shaded" land animals whose colouring is calculated to make them invisible by eliminating the contrasting shade on their undersides. As in the killer whale, in dolphins, and in penguins, the white underside of the water-shrew is divided from the dark upper side by a sharp line which runs often in very decorative curves, along the animal's flank. Curiously enough, this border-line between black and white showed considerable variations in individuals and even on both sides of one animal's body. I welcomed this, since it enabled me to recognize my shrews personally.

Three days after their arrival in Altenberg my eight shrew babies opened their eyes and began, very cautiously, to explore the precincts of their nest-box. It was now time to remove them to an appropriate container, and on this question I expended much hard thinking. The enormous quantity of food they consumed and, consequently, of excrement they produced, made it impossible to keep them in an ordinary aquarium whose water, within a day, would have become a stinking brew. Adequate sanitation was imperative for particular reasons; in ducks, grebes and all water-fowl, the plumage must be kept perfectly dry if the animal is to remain in a state of health, and the same premise may reasonably be expected to hold good of the shrew's fur. Now water which has been polluted soon turns strongly alkaline and this I knew to be very bad for the plumage of water-birds. It causes saponification of the fat to which the feathers owe their waterproof quality, and the bird becomes thoroughly wet and is unable to stay on the water. I hold the record, as far as I know hitherto unbroken by any other bird-lover, for having kept dabchicks alive and healthy in captivity for nearly two years, and even then they did not die but escaped, and may still be living. My experience with these birds proved the absolute necessity of keeping the water perfectly clean; whenever it became a little dirty I noticed their feathers beginning to get wet, a danger which they anxiously tried to counteract by constantly preening themselves. I had, therefore, to keep these little grebes in crystal-clear water which was changed every day, and I rightly assumed that the same would be necessary for my water-shrews.

I took a large aquarium tank, rather over a yard in length and about two feet wide. At each end of this, I placed two little tables, and weighed them down with heavy stones so that they would not float. Then I filled up the tank until the water was level with the tops of the tables. I did not at first push the tables close against the panes of the tank, which was rather narrow, for fear that the shrews might become trapped under water in the blind alley beneath a table and drown there; this precaution, however, subsequently proved unnecessary. The water-shrew which, in its natural state, swims great distances under the ice, is quite able to find its way to the open surface in much more difficult situations. The nest-box, which was placed on one of the tables, was equipped with a sliding shutter, so that I could imprison the shrews whenever the container had to be cleaned. In the morning, at the hour of general cage-cleaning, the shrews were usually at home and asleep, so that the procedure caused them no appreciable disturbance. I will admit that I take great pride in devising, by creative imagination, suitable containers for animals of which nobody, myself included, has had any previous experience, and it was particularly gratifying that the contraption described above proved so satisfactory that I never had to alter even the minutest detail.

When first my baby shrews were liberated in this container they took a very long time to explore the top of the table on which their nest-box was standing. The water's edge seemed to exert a strong attraction; they approached it ever and again, smelled the surface and seemed to feel along it with the long, fine whiskers which surround their pointed snouts like a halo and represent not only their most important organ of touch but the most important of all their sensory organs. Like other aquatic mammals, the water shrew differs from the terrestrial members of its class in that its nose, the guiding organ of the average mammal, is of no use whatsoever in its under-water hunting. The water-shrew's whiskers are actively mobile like the antennae of an insect or the fingers of a blind man.

Exactly as mice and many other small rodents would do under similar conditions, the shrews interrupted their careful exploration of their new surroundings every few minutes to dash wildly back into the safe cover of their nest-box. The survival value of this peculiar behaviour is evident: the animal makes sure, from time to time that it has not lost its way and that it can, at a moment's notice, retreat to the one place it knows to be safe. It was a queer spectacle to see those podgy black figures slowly and carefully whiskering their way forward and, in the next second, with lightning speed, dash back to the nest-box. Queerly enough, they did not run straight through the little door, as one would have expected, but in their wild dash for safety they jumped, one and all, first on to the roof of the box and only then, whiskering along its edge, found the opening and slipped in with a half somersault, their back turned nearly vertically downward. After many repetitions of this manoeuvre, they were able to find the opening without feeling for it; they "knew" perfectly its whereabouts yet still persisted in the leap on to the roof. They jumped on to it and immediately vaulted in through the door, but they never, as long as they lived, found out that the leap and vault which had become their habit was really quite unnecessary and that they could have run in directly without this extraordinary detour. We shall hear more about this dominance of path habits in the water-shrew presently.

It was only on the third day, when the shrews had become thoroughly acquainted with the geography of their little rectangular island, that the largest and most enterprising of them ventured into the water. As is so often the case with mammals, birds, reptiles and fishes, it was the largest and most handsomely coloured male which played the role of leader. First he sat on the edge of the water and thrust in the fore part of his body, at the same time frantically paddling with his fore-legs but still clinging with his hind ones to the board. Then he slid in, but in the next moment took fright, scampered madly across the surface very much after the manner of a frightened duckling, and jumped out on to the board at the opposite end of the tank. There he sat, excitedly grooming his belly with one hind paw, exactly as coypu and beavers do. Soon he quietened down and sat still for a moment. Then he went to the water's edge a second time, hesitated for a moment, and plunged in; diving immediately, he swam ecstatically about under water, swerving upward and downward again, running quickly along the bottom, and finally jumping out of the water at the same place as he had first entered it.

When I first saw a water-shrew swimming I was most struck by a thing which I ought to have expected but did not: at the moment of diving, the little black and white beast appears to be made of silver. Like the plumage of ducks and grebes, but quite unlike the fur of most water mammals, such as seals, otters, beavers or coypus, the fur of the water-shrew remains absolutely dry under water, that is to say, it retains a thick layer of air while the animal is below the surface. In the other mammals mentioned above, it is only the short, woolly undercoat that remains dry, the superficial hair-tips becoming wet, wherefore the animal looks its natural colour when under water and is superficially wet when it emerges. I was already aware of the peculiar qualities of the waterproof fur of the shrew, and, had I given it a thought, I should have known that it would look, under water, exactly like the air-retaining fur on the underside of a water beetle or on the abdomen of a water spider. Nevertheless the wonderful, transparent silver coat of the shrew was, to me, one of those delicious surprises that nature has in store for her admirers.

Another surprising detail which I only noticed when I saw my shrews in the water was that they have a fringe of stiff, erectile hairs on the outer side of their fifth toes and on the underside of their tails. These form collapsible oars and a collapsible rudder. Folded and inconspicuous as long as the animal is on dry land, they unfold the moment it enters the water and broaden the effective surface of the propelling feet and of the steering tail by a considerable area.

Like penguins, the water-shrews looked rather awkward and ungainly on dry land but were transformed into objects of elegance and grace on entering the water. As long as they walked, their strongly convex underside made them look pot-bellied and reminiscent of an old, overfed dachshund. But under water, the very same protruding belly balanced harmoniously the curve of their back and gave a beautifully symmetrical streamline which, together with their silver coating and the elegance of their movements, made them a sight of entrancing beauty.

When they had all become familiar with the water, their container was one of the chief attractions that our research station had to offer to any visiting naturalists or animal-lovers. Unlike all other mammals of their size, the water-shrews were largely diurnal and, except in the early hours of the morning, three or four of them were constantly on the scene. It was exceedingly interesting to watch their movements upon and under the water. Like the whirligig beetle, Gyrinus, they could turn in an extremely small radius without diminishing their speed, a faculty for which the large rudder surface of the tail with its fringe of erectile hairs is evidently essential. They had two different ways of diving, either by taking a little jump as grebes or coots do and working their way down at a steep angle, or by simply lowering their snout under the surface and paddling very fast till they reached "planing speed", thus working their way downward on the principle of the inclined plane—in other words, performing the converse movement of an ascending aeroplane. The water-shrew must expend a large amount of energy in staying down, since the air contained in its fur exerts a strong pull upwards. Unless it is paddling straight downwards, a thing it rarely does, it is forced to maintain a constant minimum speed, keeping its body as a slightly downward angle, in order not to float to the surface. While swimming under water the shrew seems to flatten, broadening its body in a peculiar fashion, in order to present a better planing surface to the water. I never saw my shrews try to cling by their claws to any underwater objects, as the dipper is alleged to do. When they seemed to be running along the bottom, they were really swimming close above it, but perhaps the smooth gravel on the bottom of the tank was unsuitable for holding on to and it did not occur to me then to offer them a rougher surface. They were very playful when in the water and chased one another loudly twittering on the surface, or silently in the depths. Unlike any other mammal, but just like water birds, they could rest on the surface; this they used to do, rolling partly over and grooming themselves. Once out again, they instantly proceeded to clean their fur-one is almost tempted to say "preen" it, so similar was their behaviour to that of ducks which have just left the water after a long swim.

Most interesting of all was their method of hunting under water. They came swimming along with an erratic course, darting a foot or so forward very swiftly in a straight line, then starting to gyrate in looped turns at reduced speed. While swimming straight and swiftly their whiskers were, as far as I could see, laid flat against their head, but while circling they were erect and bristled out in all directions, as they sought contact with some prey. I have no reason to believe that vision plays any part in the water-shrew's hunting, except perhaps in the activation of its tactile search. My shrews may have noticed visually the presence of the live tadpoles or little fishes which I put in the tank, but in the actual hunting of its prey the animal is exclusively guided by its sense of touch, located in the wide-spreading whiskers on its snout. Certain small free-swimming species of cat-fish find their prey by exactly the same method. When these fishes swim fast and straight, the long feelers on their snout are depressed but, like the shrew's whiskers, are stiffly spread out when the fish becomes conscious of the proximity of potential prey; like the shrew, the fish then begins to gyrate blindly in order to establish contact with its prey. It may not even be necessary for the water-shrew actually to touch its prey with one of its whiskers. Perhaps, at very close range, the water vibration caused by the movements of a small fish, a tadpole or a water-insect is perceptible by those sensitive tactile organs. It is quite impossible to determine this question by mere observation, for the action is much too quick for the human eye. There is a quick turn and a snap and the shrew is already paddling shorewards with a wriggling creature in its maw.

In relation to its size, the water-shrew is perhaps the most terrible predator of all vertebrate animals, and it can even vie with the invertebrates, including the murderous Dytiscus larva described in the third chapter of this book. It has been reported by A. E. Brehm that water-shrews have killed fish more than sixty times heavier than themselves by biting out their eyes and brain. This happened only when the fish were confined in containers with no room for escape. The same story has been told to me by fishermen on Lake Neusiedel, who could not possibly have heard Brehm's report. I once offered to my shrews a large edible frog. I never did it again, nor could I bear to see out to its end the cruel scene that ensued. One of the shrews encountered the frog in the basin and instantly gave chase, repeatedly seizing hold of the creature's legs; although it was kicked off again it did not cease in its attack and finally, the frog, in desperation, jumped out of the water and on to one of the tables, where several shrews raced to the pursuer's assistance and buried their teeth in the legs and hindquarters of the wretched frog. And now, horribly, they began to eat the frog alive, beginning just where each one of them happened to have hold of it; the poor frog croaked heartrendingly, as the jaws of the shrews munched audibly in chorus. I need hardly be blamed for bringing this experiment to an abrupt and agitated end and putting the lacerated frog out of its misery. I never offered the shrews large prey again but only such as would be killed at the first bite or two. Nature can be very cruel indeed; it is not out of pity that most of the larger predatory animals kill their prey quickly. The lion has to finish off a big antelope or a buffalo very quickly indeed in order not to get hurt itself, for a beast of prey which has to hunt daily cannot afford to receive even a harmless scratch in effecting a kill; such scratches would soon add up to such an extent as to put the killer out of action. The same reason has forced the python and other large snakes to evolve a quick and really humane method of killing the well-armed mammals that are their natural prey. But where there is no danger of the victim doing damage to the killer, the latter shows no pity whatsoever. The hedgehog which, by virtue of its armour, is quite immune to the bite of a snake, regularly proceeds to eat it, beginning at the tail or in the middle of its body, and in the same way the water-shrew treats its innocuous prey. But man should abstain from judging his innocently-cruel fellow creatures, for even if nature sometimes "shrieks against his creed", what pain does he himself not inflict upon the living creatures that he hunts for pleasure and not for food?

The mental qualities of the water-shrew cannot be rated very high. They were quite tame and fearless of me and never tried to bite when I took them in my hand, nor did they ever try to evade it, but, like little tame rodents, they tried to dig their way out if I held them for too long in the hollow of my closed fist. Even when I took them out of their container and put them on a table or on the floor, they were by no means thrown into a panic but were quite ready to take food out of my hand and even tried actively to creep into it if they felt a longing for cover. When, in such an unwonted environment, they were shown their nest-box, they plainly showed that they knew it by sight and instantly made for it, and even pursued it with upraised heads if I moved the box along above them, just out of their reach. All in all, I really may pride myself that I have tamed the shrew, or at least one member of that family.

In their accustomed surroundings, my shrews proved to be very strict creatures of habit. I have already mentioned the remarkable conservatism with which they persevered in their unpractical way of entering their nest-box by climbing on to its roof and then vaulting, with a half turn, in through the door. Something more must be said about the unchanging tenacity with which these animals cling to their habits once they have formed them. In the water-shrew, the path-habits, in particular, are of a really amazing immutability; I hardly know another instance to which the saying, "As the twig is bent, so the tree is inclined", applies so literally.

In a territory unknown to it, the water-shrew will never run fast except under pressure of extreme fear, and then it will run blindly along, bumping into objects and usually getting caught in a blind alley. But, unless the little animal is severely frightened, it moves, in strange surroundings, only step by step, whiskering right and left all the time and following a path that is anything but straight. Its course is determined by a hundred fortuitous factors when it walks that way for the first time. But, after a few repetitions, it is evident that the shrew recognizes the locality in which it finds itself and that it repeats, with the utmost exactitude, the movements which it performed the previous time. At the same time, it is noticeable that the animal moves along much faster whenever it is repeating what it has already learned. When placed on a path which it has already traversed a few times, the shrew starts on its way slowly, carefully whiskering. Suddenly it finds known bearings, and now rushes forward a short distance, repeating exactly every step and turn which it executed on the last occasion. Then, when it comes to a spot where it ceases to know the way by heart, it is reduced to whiskering again and to feeling its way step by step. Soon, another burst of speed follows and the same thing is repeated, bursts of speed alternating with very slow progress. In the beginning of this process of learning their way, the shrews move along at an extremely slow average rate and the little bursts of speed are few and far between. But gradually the little laps of the course which have been "learned by heart" and which can be covered quickly begin to increase in length as well as in number until they fuse and the whole course can be completed in a fast, unbroken rush.

Often, when such a path-habit is almost completely formed, there still remains one particularly difficult place where the shrew always loses its bearings and has to resort to its senses of smell and touch, sniffing and whiskering vigorously to find out where the next reach of its path "joins on". Once the shrew is well settled in its path-habits it is as strictly bound to them as a railway engine to its tracks and as unable to deviate from them by even a few centimetres. If it diverges from its path by so much as an inch, it is forced to stop abruptly, and laboriously regain its bearings. The same behaviour can be caused experimentally by changing some small detail in the customary path of the animal. Any major alteration in the habitual path threw the shrews into complete confusion. One of their paths ran along the wall adjoining the wooden table opposite to that on which the nest box was situated. This table was weighted with two stones lying close to the panes of the tank, and the shrews, running along the wall, were accustomed to jump on and off the stones which lay right in their path. If I moved the stones out of the runway, placing both together in the middle of the table, the shrews would jump right up into the air in the place where the stone should have been; they came down with a jarring bump, were obviously disconcerted and started whiskering cautiously right and left, just as they behaved in an unknown environment. And then they did a most interesting thing: they went back the way they had come, carefully feeling their way until they had again got their bearings. Then, facing round again, they tried a second time with a rush and jumped and crashed down exactly as they had done a few seconds before. Only then did they seem to realize that the first fall had not been their own fault but was due to a change in the wonted pathway, and now they proceeded to explore the alteration, cautiously sniffing and be-whiskering the place where the stone ought to have been. This method of going back to the start, and trying again always reminded me of a small boy who, in reciting a poem, gets stuck and begins again at an earlier verse.

In rats, as in many small mammals, the process of forming a path-habit, for instance in learning a maze, is very similar to that just described; but a rat is far more adaptable in its behaviour and would not dream of trying to jump over a stone which was not there. The preponderance of motor habit over present perception is a most remarkable peculiarity of the water-shrew. One might say that the animal actually disbelieves its senses if they report a change of environment which necessitates a sudden alteration in its motor habits. In a new environment a water-shrew would be perfectly able to see a stone of that size and consequently to avoid it or to run over it in a manner well adapted to the spatial conditions; but once a habit is formed and has become ingrained, it supersedes all better knowledge. I know of no animal that is a slave to its habits in so literal a sense as the water-shrew. For this animal the geometric axiom that a straight line is the shortest distance between two points simply does not hold good. To them, the shortest line is always the accustomed path and, to a certain extent, they are justified in adhering to this principle: they run with amazing speed along their pathways and arrive at their destination much sooner than they would if, by whiskering and nosing, they tried to go straight. They will keep to the wonted path, even though it winds in such a way that it crosses and recrosses itself. A rat or mouse would be quick to discover that it was making an unnecessary detour, but the water-shrew is no more able to do so than is a toy train to turn off at right angles at a level crossing. In order to change its route, the water-shrew must change its whole path-habit, and this cannot be done at a moment's notice but gradually, over a long period of time. An unnecessary, loop-shaped detour takes weeks and weeks to become a little shorter, and after months it is not even approximately straight. The biological advantage of such a path-habit is obvious: it compensates the shrew for being nearly blind and enables it to run exceedingly fast without wasting a minute on orientation. On the other hand it may, under unusual circumstances, lead the shrew to destruction. It has been reported, quite plausibly, that water-shrews have broken their necks by jumping into a pond which had been recently drained. In spite of the possibility of such mishaps, it would be short-sighted if one were simply to stigmatize the water-shrew as stupid because it solves the spatial problems of its daily life in quite a different way from man. On the contrary, if one thinks a little more deeply, it is very wonderful that the same result, namely a perfect orientation in space, can be brought about in two so widely divergent ways: by true observation, as we achieve it, or, as the water-shrew does, by learning by heart every possible spatial contingency that may arise in a given territory.

Among themselves, my water-shrews were surprisingly good-natured. Although, in their play, they would often chase each other, twittering with a great show of excitement, I never saw a serious fight between them until an unfortunate accident occurred: one morning, I forgot to reopen the little door of the nest-box after cleaning out their tank. When at last I remembered, three hours had elapsed—a very long time for the swift metabolism of such small insectivores. Upon the opening of the door, all the shrews rushed out and made a dash for the food tray. In their haste to get out, not only did they soil themselves all over but they apparently discharged, in their excitement, some sort of glandular secretion, for a strong, musk-like odour accompanied their exit from the box. Since they appeared to have incurred no damage by their three hours' fasting, I turned away from the box to occupy myself with other things. However, on nearing the container soon afterwards, I heard an unusually loud, sharp twittering and, on my hurried approach, found my eight shrews locked in deadly battle. Two were even then dying and, though I consigned them at once to separate cages, two more died in the course of the day. The real cause of this sudden and terrible battle is hard to ascertain but I cannot help suspecting that the shrews, owing to the sudden change in the usual odour, had failed to recognize each other and had fallen upon each other as they would have done upon strangers. The four survivors quietened down after a certain time and I was able to reunite them in the original container without fear of further mishap.

I kept those four remaining shrews in good health for nearly seven months and would probably have had them much longer if the assistant whom I had engaged to feed them had not forgotten to do so. I had been obliged to go to Vienna and, on my return in the late afternoon, was met by that usually reliable fellow who turned pale when he saw me, thereupon remembering that he had forgotten to feed the shrews. All four of them were alive but very weak; they ate greedily when we fed them but died none the less within a few hours. In other words, they showed exactly the same symptoms as the shrews which I had formerly tried to keep; this confirmed my opinion that the latter were already dying of hunger when they came into my possession.

To any advanced animal keeper who is able to set up a large tank, preferably with running water, and who can obtain a sufficient supply of small fish, tadpoles and the like, I can recommend the water-shrew as one of the most gratifying, charming and interesting objects of care. Of course it is a somewhat exacting charge. It will eat raw chopped heart (the customary substitute for small live prey) only in the absence of something better and it cannot be fed exclusively on this diet for long periods. Moreover, really clean water is indispensable. But if these clear-cut requirements be fulfilled, the water-shrew will not merely remain alive but will really thrive, nor do I exclude the possibility that it might even breed in captivity.

NIKOLASS TINBERGEN

Mating Behavior

The Functions of Mating Behavior

Nikolass Tinbergen's Social Behavior in Animals *is one of the truly great works in the field of animal behavior and ranks alongside Konrad Lorenz's* King Solomon's Ring. *Professor Tinbergen's books include* Eskimoland, The Study of Instinct, The Herring Gull's World, Social Behaviour in Animals, *and* Curious Naturalists. *At present he is Reader in Animal Behaviour at Oxford University.*

Many animals, particularly species living in the sea, ensure the fertilization of the egg cells in such a simple way that we can scarcely speak of mating behaviour. Oysters for instance simply eject their sperm cells in huge numbers at a certain time of the year; for a while each individual is enveloped in a cloud of sperm cells. The egg cells, it seems, cannot avoid being fertilized. Yet even here an important sort of behaviour is involved: fertilization would not succeed if the various oyster individuals did not produce their sperm cells and their eggs at the same time. A certain synchronization therefore is necessary. As I hope to show, this applies equally to land animals.

In many higher animals, particularly land animals, fertilization involves mating, or copulation. This requires more than mere synchronization. It means bodily contact. This is a thing most

233

animals avoid. This avoidance is an adaptation, part of their defence against predators. Being touched usually means being captured. Also, during actual mating the animals, and above all the females, are in a dangerous, defenceless position. In such animals the mating behaviour therefore involves the suppression of the escape behaviour. Since the female carries the eggs for some time, often even after fertilization, and since in so many species the female takes a larger share than the male in feeding and protecting the young, she is the more valuable part of the species' capital. Also, one male can often fertilize more than one female, an additional reason why individual males are biologically less valuable than females. It is therefore not surprising that the female needs persuasion more than the male, and this may be the main reason why courtship is so often the concern of the male. Often the male needs persuasion as well, but for a different reason. The males of most species are extremely pugnacious in the mating season, and unless the females can appease the males, they may be attacked instead of courted.

Further, apart from synchronization, which is a matter of coordinating the time pattern of mating, there must be close spatial co-ordination: the males and females must find each other; during actual copulation they must bring their genital organs in contact with each other; and next, the sperm must find the egg cell. This orientation is also a task of mating behaviour.

Finally, there is a premium on the avoidance of mating with members of another species. Since the genes, and the highly complicated growth processes started by them, are different in each species, mating between animals of different species brings widely different genes together, and this easily disturbs the delicately balanced growth pattern. Mating between different species therefore often results in fertilized eggs which are unable to live, and which die at the beginning of their growth; in less serious cases the hybrids may live but are less vital, or infertile. This premium on intraspecific mating has led to the development of differences between the mating patterns of different species, so that each individual can easily "recognize" its own species.

From *Social Behavior in Animals* by Nikolass Tinbergen. Reprinted by permission of John Wiley & Sons, Inc.

Apart from actual insemination, therefore, synchronization, persuasion, orientation, and reproductive isolation are the functions of mating behaviour.

Our problem in this chapter is: how are these functions fulfilled? What part does social behaviour play, and how does it attain these results? Let me say right at the beginning that our knowledge is very patchy. We have bits of information on each of these problems, but part of our knowledge applies to one species, and other parts to other species. In not a single species do we know the whole picture. The only thing I can do, therefore, is to present some examples of the various ways in which mating behaviour attains these ends, leaving it to future research to find out to what extent we are entitled to generalize our findings.

One thing seems to be obvious already: all the behaviour involved is of a relatively low "psychological" level, and does not imply foresight of these ends, nor deliberate action with the aim of attaining them. As we shall see, mating behaviour in all animals except Man and, perhaps, some of the apes, consists of immediate reactions to internal and external stimuli. There is no way in which "foreseen" effects of the behaviour can be brought into play as causes of the behaviour, as it does, in some as yet completely mysterious way, in Man.

Some Instances of Timing

The timing of the reproductive behaviour of Oysters (*Ostrea edulis*) has been shown recently to be the work of a rather unexpected outside factor, and therefore it is not, strictly speaking, a sociological problem. Yet it is perhaps useful to discuss it here as an example of the way in which the action of outside factors may often, so to speak, "fake" social co-operation.

About eight days after the oysters spawn, the larvae "swarm." They lead a very short floating life, and soon settle down on a solid substratum. In the muddy estuaries of the Scheldt, in Holland, oyster breeders increase their oyster stock by depositing roof tiles as artificial substrates on the bottom of the sea. This must not be done too much in advance of swarming, since the tiles would then become overgrown with other organisms before the oyster larvae could settle. A zoologist therefore had to find out whether he could forecast when the swarming would take place. His forecast, based upon many years of study, seems astonishing: "The big maximum in swarming is to be expected each year between June 26 and July 10, at about 10 days after full or new moon." This sounds like a fable, yet it is the hard truth. Since swarming takes place eight days after spawning, this means that spawning is to be expected two days after full or new moon. This gives us the key to the factor that is responsible for the timing: the tides. Spawning takes place at spring tide. How the spring tide affects the oysters is not yet known; it is not improbable that it is a matter of water pressure, which reaches its greatest oscillations at spring tide. Also, the intensity of the light penetrating to the bottom shows its maximum fluctuations at that time, and this might also be a factor.

Since the oysters do not spawn at each spring tide, there must be another factor preparing them to be ready in June to react to the spring tides; the nature of this factor is not known yet. It works much less precisely than the tides, for although the maximum of spawning occurs between June 18 and July 2, there are minor peaks during the preceding and the following spring tide. This factor is not known in the oyster, but in other animals we know something about it.

Not only the oyster but several other marine animals are known to be timed by the tides, among them the famous Palolo worm of the Pacific, and various other worms and molluscs.

Timing in the higher animals is a more complicated affair. Something is known of fish, birds, and mammals of the Northern temperate zone. Reproduction of most of these begins in spring. The first phase is migration towards the breeding grounds. This is done by all individuals at approximately the same time, though there may be weeks between the arrival of the first and the last comers. This rough timing is again due not to social behaviour but to reactions to an outside factor. The main factor here is the gradual lengthening of the day in late winter. Various mammals, birds, and fish have been subjected to artificial day-lengthening. The result was that the pituitary gland in the brain began to secrete a hormone which in its turn affected the growth of the sex glands. These then began to secrete sex hormones, and the action of these sex hormones on the central nervous system brought about the first reproductive behaviour pattern, migration. Often a rise in the temperature of the environment has an additional effect.

As I said, this timing process is not very accurate. The different individuals do not all react to the lengthening of the day with the same promptness. There may be a considerable difference between the male and the female of a pair. It has been found, in pigeons and in other animals, that if the male is further advanced than the female, his persistent courtship may speed up the female's development. This has been found in the following way. When a male and a female are kept separately in adjoining cages so that they can see and even touch each other, but are prevented from copulating, the persistent courtship of the male will finally induce the female to lay eggs. These of course are infertile. It may occur in captivity, when no males are available, that two female pigeons form a pair. Of these two, one then shows all the behaviour normally shown by the male. And although their reproductive rhythms may have been out of step at the beginning, the final result is that they both lay eggs at the same time. Somehow their mutual behaviour must have produced synchronization, not merely of behaviour, but also of the development of eggs in the ovary.

It is possible that this effect may be found in other species as well. It has been suggested by Darling that the communal courtship of birds breeding in colonies may have the same effect.

A further refinement of synchronization however is necessary. In all species that copulate, and in many other species as well, the co-operation between male and female must run according to an exact time schedule, and without exact co-operation no fertilization would be possible. In only very few species can the male force the female against her will to copulate. This means that in many species some form of very accurate synchronization must occur, which is a matter of fractions of a second. This is done by a kind of signal system. As an example I will discuss the mating of the Three-spined Stickleback. In the scheme of the mating behaviour, there is not merely a temporal sequence, but also a causal relation: each reaction really acts as a signal which releases the next reaction in the partner. Thus the male's zigzag dance releases approach in the female. Her approach in its turn releases leading in the male. His leading stimulates her to follow, and so on. This can easily be shown by the use of models or dummies. When a very crude imitation of a pregnant female is presented to the male in its territory, he will approach it and perform the zigzag dance. As soon as the model is then turned in his direction and "swims" towards him, he turns round, and leads it to the nest.

Pregnant females can be induced in a similar way to react to a model of the male. A crude fish model again is sufficient, provided it is painted red underneath. A bright blue eye will also help, but beyond that no details are necessary. If such a model is moved round a pregnant female in a crude imitation of the zigzag dance, the female will turn towards the model and approach it. If we then let the model swim away, the female follows it, and it is even possible to make her try to "enter" anywhere in the bottom of the aquarium by making the male model "show the nest entrance." No nest is necessary; the movement of the model is sufficient stimulus for the female to react.

Now in these cases the fish do not react exclusively to the partner's movements, but also to certain aspects of shape and colour. If the female dummy does not have the swollen abdomen of the real female, it will not or scarcely stimulate the male to dance. If the model of the male does not show a red underside, the female shows no interest in it. On the other hand, all other details have little or no influence, so that it is easier to release mating behaviour by using a very crude but "pregnant" dummy than with a live but non-pregnant female. However, the swollen abdomen, and the red colour, which are displayed continuously, are not responsible for the timing of the response of the male. It is the movements, which appear suddenly and immediately elicit a response, that are responsible for the exact timing.

The mating behaviour of Sticklebacks is a complicated series of such signal-response sequences, and the end result is that the male fertilizes the eggs immediately after they are laid by the female. It is not at all difficult to observe this behaviour, and to carry out all the model tests described. The Three-spined Stickleback will readily breed in an aquarium of a cubic foot or larger. It should have sand on the bottom, and plenty of green vegetation, including some green thread-algae.

The mating behaviour of many species involves such signal-movements which serve this ultimate refinement of synchronization.

Persuasion and Appeasement

Even when an animal is in a sexually active condition, it does not always react immediately to the partner's courtship. It may take a considerable time to overcome the female's reluctance. The zigzag dance of a male Stickleback for instance does not always elicit the female's response at once. She may approach in a half-hearted way, and stop when the male tries to lead her to the nest. In that case the male returns, and again performs his zigzag dance. After a number of repetitions the female may eventually yield, follow him, and enter the nest.

A similar repetition of signals is necessary when the female has entered the nest. The male's prolonged "quivering" is required to make her spawn. When you take the male away just after the female has entered the nest, she is unable to spawn. When you touch such a female gently with a light glass rod, imitating the male's quivering with it, she spawns just as easily as when the male has delivered the stimuli. Both male and rod have to touch her a great number of times.

In many species this repetition of signals is the rule. The copulation of Avocets for instance is preceded by curious antics: both male and female stand and preen their feathers in a hasty, "nervous" fashion. After some time the female stops preening, and adopts a flat attitude. This is the signal indicating that she is willing to mate, and only then does the male mount and copulate. Sometimes he does not react at once, but only after a certain time.

Herring Gulls have a similar introduction to coition. Both male and female bob their heads upwards, uttering a soft, melodious call with each bob. Here it is the male which takes the initiative in copulation: after a series of such mutual head-tossings he suddenly mounts and mates.

Sometimes persuasion has another function. In many birds, and in other species as well, the males become very aggressive in the breeding season. Actually, most of the fighting seen in animals is fighting between rival males in spring. This fighting is essential. Since it is always aimed at a rival male, the female has to differ from the male lest she should be attacked as well. In species such as the Chaffinch, the Redstart, or various Pheasants, the differences in plumage partly serve this purpose. In many other species however, such as the Wren, the plumages of male and female are not very different, or they are even identical, and here the female has to show special behaviour to suppress the male's aggressiveness. The essence of this "female courtship" therefore is to avoid provoking attack. Whereas a strange male may either flee from the displaying male—in which case it immediately elicits pursuit—or strut and threaten in reply (which also provokes the displaying male's aggressiveness), a female does neither. In the Bitterling (*Rhodeus amarus*) the female is at first attacked. She either withdraws quietly or merely avoids the attack by swimming under the male. The male then seems to be unable to attack her, and after a while it ceases to try and begins to court the female. A similar unobtrusive appeasement can be observed in many Cichlids. In other species the female shows infantile behaviour, that is to say, it resorts to the same method of appeasement as employed by the young, which probably stimulates the male's parental drive. That is why in so many species the male feeds the female during courtship. This happens, as we have seen, in the Herring Gull. There are also species in which the appeasing postures used during courtship are different from those used by the young. The female, or in other species both sexes, then show a type of behaviour which in many respects is the exact opposite of the threat behaviour. When, for instance, Blackheaded Gulls (*Larus ridibundus*) meet in the mating season, they show the "forward display," lowering the head and pointing the beak towards each other. This threat gesture is emphasized by the brown face, which surrounds the bill, the actual weapon. Mates however show their friendly intentions by "head flagging"; they stretch the neck, and then, by a sudden jerky movement, they turn their faces away from each other. Here, since both sexes are rather aggressive, the male appeases the female, as well as vice versa.

In some web-building spiders, the male visits the female on her web. Here the male has to appease the female, because he might be mistaken for prey.

Orientation

The spatial directing of mating movements is another important function of courtship. The most obvious function to be fulfilled is attraction. Many songbirds, such as the Nightingale, spend the winter far from the breeding grounds. The males, as mentioned above, return from the south well in advance of the females. How do the females find the males? This is made possible by the song. Many birds attract the other sex by some loud noise. In the Nightingale we happen to find this noise beautiful and have called it song. But the spring call of a male Grey Heron (*Ardea cinerea*), a harsh cry, does not appeal to human ears. Yet it does to the female Heron. It serves exactly the same function as the Nightingale's song. The Nightjar's rattling, the Woodpecker's drumming and the croaking of toads belong to the same category. So exactly is the song of many birds tuned to this function that the song is most intense as long as the males are still unmated, and it stops as soon as a female arrives. This again is due to a conflict between various interests. Song serves the species in that it attracts females (and, as we shall see later, repels rival males), but it endangers the male because it attracts predators as well. Nature, as always, has evolved a compromise: song is only produced when it is really needed, or at least when the advantages outweigh the disadvantages.

Since most animals are deaf (only the vertebrates and some other groups are exceptions), we find auditory advertisement in relatively few groups. It is well developed in birds, in frogs and toads, and in various insects such as crickets and grasshoppers. Special organs have evolved in such groups exclusively for the production of sound.

Other groups use scent as a means of attracting the opposite sex. Extreme cases are found among moths. The Psychid Moths have been studied to some extent and will be chosen as examples. The females have lost the capacity to fly; they are practically wingless. Soon after hatching, a female leaves the tubular shelter in which she has been living as a caterpillar and as a pupa. She does not move beyond her doorstep however, but remains hanging beneath her shelter. The males can fly. Shortly after hatching they leave their house, and take wing in order to search for a female. This search is guided by a scent which emanates from a virgin female. This attraction by female scent is highly developed in many other moths, such as Saturnia and Lasiocampa species. In such species the male is often able to find a female from a considerable distance, and his organs of smell, situated on the plume-like antennae, are highly sensitive. It is not at all difficult to collect caterpillars of those species, let them pupate and hatch, and watch the wild males come and enter the house in their search for the virgin females.

Visual attraction plays a part in many species. It is beautifully developed in the Sticklebacks. The male Three-spined Stickleback develops its most brilliant nuptial colours after the nest is finished. The red of the underside becomes more brilliant, and the dark shade which has covered his back during nest building becomes a fluorescent bluish white. Simultaneously, his behaviour changes. While during nest building he moved about smoothly, avoiding sudden movements, he now keeps swimming round the territory in a jerky abrupt fashion, which together with his conspicuous dress makes him visible from afar.

Many birds add visual displays to their auditory attraction devices. This is developed most impressively in birds of wide open plains. The waders of the Arctic tundra and many marsh birds in this country specialize in this respect. Again we often find a combination of conspicuous colours and movements. Lap-wing, Blacktailed Godwit, Dunlin and other waders are good examples. Other species have entirely specialized on movement, and are lacking in colour; such are found among the more vulnerable songbirds: Pipits, Larks. Specialization on colour has also occurred: the Ruff (*Philomachus pugnax*) has no special song flight, but relies on gorgeous coloration. Yet it has evolved another signal movement: now and then the males on a "lek" lift their wings, the light undersides of which make them very conspicuous. This wing lifting occurs particularly as a reaction to females flying in the distance, and it seems to attract these females. These lek birds apply still another principle, which has been called the "flower-bed principle": by crowding together their individual colour-effects are added together; they form a large gaudy patch somewhat like a flower bed.

In only a few of these cases has experiment proved the attracting influence. The red colour of male Sticklebacks has been proved to attract the females; models lacking red do not attract them. The influence of song has been nicely demonstrated in various locust. In one cage, hidden in the heather, singing males of Ephippiger were kept; in the next cage there were the same number of males, which were silenced by gluing their stridulation organs together. This is a minor operation, which leaves this wingless form free to pursue all other activities. At a distance of ten yards, females in mating condition were released. They invariably made their way in a short time to the cage containing singing males.

Experiments of this type justify the conclusions drawn in these paragraphs concerning the attracting influence of various types of display. Yet further experimental work is needed.

The orientation task of courtship is not finished when attraction has been effected. In actual copulation, the male has to bring his copulation apparatus into contact with that of the female, and this again requires powers of orientation. This is most obvious in many insects, where the males possess a complicated system of claspers to be fitted into the closely corresponding "negative" counterparts of the females. But in less "mechanized" animals such as birds this problem exists as well: the male cannot bring its cloaca in touch with that of the female without first reacting to orienting stimuli from the female. However, very little is known about these behaviour mechanisms.

Reproductive Isolation

Hybridization between species is exceedingly rare in nature. This is only partly due to differences in habitat preference between different species. Closely related species which breed in entirely separated geographical regions, and species which, though living in the same general region, go to different habitats to breed, are prevented from cross breeding by this spatial separation. But even when there is no such separation, species do not ordinarily interbreed. This is due to the fact that the various signals serving attraction, persuasion, appeasement, and synchronization, are so very different from one species to another. Also, the tendency to react to such signals is specific; every animal is innately equipped with the tendency both to give its species' signals and to react only to the signals of its own species. Yet one often sees, in nature, sexual reactions to other species. The males of the Grayling, which I have studied for several seasons, start their courtship by following the females in flight. This sexual pursuit is not released by females only: butterflies of other species, beetles, flies, small birds, falling leaves, even their own shadow on the ground attracts them. How is it that they never mate with these other species? Similar observations, leading to the same query, can be made on birds, fish, and many other animals.

The answer seems to be found in the chain character of mating and pair formation activities. When a female Grayling is willing to mate, it reacts in a special way to the male's sexual pursuit: it alights. All the other species usually do the opposite: if bothered by a pursuing male, they fly off as fast as they can, and this makes the male abandon its pursuit. Only closely related species react occasionally, but this has never been observed to lead to mating. Sticklebacks show essentially similar behaviour. The male may react to a small Tench entering its territory by zigzag-dancing. For a continuation of his mating behaviour, however, it is necessary that the partner swims toward him. Even if a Tench does this inadvertently, it has to follow the male to the nest, it has to enter the nest, and it has to spawn there before it can release sperm-ejaculation in the Stickleback. In other words, it must show the correct series of responses to the whole succession of the male's courtship activities, including the final "quivering." And this is so extremely improbable that it has never been observed. The sign stimuli of each separate reaction of the chain may not be sufficient to prevent reactions to other species, but since the separate reactions are each released by different stimuli, these together are sufficiently typical to prevent interspecific mating. This is obvious in species with "mutual" courtship, for here each sex shows a series of courtship activities. But even in a species such as the Grayling, where the female just sits while the male performs his courtship sequence, the female supplies a series of stimuli: experimental analysis has shown that the various activities of the male are released by stimuli which differ from one reaction to the next.

This specificity is particularly needed in closely related species. As we will see later, the behaviour patterns of closely related species are always very similar, just as their morphological characters are. They simply have not had the time for wide evolutionary divergence. But in such species there is always some striking difference between mating patterns, at least if spatial (geographical or ecological) or temporal (differences in breeding season) separation does not render this unnecessary. For instance, the Ten-spined Stickleback's

(*Pungitius pungitius*) mating behaviour is rather similar to that of the Three-spined species. It has however evolved very different nuptial colours in the male. The male of the Ten-spined species is pitchblack in spring. Just as the red colour attracts Three-spined females, so the black colour appeals to the females of the Ten-spined species. This, together with some minor behaviour differences, is sufficient to make interbreeding rare.

A systematic study of this problem of reproductive isolation has been undertaken in only one group: the fruit flies (*Drosophila*). The first results indicate that mating attempts between different species break off at various stages of the courtship, depending on which species are involved. Whenever such an interruption of courtship is found to be consistent in a series of observations, it is a sign that we are dealing with a specific response which cannot be released by the partner. The results obtained thus far show that in some cases the male fails to give the correct stimulus, in other cases the "fault" is with the female.

Conclusion

This very brief and sketchy review may be sufficient to show the intricate nature of behaviour patterns serving co-operation between the members of a pair. It has been shown that we must distinguish between four different types of functions served by courtship. This does not mean that each particular courtship activity serves only one of these ends. The zigzag dance of the male Stickleback for instance certainly serves timing, persuasion, orientation, and isolation, but the difference between the nuptial colours of Three-spined and Ten-spined Sticklebacks can only be understood from the viewpoint of isolation. Also, we know of courtship activities which have to do with timing and persuasion but not with orientation: Grayling females for instance can be timed and persuaded by the courtship of one male, and then mate with another male, which shows that the first male did not orient the female's response towards himself. Similarly, in pigeons, the persistent cooing and bowing of the male does not so much orient the female but it makes her gonads start ovulation. The various closely related "Darwin's Finches" of the Galapagos islands were found to have almost identical courtships. Yet there is no interbreeding. Here reproductive isolation is effected partly by ecological isolation, partly by each species reacting specifically to its own species' type of bill, which, in relation to the type of food taken, is different from one species to another. In this case therefore the courtship activities have nothing to do with reproductive isolation, but they do serve all the other functions.

In all these cases courtship activities, however different their functions may be in detail, have one thing in common: they send out signals to which the sex partner responds. In a later chapter I will discuss the nature and function of these signals more closely. It will then become clear that many of the conclusions and generalizations are still tentative, because experimental evidence is fragmentary. Further experiments with the aid of models are much needed.

GEORGE B. SCHALLER

"*Am I Satyr or Man?*"

George B. Schaller's The Year of the Gorilla *is exciting, refreshing, and captivating. He describes with scientific exactitude wild African gorillas in their jungle world. Dr. Schaller is currently studying deer and tiger behavior and is teaching at the University of Calcutta.*

When I began to study gorillas, I was tremendously impressed with their human appearance—they gave the superficial impression of slightly retarded persons with rather short legs, wrapped in fur coats. They stretch their arms to the side and yawn in the morning when they wake up, they sit on a branch with legs dangling down, and they rest on their back with arms under the head. In their emotional expressions too the gorillas resemble man: they frown when annoyed, bite their lips when uncertain, and youngsters have temper tantrums when thwarted. The social interactions between members of a gorilla group are close and affectionate, much like that of a human family, and their mating system is polygamous, a type for which man certainly has a predilection.

One hundred years ago the explorer Du Chaillu first described a male gorilla "beating his chest in rage." Almost every hunter, traveler, and scientist who since that time has encountered gorillas in the wild mentions this striking display in which the animal rises on its hind legs and beats a rapid tattoo on its chest with its hands. But none of these observers noted that beating the chest is the climax of a complex series of actions, which more than anything else are typical of the gorilla and constitute the most exciting aspect of its behavior. The complete sequence, which is rarely given and then only by silverbacked males, consists of nine more or less distinct acts. At the beginning of the display, the male often sits, tips up his head, and through pursed lips emits a series of soft, clear hoots that start slowly but grow faster and faster until they fuse into a slurred growling sound at the climax of the display. The hoots seem to generate excitement in the male, helping him to build up to the desired climax, much as natives use a drum in their frenzied dances. The gorillas have a look of great concentration on their faces when they hoot, and if another member of the group interrupts the even rhythm of the vocalization in some way, the male may stop abruptly and look around as if annoyed before continuing his display. Sometimes the male stops vocalizing briefly and plucks a single leaf from a nearby plant and places it between the lips, an act of such daintiness and seeming irrelevance that it never ceased to amaze me. The females and youngsters in the group know that the hoots and the placing of a leaf between the lips are preliminaries to rather vigorous, even violent, actions on the part of the male, and they generally retreat to a safe distance.

Just before the climax, the male rises on his short, bowed legs and with the same motion rips off some vegetation with his hand and throws it into the air. The climax consists of the chest beat, which is the part of the display most frequently seen and heard. The open, slightly cupped hands are slapped alternately some two to twenty times against the lower part of the chest at the rate of about ten beats a second. Gorillas do not pound their chests with the fists, as is often stated, except on very rare occasions. Chest beating is not at all stereotyped in its application, and the animal may slap its belly, the outside of its thigh, a branch, a tree trunk, or the back of another gorilla. One juvenile patted the top of its head about thirty times, and once a blackbacked male lay on his back with legs stretched skyward, beating the soles of his feet. Two females did not slap their chests directly, but rotated their arms, making their breasts flap in passing. While beating its chest, the gorilla often kicks a leg into the air.

Immediately after and sometimes during chest beating, the animal tends to run bipedally sideways for a few steps before dropping to quadrupedal position and dashing along. The male often slaps, breaks, and tears at anything in its path during the run, and this is dangerous, not only because of the violence of the act, but also because the male is not at all selective in what he swats. Any member of the group may be hit. One juvenile was picked up by a male and bowled down the slope. Even a man in the path of a running male may be swatted, as observed by Fred Merfield: "N'Denge was holding his gun loosely pointing downward, and was looking toward me, when a big male gorilla suddenly crashed out of the bush and swept him aside with a terrible full blow in the face." The grand finale of the display consists of a vigorous thump of the ground with the palm of the hand. The performer then settles back quietly, the display completed. It is a magnificent act, unrivaled among mammals, which Dr. Emlen likened to a symphony when he wrote (in the Transactions of the Philadelphia Academy of Science): "The hooting comes first, an effective introduction, rich in restraint and suspense to the human connoisseur of sonata and symphony. This leads with dramatic crescendo into the powerful climax of the display as the animal leaps to its feet, hurls leaves and branches into the air, and then pounds out a resounding percussion on its massive chest. Then follows the crashing finale, a free-swinging run ending in a tremendous thump."

Infants display various acts at an early age. When only about four months old they rise shakily and very briefly on their hind legs and beat their chests, and at a year and a half they throw vegetation and place a leaf between the lips. Although all parts of the sequence, except for the hooting and possibly the kick, are given by the females as well as the males, the former display less frequently and less intensely. To what extent the display is inherited or learned, and how age and sex of the animal affects the behavior cannot be determined in the wild. Goma, the infant born at the Basel zoo, beat its chest and the ground without having had the opportunity to learn the act from other gorillas. This, and similar data, suggests that gorillas have an inborn tendency to beat something when excited.

A display like that of the gorilla poses some challenging problems of interpretation. The remarkable series of sounds, movements, and postures must be of survival value to the species or it would not have evolved or persisted. A clue to the function of the display and to its underlying cause can be obtained by noting the situations that elicit it. The most intense, prolonged, and diverse displays are given in response to the presence of man. Other situations include the proximity of another gorilla group or a lone male, an undetermined disturbance, displays by another member of the group, and play. The hooting, the bipedal stance, the thrown vegetation, the running—all are actions which draw attention to the animal and make it conspicuous. It seems to advertise its presence, to show off. Studies of many animals, especially birds, have shown that certain prominent gestures are of significance in signaling information to others of the same and even different species—they are a means of communication. Judging from the effect that the display of the gorilla has on other gorillas and on man, it appears to function in two ways: it is a communicatory signal, revealing, for example, that another group is in the vicinity, and it serves to intimidate other gorillas and human intruders.

But what is the motivation underlying this remarkable display? Intimidation and communication do not explain the cause. Why, for instance, does it occur in play and in situations where there is nothing to intimidate or communicate? The most general emotional term which encompasses all the diverse manifestations is excitement. During the display the gorillas find release for the tension which has accumulated in their system in an excitable situation. After the display, the level of excitement temporarily drops, and the animals behave calmly until a new accumulation of tension erupts in display.

The evolutionary derivation of the display is of particular interest, and my explanation of it is based on the concepts developed in recent years by Niko Tinbergen, Konrad Lorenz, and other behaviorists. When two conflicting impulses, such as attack and flight, operate at the same time, the result is often a displacement activity, an activity which seems irrelevant and out of context in the situation at hand. A conflict of this type may produce preening in birds; but in gorillas it results in feeding, scratching, yawning, and the tendency to beat something. Natural selection may act on such displacement activities by enhancing their effectiveness as communicatory signals; they may become stereotyped and be incorporated into a definite display—they become ritualized. The fact that the gorilla often places a leaf between its lips suggests that this curious gesture may be a ritualized act of displacement feeding, and beating the chest may be the fairly stereotyped outcome of the tendency to slap something.

The gorilla shares various aspects of the display with other apes and with man. In Borneo I watched grey gibbons swinging from branch to branch by their arms, almost flying it seemed through the canopy of the rain forest. When they spotted me and grew excited, they hooted several times, faster and faster, until at the climax their sounds were of very high pitch and they ran bipedally along a branch. There is obvious similarity to the hooting, rising, and running of gorillas.

The gorilla's habit of throwing branches and other vegetation when excited is also found in the orangutan. I remember one evening toward dusk in Sarawak as my Dyak guide and I came across a female orangutan with a large infant both feeding on small green fruit in the forest canopy. The infant was about five feet from her when she saw us. Immediately she reached over, snatched the infant to her chest, and climbed from tree to tree for some five hundred feet, the youngster either clinging to her back or to her side. She grew very excited as we followed her. Three times she held the knuckles of her hand to her mouth and kissed them loudly, a sound which was followed by a *gluck-gluck*, resembling the gulping of liquid, and ended with a loud, two-toned burp. Then she peered down at us from a height of one hundred feet, a shaggy almost grotesque creature, black against the evening sky. Over a period of fifteen minutes she ripped off twigs and branches and hurled them at us. Several times she swung a branch like a large pendulum and at the peak of the arc closest to me she released it. The behavior of this female orangutan certainly seemed purposeful; at any rate, with the branches crashing down around me I had to jump nimbly at times to escape being hit. Dr. C. R. Carpenter has also observed that gibbons in Thailand, and howler and spider monkeys in Central America, break off branches and drop them in the direction of the observer. None of the gorillas I watched ever used branches and leaves as missiles, although vegetation sometimes inadvertently flew in my direction.

The chimpanzee exhibits nearly all aspects of the display sequence, although its behavior is, on the whole, not as stereotyped as that of the gorilla. Captive chimpanzees hoot, throw objects, slap floors, walls, and themselves, jump around, shake the bars of the cage, and stamp their feet when excited. Once when I surprised a male chimpanzee in the Maramagambo Forest of Uganda he raced along a branch and hid in a nest with only the top of his head poking inquisitively over the rim. We looked silently at each other until he suddenly slapped the edge of the nest and with an agility unheard of in a gorilla descended the tree. My most hair-raising experience in Africa was an encounter with a group of displaying chimpanzees in the Budongo Forest of Uganda. With Richard Clark, an anthropology student from Cambridge, I visited this forest for several days in early July, 1960, to observe chimpanzees. At dawn we crawled through the wet undergrowth in the direction of some hooting, barking, and gibbering champanzees that sounded like a conclave of maniacs. It had been light for half an hour when we reached the apes. Most of them were still in bed, squatting in their nest of branches anywhere from fifteen to ninety feet above ground. One juvenile left its nest and fed nearby on the olive-sized fruits of the *Maesopsis* tree. A female walked leisurely along a branch, but when she saw us she raced away through the tree and jumped twenty feet down into the leafy crown of a sapling, and from there to the ground. The others left their nests, hooting as they fled, and soon they were spread out in the distant trees, and on the ground where we could not see them. We followed the retreating animals, of which there were about thirty. Suddenly, as if by signal, all hooting ceased. The chimpanzees disappeared from sight, and we waited in the silent forest, scanning the tree tops and listening. Minutes passed. Without warning the hooting began again, this time all around us in the obscurity of the undergrowth, drawing closer and closer until the sounds seemed to come out of the earth itself. Not a single animal revealed itself, and this, coupled with the high-pitched screeches that appeared to erupt from the throats of a thousand furious demons, brought fear to our hearts. It was fear of the unknown, of being unable to do anything except wait. When the hoots reached their screaming climax, strange and new sounds reverberated through the forest—rolling, hollow, *bum-bum-bum*. Later we were to discover that the chimpanzees pound the hollow buttresses of ironwood trees much like an African beats a drum. The pandemonium subsided, and the chimpanzees retreated, leaving us thoroughly intimidated by their fascinating display.

Man behaves like a gorilla in conflicting situations. A marital squabble, for example, in which neither person cares to attack or retreat, may end with shouting, thrown objects, slamming doors, furniture pounded and kicked—all means of reducing tension. Sporting events, where man is excited and emotionally off guard, provide the ideal location for people-watching. A spectator at a sporting event perceives behavior that excites him. Yet he cannot participate directly in the action, nor does he want to cease observing it. The tension thus produced finds release in chanting, clapping hands, stamping feet, jumping up and down, and throwing objects into the air. This behavior may be guided into a pattern by the efforts of cheer leaders who, by repeating similar sounds over and over again with increasing frequency, channel the display into a violent and synchronized climax. Two of the functions of this display are communication with and intimidation of the opponent. Wherein lies the difference between gorilla and man?

What indeed are the differences between gorilla and man?

> Am I satyr or man?
> Pray tell me who can
> And settle my place in the scale;
> A man in ape's shape,
> An anthropoid ape,
> Or a monkey deprived of a tail?

When I began to study gorillas, I was at first tremendously impressed by their human appearance—they gave the superficial impression of slightly retarded persons with rather short legs wrapped in fur coats. These gestures and body positions of gorillas, and for that matter also those of other apes, resemble those of man rather than the monkeys. They stretch their arms to the side and yawn in the morning when they wake up, they sit on a branch with legs dangling down, and they rest on their back with their arms under the head. The great structural similarity between man and apes has been noted repeatedly since the time of Linnaeus and Darwin, and it is for this reason that all have been placed taxonomically into the super-family *Hominoidea*. In their emotional expressions too the gorillas resemble man: they frown when annoyed, bite their lips when uncertain, and youngsters have temper tantrums when thwarted. The social interactions between members of a gorilla group are close and affectionate, much like that of a human family, and their mating system is polygamous, a type for which man certainly has a predilection. These and many other basic similarities are to be expected, for man and the apes evolved from a common ancestral stock of monkey-like apes which diverged, one line leading to the apes, the other to man. It must be assumed from the evidence of evolution that man became man by the slow accumulation of certain characteristics, he became man by degrees, but still retained in his mind and frame the stamp of his origin.

Because of the many similarities between the apes and man, scientists and philosophers have the years been bedeviled by the problem of pointing to basic distinguishing characters other than minor anatomical ones. Some, like the famous French naturalist Buffon in 1791, glorified the mental capabilities of man by belittling those of the ape:

> Thus the ape, which philosophers, as well as the vulgar, have regarded as being difficult to define, and whose nature was at least equivocal, and intermediate between that of man and the animals, is, in fact, nothing but a real brute, endowed with the external mark of humanity, but deprived of thought and of every faculty which properly constitutes the human species . . .

Others, like Lord Monboddo in his *Of the Origin and Progress of Language*, published in 1774, looked upon the apes almost as our equals:

> The substance of all these different relations is, that the Orang Outang is an animal of the human form, inside as well as outside: that he has the human intelligence, as much as can be expected in an animal living without civility or arts: that he has a disposition of mind, mild, docile, and humane: that he has the sentiments and affections peculiar to our species, such as the sense of modesty, of honor, and of justice; and likewise an

attachment of love and friendship to one individual, so strong in some instances, that the one friend will not survive the other: that they live in society, and have some arts of life; for they build huts, and use an artificial weapon for attack and defense, viz. a stick; which no animal, merely brute, is known to do. . . . They appear likewise to have some kind of civility among them, and to practice certain rites, such as that of burying the dead.

In more recent times man has often been defined by one criterion like tool-using and tool-making, the presence of language, or the possession of culture.

The use of tools is certainly not confined to man, as has often been pointed out, but is found in a variety of other animals, including the insects. One species of solitary wasp, *Ammophila urnaria,* holds a small pebble in its mandibles and uses it as a hammer to pound dirt into its nesting burrow. A Burmese elephant was observed to pick up a stick with its trunk and scratch its back. However, the mammal that uses a tool more frequently than any other except man is not an ape but the sea otter (*Enhydra lutris*). This large member of the weasel family was once almost hunted to extinction for its valuable fur, but in recent years it has again become abundant in the Aleutian Islands and along certain parts of the California coast. With Dr. K. R. L. Hall, of the University of Bristol, England, I studied the feeding and tool-using behavior of the sea otter at Point Lobos, California, in January, 1963. When feeding, the otters generally swam along the shore and around the reefs, diving and reappearing many times in a small area. After a dive, they popped to the surface, immediately rolled onto their backs and, holding a sea urchin, crab, or other item between the paws, began to eat. Occasionally an otter surfaced with a small black mussel and a fist-sized stone. The animal then rolled onto its back, placed the stone on its chest, held the mussel pressed between its stubby hands, and brought the arms down forcefully so that the hard shell of the mollusk struck the stone with a click. The otter banged the shell against this "anvil" many times in succession, pausing only briefly at intervals to see if the shell was cracked and the soft insides of the mussel exposed. One otter brought up 54 mussels in an hour and a half and banged the shells against a stone 2,237 times, truly an energetic tool-using performance. An otter sometimes uses the same stone to open several mussels in succession. Once, after an animal had fed on mussels, it dove with the stone, only to reappear with two crabs. After the crabs were eaten, it reached under one arm and placed on its chest the same distinctive stone it had used previously. Such retention of a tool suggests that sea otters may have the rudimentary ability to think about the relationship between objects even though one of these objects is not in sight, something for which apes have a very limited capacity. In general, sea otters seem to have the inborn tendency to handle and pound objects, and we suspect that the tool-using habit is learned by youngsters while watching their mothers feed.

The woodpecker finch, *Cactospiza pallida,* a drab little bird inhabiting the Galapagos Islands, provides a most remarkable example of tool-using. This finch resembles a woodpecker in that it climbs along tree trunks and branches in search of food, but, unlike the woodpecker, it has no long pointed bill with which to get at the insects. Instead, it picks up a cactus spine or twig, holds it lengthwise in its beak, pokes it into the cracks of the bark, and grabs the insects as they come out. Anthropologists point out that simple tool-using is of an entirely different order of mental activity than actual tool-making, and it is usually inferred that only man, and perhaps also the apes, have attained the level of cerebral development necessary to do this. The zoölogist R. Bowman made the following observation on the woodpecker finch: "One such bird was holding a spine about six inches long. Only about two inches of the spine protruded from the tip of the bill, the remainder passed along one side of the face and neck. Apparently the bird realized that the stick was excessively long, for it made an unsuccessful attempt to twist off approximately three inches of the spine by holding it with the feet." This was clearly a rudimentary attempt at tool-making.

The fact that captive monkeys and apes may pick up a stick and use it to rake in food has been noted many times. One chimpanzee, observed by the animal psychologist W. Köhler, fitted a small bamboo cane into a larger one to make a stick long enough to reach some bananas, a simple form of tool-making. Observations of this type on free-living primates are very rare. I never saw tool-using in wild gorillas, and the only reliable accounts are for chimpanzees. In

Liberia, Beatty watched wild chimpanzees as they cracked open palm nuts. "He then picked up a chunk of rock and pounded the nut which had been placed on a flat-surfaced rock." The hunter Merfield observed several chimpanzees around a hole which led to a nest of subterranean bees: "Each ape held a long twig, poked it down the hole, and withdrew it coated with honey. There was only one hole, and, though for the most part they took turns at using their twigs, quarrels were constantly breaking out, and those who had licked off most of their honey tried to snatch the newly coated twigs." Jane Goodall, during her study of chimpanzees in Tanganyika, saw them push twigs into termite nests and eat the insects which adhered to them.

But, as Pascal once noted, "It is dangerous to let man see too clearly how closely he resembles the beasts unless, at the same time, we show him how great he is." Even though other animals share with man tool-using and to a minor extent tool-making ability, there still appears to be a wide mental gap between preparing a simple twig for immediate use and shaping a stone for a particular purpose a day or two hence. This was emphasized by the anthropologist Oakley when he wrote: "There is the possibility of gradation between these two extremes, perceptual thought in apes, conceptual thought in man; but it seems necessary to stress the contrast because one is apt to be so impressed by the occasional manufacture of tools by apes that there is danger of minimizing the gap in quality of mind needed for such efforts, compared with even the crudest tools of early man, which indicate forethought."

The most interesting archaeological discovery in recent years was the association of definite stone tools with the man-apes of Africa, the *Australopithecine*. In the Olduvai Gorge of Tanganyika, Dr. and Mrs. L. S. B. Leakey uncovered the skull of a man-ape with some simple chipped pebble tools, dating to the lower pleistocene, well over 600,000 years ago; and in South Africa similar tools were found in deposits that had also yielded the bones of man-apes. Two basic types of man-apes are known in Africa: *Australopithecus,* who was about four feet tall and weighed some fifty pounds, and *Paranthropus,* who was somewhat taller than the former type and weighed perhaps twice as much. Both walked fully upright through the savannahs which they inhabited and probably used their crude tools to kill and cut apart any small animal that crossed their path. The deposit at Olduvai Gorge, for example, contained the bones of frogs, rats, young pigs, and antelopes. But the remarkable thing about these tool-making man-apes is the fact that their heads are in many ways apelike and their brain capacity is only 450 to 750 cc., or no larger than that of gorillas. Brain size is, of course, not an accurate reflection of mental capacity, and judging from their systematic use of tools, the quality of the brain of the man-apes was considerably higher than that of gorillas.

Perhaps no aspect of ape behavior has more general interest than the way in which members of the group communicate with each other. Do apes have a rudimentary language, or do they merely emit a series of grunts and barks without meaning and without function? As I watched the gorillas over the weeks and months, a subtle change occurred in my thinking about the apes. At first I was highly impressed with their human ways, but there was something basic lacking, something that their brown eyes, no matter how expressive, could not convey, namely, a means of communication with each other about the past and the future and about things that were not immediately apparent. In other words, the gorillas lacked a language in the true sense of the word.

The apes seem to lack the tendency to vocalize for the sake of vocalizing, a trait which is so important in man. No infant gorilla ever babbled like a human baby. The gorillas had no interest in imitating sounds, in practicing with various combinations of sounds. The speech organs of gorillas and chimpanzees are perfectly adequate for talking. The failure of the apes to do so lies not in the anatomy but in the brain. Only with the greatest difficulty has a chimpanzee been taught to say the whispered approximations of "mama," "papa," and "cup." The apes are at the dawn of abstract and conceptual thought, but their neurological connections appear to be such that ideas fade away quickly. Thus, symbolic language, made possible through the ability to think in abstract terms, is the most unique feature of man. As Thomas H. Huxley wrote in an 1863 essay on *Man's Place in Nature:*

> Our reverence for the nobility of manhood will not be lessened by the knowledge that Man is, in substance and structure, one with the brutes; for, he alone possesses the marvellous

endowment of intelligible and rational speech, whereby, in the secular period of his existence, he has slowly accumulated and organized the experience which is almost wholly lost with the cessation of every individual life in other animals; so that now he stands raised upon it as on a mountain top, far above the level of his humble fellows, and transfigured from his grosser nature by reflecting, here and there, a ray from the infinite source of truth.

Or, as G. W. Corner noted more briefly: "After all, if he is an ape he is the only ape that is debating what kind of ape he is."

This is not to say that gorillas lack a way of communicating with each other, and that their method is not perfectly adequate for their simple mode of life. But the gorilla's ability to impart information to a neighbor is confined entirely to the situation at hand; there is no way to convey something that happened yesterday. On the whole, their signaling system is no more complex than that used by dogs and many other mammals. Gorillas coordinate their behavior within the group primarily by employing certain gestures and postures. For instance, a dominant male who walks away from a rest area without hesitation imparts not only the information that he is leaving but also the direction which he intends to take. In order to be groomed, a gorilla merely presents a certain part of its body to another animal. Each gorilla simply keeps its eyes on the rest of the group most of the time and does what the others are doing. Vocalizations, which feature prominently in our society, occupy a position of secondary importance in the gorillas; the animals are remarkably silent during their daily routine. I counted twenty-one more or less distinct vocalizations in free-living gorillas, with all but eight being infrequent. The apes grumble and grunt when contented, they emit a series of abrupt grunts when the group is scattered in the dense vegetation, they grunt harshly or bark when annoyed in some way, and they scream and roar when angry. These and other sounds appear to be mere expressions of the emotions: the sounds are not given for the purpose of communicating something; they are not symbolic. But the other members of the group have learned that certain vocalizations are given only in certain situations, with the result that many of the sounds have become definite signals. When, for example, the male suddenly roars, the other animals know that something potentially dangerous is in the vicinity, and they congregate around their leader. In general, vocalizations draw attention to the performer so that he can then impart further news through postures and gestures.

Although the number of basic vocalizations emitted by gorillas is fairly small, there is considerable variation in the pitch, intensity, and pattern of each sound. These variations greatly broaden the scope of the vocal repertoire, for the animals respond selectively to the sounds they hear. Their reaction depends not only on the sound but also on the condition under which it is given and the member of the group who gives it. For example, no member would mistake the deep, full grunt of a male for that of a female. One female had the tendency to scream loudly every time I arrived near the group. The others ignored her warning even when she was out of sight, indicating that they recognized her voice. Apparently she cried "Wolf!" too often. A sound may also have two meanings, depending on the situation. Harsh staccato grunts given by the leader when females quarrel causes them to subside. If, however, the male emits the same sound for no obvious reason, all members first look at him and then face the direction that occupies his attention.

One supposedly unique feature of man is his lack of precise instinctive responses to certain situations, a lack which has freed him from the strict biological control of most animals to let him to some extent choose his own destiny. The anthropologist Ashley Montagu expressed it as follows:

> The development of intelligence increasingly freed man from the bondage of biologically predetermined response mechanisms, and the limiting effects they exercise upon behavior. In the evolution of man the rewards have gone not to those who could react instinctively, but to those who were able to make the best or most successful response to the conditions with which they were confronted. Those individuals who responded with intelligence were more likely to prosper and leave progeny than those who were not so able. If there is one thing of which we can be certain it is of the high adaptive value of intelligence as a factor in both the mental and physical evolution of man. In the course of human evolution the power of instinctual drives has gradually withered away, until man has virtually lost all

his instincts. If there remain any residues of instincts in man, they are, possibly, the automatic reaction to a sudden loud noise, and, in the remaining instance, to a sudden withdrawal of support; for the rest man has no instincts.

Nobody, I think, would question the fact that much of man's behavior is the outcome of the culture into which he is born, that through learning, through social inheritance, he thinks and acts and makes those things which over the generations his particular culture has thought of as proper. But man's ability to learn from others and from experience, and to adapt his actions to conform with a predetermined set of rules, have merely masked the inherent aspects of his behavior. Man still possesses many instincts, and perhaps the most striking and unique one is the smile. An infant often begins to smile by the age of one month when the corner of its mouth is stimulated and when it hears various sounds. Later, during the second month, any smiling face, whether it is a person or merely a crude drawing of a face, will elicit a smile. A smile in the baby tends to evoke a smile in the mother, which in turn stimulates the baby to smile some more, a self-reinforcing mechanism which is very important in establishing the social bond between mother and child. Even infants born blind smile in response to certain stimuli. Although the smile as an important social pattern is unique to man, many other inherited types of behavior are shared with the apes— the tendency to throw and beat things when excited, to crouch down in submissiveness when threatened, and to develop a fear of strange objects at a certain age.

And yet the apes—and this is true of other animals—are not under the total grip of their instincts. Learning and tradition play an important role in their lives, a role which is difficult to assess with precision in the wild, because each youngster gradually and unobtrusively learns the things that help it to fit into its group and its environment. Knowledge of food plants, route of travel, the proper way to respond to vocalizations and gentures—these and many other aspects are undoubtedly part of the gorilla's tradition, handed down as a result of individual experience from generation to generation and constituting a rudimentary form of culture. The importance of tradition in animal society often becomes apparent only when a new trait appears. In recent years, for example, the blue tit, a European bird related to the American chickadee, acquired the remarkable habit of opening milk bottles on doorstops and taking the cream. This useful trait was apparently invented by a few tits in several localities, and it soon spread widely over western Europe.

The brain among the higher animals has evolved to increasing heights of complexity, growing more and more efficient and better capable of integrating the information received, and of becoming more aware of its surroundings as a whole. The ape brain seems to have evolved to or just over the threshold of insightful behavior, but it has not bridged the gaps that make it truly human. Why was *Australopithecus,* with the brain capacity of a large gorilla, a maker of stone tools, a being with a culture in the human sense, while the free-living gorilla in no way reveals the marvelous potential of its brain? I suspect that the gorilla's failure to develop further is related to the ease with which it can satisfy its needs in the forest. In its lush realm there is no selective advantage for improvement of manipulative skills like tool-making, or of mental activity along the lines that characterized human evolution. There is no reason to make, carry, and use a tool if vegetable food is abundant everywhere and at all times and no preparation of this food is required beyond stripping and shredding it with the teeth and fingers. There is no selective pressure to try anything new or improve on the old. The need for tools and for new additions to the diet, like mice, antelopes, and other meat, is more likely in harsh and marginal habitats where a primium is placed on an alert mind and new modes of fulfilling bodily requirements. *Australopithecus* lived in such an environment, and man must have continued to evolve in a similar one. But the very existence of the gorilla, free from want and free from problems, is mentally an evolutionary dead-end.

LOREN EISELEY

The Bird and the Machine

Loren Eiseley's The Bird and the Machine *is one of those once in a lifetime essays that combines scientific accuracy with simple eloquence and real feeling for life. It is delightfully unpretentious. Currently Dr. Eiseley is professor of anthropology and history of science at the University of Pennsylvania. For a number of years he was active in the search for early post-glacial man in the western United States and has worked extensively in the high plains, mountains, and deserts bordering the Rocky Mountains from Canada into Mexico. His books include* The Immense Journey, Darwin's Century, The Firmament of Time, *which received the John Burroughs' Association Medal in* 1961, The Mind and Nature, *and* Francis Bacon and the Modern Dilemma. *Dr. Eiseley's beautifully written articles also have appeared in scientific periodicals and popular magazines such as* Harpers *and* American Scholar.

I suppose their little bones have years ago been lost among the stones and winds of those high glacial pastures. I suppose their feathers blew eventually into the piles of tumbleweed beneath the straggling cattle fences and rotted there in the mountain snows, along with dead steers and all the other things that drift to an end in the corners of the wire. I do not quite know why I should be thinking of birds over the *New York Times* at breakfast, nor particularly of the birds of my youth half a continent away. It is a funny thing what

263

the brain will do with memories and how it will treasure them and finally bring them into odd juxtapositions with other things, as though it wanted to make a design, or get some meaning out of them, whether you want it or not, or even see it.

It used to seem marvelous to me, but I read now that there are machines that can do these things in a small way, machines that can crawl about like animals, and that it may not be long now until they do more things—maybe even make themselves—I saw that piece in the *Times* just now—and then they will, maybe—well, who knows —but you read about it more and more with no one making any protest, and already they can add better than we and reach up and hear things through the dark and finger the guns over the night sky.

This is the new world that I read about at breakfast. This is the world that confronts me in my biological books and journals, until there are times when I sit quietly in my chair and try to hear the little purr of the cogs in my head and the tubes flaring and dying as the messages go through them and the circuits snap shut or open. This is the great age, make no mistake about it; the robot has been born somewhat appropriately along with the atom bomb, and the brain they say now is just another type of more complicated feedback system. The engineers have its basic principles worked out; it's mechanical, you know; nothing to get superstitious about; and man can always improve on nature once he gets the idea. Well, he's got it all right and that's why, I guess, that I sit here in my chair, with the article crunched in my hand, remembering those two birds and that blue mountain sunlight. There is another magazine title on my desk that reads "Machines Are Getting Smarter Every Day." I don't deny it, but I'll stick with the birds. It's life I believe in, not machines.

Maybe you don't believe there is any difference. A skeleton is all joints and pulleys, I'll admit. And when man was in his simpler stages of machine building in the eighteenth century, he quickly saw the resemblances. "What," wrote Hobbes, "is the heart but a spring, and the nerves so many springs, and the joints but so many wheels, giving motion to the whole body?" Tinkering about in their shops it was inevitable in the end that men would see the world as a huge machine "subdivided into an infinite number of lesser machines."

From *The Immense Journey* by Loren Eiseley. Reprinted by permission of Random House, Inc. Copyright 1955 by Loren Eiseley.

The idea took on with a vengeance. Little automatons toured the country—dolls controlled by clockwork. Clocks described as little worlds were taken on tours by their designers. They were made up of moving figures, shifting scenes, and other remarkable devices. The life of the cell was unknown. Man, whether he was conceived as possessing a soul or not, moved and jerked about like these tiny puppets. A human being thought of himself in terms of his own tools and implements. He had been fashioned like the puppets he produced and was only a more clever model made by a great designer.

Then in the nineteenth century, the cell was discovered, and the single machine in its turn was found to be the product of millions of infinitesimal machines—the cells. Now, finally, the cell itself dissolves away into an abstract chemical machine—and that into some intangible, inexpressible flow of energy. The secret seems to lurk all about, the wheels get smaller and smaller, and they turn more rapidly, but when you try to seize it the life is gone—and so, it is popular to say, the life was never there in the first place. The wheels and the cogs are the secret and we can make them better in time—machines that will run faster and more accurately than real mice to cheese.

I have no doubt it can be done, though a mouse harvesting seeds on an autumn thistle is to me a fine sight and more complicated, I think, in his multiform activity, than a machine "mouse" running a maze. Also, I like to think of the possible shape of the future brooding in mice, just as it brooded once in a rather ordinary mousy insectivore who became a man. It leaves a nice fine indeterminate sense of wonder that even an elcetronic brain hasn't got, because you know perfectly well that if the electronic brain changes it will be because of something man has done to it. But what man will do to himself he doesn't really know. A certain scale of time and a ghostly intangible thing called change are ticking in him. Powers and potentialities like the oak in the seed, or a red and awful ruin. Either way, it's impressive; and the mouse has it, too—or those birds, I'll never forget those birds, though I learned the lesson of time first of all. I was young then and left alone in a great desert— part of an expedition that had scattered its men over several hundred miles in order to carry on research more effectively. I learned there that time is a series of planes existing superficially in the same universe. The tempo is a human illusion, a subjective clock ticking in our kind of protoplasm.

As the long months passed, I began to live on the slower planes and to observe more readily what passed for life there. I sauntered, I passed more and more slowly up and down the canyons in the dry baking heat of midsummer. I slumbered for long hours in the shade of huge brown boulders that had gathered in tilted companies out on the flats. I had forgotten the world of men and the world had forgotten me. Now and then I found a skull in the canyons and these justified my remaining there. I took a serene cold interest in these discoveries. I had come, like many a naturalist before me, to view life with a wary and subdued attention. I had grown to take pleasure in the divested bone.

I sat once on a high ridge that fell away before me into a waste of sand dunes. I sat through hours of a long afternoon. Finally glancing by my boot an indistinct configuration caught my eye. It was a coiled rattlesnake, a big one. How long he had sat with me I do not know. I had not frightened him. We were both locked in the sleep-walking tempo of the earlier world, baking in the same high air and sunshine. Perhaps he had been there when I came. He slept on as I left, his coils, so ill discerned by me, dissolving once more among the stones and gravel from which I had barely made him out.

Another time, I got on a higher ridge, among some tough little wind-warped pines half covered over with sand in a basin-like depression that caught everything carried by the air up to those heights. There were a few thin bones of birds, some cracked shells of indeterminable age, and the knotty fingers of pine roots bulged out of shape from their long and agonizing grasp upon the crevices of the rock. I lay under the pines in the sparse shade and went to sleep once more.

It grew cold finally, for autumn was in the air by then, and the few things that lived thereabouts were sinking down into an even chillier scale of time. In the moments between sleeping and waking I saw the roots about me and slowly, slowly, a foot in what seemed many centuries, I moved by sleep-stiffened hands over the scaling bark and lifted my numbed face after the vanishing sun. I was a great awkward thing of knots and aching limbs, trapped up there in some long patient endurance that involved the necessity of putting living fingers into rock and by slow, aching expansion bursting those rocks asunder. I suppose, so thin and slow was the time of my pulse by then, that I might have stayed on to drift still deeper into the lower cadences of the frost, or the crystalline life that glisters pebbles or shines in a snow flake, or dreams in the meteoric iron between the worlds.

It was a dim descent but time was present in it. Somewhere far down in that scale the notion struck me that one might come the other way. Not many months thereafter, I joined some colleagues heading higher into a remote windy tableland where huge bones were reputed to protrude like boulders from the turf. I had drowsed with reptiles and moved with the century-long pulse of trees; now, lethargically, I was climbing back up some invisible ladder of quickening hours. There had been talk of birds in connection with my duties. Birds are intense, fast-living creatures—reptiles, I suppose one might say—that have escaped out of the heavy sleep of time, transformed fairy creatures dancing over sunlit meadows. It is a youthful fancy, no doubt, but because of something that happened up there among the escarpments of that range, it remains with me a life-long impression. I can never bear to see a bird imprisoned.

We came into that valley through the trailing mists of a spring night. It was a place that looked as though it might never have known the foot of man, but our scouts had been ahead of us and we knew all about the abandoned cabin of stone that lay far up on one hillside. It had been built in the land rush of the last century and then lost to the cattlemen again as the marginal soils failed to take to the plow.

There were spots like this all over that country. Lost graves marked by unlettered stones and old corroding rim-fire cartridge cases lying where somebody had made a stand among the boulders that rimmed the valley. They are all that remain of the range wars; the men are under the stones now. I could see our cavalcade winding in and out through the mist below us: torches, and lights reflected on collecting tins, and the far-off bumping of a loose dinosaur thigh bone in the bottom of a trailer. I stood on a rock a moment looking down and thinking what it cost in money and equipment to capture the past.

We had, in addition, instructions to lay hands on the present. The word had come through to get them alive, birds, reptiles, anything. A zoo somewhere abroad needed restocking. It was one of those reciprocal matters in which science involves itself. Maybe our museum needed a stray ostrich egg and this was the payoff. Anyhow, my job was to help capture some birds and that was why I was there before the trucks.

The cabin had not been occupied for years. We intended to clean it out and live in it, but there were holes in the roof and the birds had come in and were roosting in the rafters. You could depend on it in a place like this where everything blew away and even a bird needed some place out of the weather and away from coyotes. A cabin going back to nature in a wild place draws them till they come in, listening at the eaves, I imagine, pecking softly among the shingles till they find a hole and then suddenly the place is theirs and man is forgotten.

Sometimes of late years I find myself thinking the most beautiful sight in the world might be the birds taking over New York after the last man has run away to the hills. I will never live to see it, of course, but I know just how it will sound because I've lived up high and I know the sort of watch birds keep on us. I've listened to sparrows tapping tentatively on the tin of the air conditioners when they thought no one was listening, and I know how other birds test the vibrations that come up to them through the television aerials.

"Is he gone?" they ask, and the vibrations come up from below, "not yet, not yet."

Well, to come back, I got the door open softly and I had the spotlight all ready to turn on and blind whatever birds were there so they couldn't see to get out through the roof. I had a short piece of ladder to put against the far wall where there was a shelf on which I expected to make the biggest haul. I had all the information I needed just like any skilled assassin. I pushed the door open with the hinges only squeaking a little after the oil was put on them. A bird or so stirred—I could hear them—but nothing flew and there was a faint starshine through the holes in the roof.

I padded across the floor, got the ladder up, and the light ready, and slithered up the ladder till my head and arms were over the shelf. Everything was dark as pitch except for the starlight at a little place back of the shelf near the eaves. With the light to blind them, they'd never make it. I had them. I reached my arm carefully over in order to be ready to seize whatever was there and I put the flash on the edge of the shelf where it would stand by itself when I turned it on. That way I'd be able to use both hands.

Everything worked perfectly except for one detail—I didn't know what kind of birds were there. I never thought about it at all and it wouldn't have mattered if I had. My orders were to get something interesting. I snapped on the flash and sure enough there was a great beating and feathers flying, but instead of my having them, they, or rather he, had me. He had my hand, that is, and for a small hawk not much bigger than my fist he was doing all right. I heard him give one short metallic cry when the light went on and my hand descended on the bird beside him; after that he was busy with his claws and his beak was sunk in my thumb. In the struggle I knocked the lamp over on the shelf and his mate got her sight back and whisked neatly through the hole in the roof, and off among the stars outside. It all happened in fifteen seconds and you might think I would have fallen down the ladder, but no, I had a professional assassin's reputation to keep up and the bird, of course, made the mistake of thinking the hand was the enemy and not the eyes behind it. He chewed my thumb up pretty effectively and lacerated my hand with his claws, but in the end I got him, having two hands to work with.

He was a sparrow hawk and a fine young male in the prime of life. I was sorry not to catch the pair of them, but as I dripped blood and folded his wings carefully, holding him by the back so he couldn't strike again, I had to admit the two of them might have been a little more than I could have handled under the circumstances. The little fellow had saved his mate by diverting me, and that was that. He was born to it, and made no outcry now, resting in my hand hopelessly, but peering toward me in the shadows behind the lamp with a fierce, almost indifferent glance. He neither gave nor expected mercy and something out of the high air passed from him to me, stirring a faint embarrassment.

I quit looking into that eye and managed to get my huge carcass with its fist full of prey back down the ladder. I put the bird in a box too small to allow him to injure himself by struggle and walked out to welcome the arriving trucks. It had been a long day and camp was still to make in the darkness. In the morning that bird would be just another episode. He would go back with the bones in the truck to a small cage in a city where he would spend the rest of his life. And a good thing, too. I sucked my aching thumb and spat out some blood. An assassin has to get used to these things. I had a professional reputation to keep up.

In the morning with the change that comes on suddenly in that high country, the mist that had hovered below us in the valley was gone. The sky was a deep blue and one could see for miles over the high outcroppings of stone. I was up early and brought the box in which the little hawk was imprisoned out onto the grass where I was building a cage. A wind as cool as a mountain spring ran over the grass and stirred my hair. It was a fine day to be alive. I looked up and all around and at the hole in the cabin roof out of which the other little hawk had fled. There was no sign of her anywhere that I could see.

"Probably in the next county by now," I thought cynically, but before beginning work I decided I'd have a look at my last night's capture.

Secretively, I looked again all around the camp and up and down and opened the box. I got him right out in my hand with his wings folded properly and I was careful not to startle him. He lay limp in my grasp and I could feel his heart pound under the feathers but he only looked beyond me and up.

I saw him look that last look away beyond me into a sky so full of light that I could not follow his gaze. The little breeze flowed over me again, and nearby a mountain aspen shook all its tiny leaves. I suppose I must have had an idea about then of what I was going to do, but I never let it come up into consciousness. I just reached over and laid the hawk on the grass.

He lay there a long minute without hope, unmoving, his eyes still fixed on that blue vault above him. It must have been that he already was so far away in heart that he never felt the release from my hand. He never even stood. He just lay with his breast against the grass and my eye upon him.

In the next second after that long minute he was gone. Like a flicker of light, he had vanished with my eyes full on him, but without actually seeing even a premonitory wing beat. He was gone straight into that towering emptiness of light and crystal that my eyes could scarcely bear to penetrate. For another long moment there was silence. I could not see him. The light was too intense. Then from far up somewhere a cry came ringing down.

I was young then and had seen little of the world, but when I heard that cry my heart turned over. It was not the cry of the hawk I had captured, for, by shifting my position against the sun, I was now seeing further up. Straight out of the sun's eye, where she must have been soaring restlessly above us for untold hours, hurtled his mate. And from far up, ringing from peak to peak of the summits over us, came a cry of such unutterable and ecstatic joy that it sounds down cross the years and tingles among the cups on my quiet breakfast table.

I saw them both now. He was rising fast to meet her. They met in a great soaring gyre that turned to a whirling circle and a dance of wings. Once more, just once, their two voices, joined in a harsh wild medley of question and response, struck and echoed against the pinnacles of the valley. Then they were gone forever somewhere into those upper regions beyond the eyes of men.

I am older now, and sleep less, and have seen most of what there is to see and am not very impressed any more, I suppose, by anything. "What Next in the Attributes of Machines?" my morning headline runs. "It Might Be the Power to Reproduce Themselves."

I lay the paper down and across my mind a phrase floats insinuatingly: "It does not seem that there is anything in the construction, constituents, or behavior of the human being which it is essentially impossible for science to duplicate and synthesize. On the other hand . . ."

All over the city the cogs in the hard, bright mechanisms have begun to turn. Figures move through computers, names are spelled out, a thoughtful machine selects the fingerprints of a wanted criminal from an array of thousands. In the laboratory an electronic mouse runs swiftly through a maze toward the cheese it can neither taste nor enjoy. On the second run it does better than a living mouse.

"On the other hand . . ." Ah, my mind takes up, on the other hand the machine does not bleed, ache, hang for hours in the empty sky in a torment of hope to learn the fate of another machine, nor does it cry out with joy nor dance in the air with the fierce passion of a bird. Far off, over a distance greater than space, that remote cry from the heart of heaven makes a faint buzzing among my breakfast dishes and passes on and away.

8